STATESMEN OF SCIENCE

By the same Author

FRANCIS BACON: THE FIRST STATESMAN OF SCIENCE
FOUNDERS OF BRITISH SCIENCE
SCIENTISTS OF THE INDUSTRIAL REVOLUTION
BRITISH SCIENTISTS OF THE NINETEENTH CENTURY
BRITISH SCIENTISTS OF THE TWENTIETH CENTURY

FAMOUS AMERICAN MEN OF SCIENCE
THE SOCIAL RELATIONS OF SCIENCE
SOVIET SCIENCE
SCIENCE UNFOLDS THE FUTURE
THE SCIENCES OF ENERGY
NUCLEAR ENERGY IN INDUSTRY
SCIENCE IN LIBERATED EUROPE
THE PROGRESS OF SCIENCE
AN OUTLINE OF THE UNIVERSE
INDUSTRY AND EDUCATION IN SOVIET RUSSIA
SCIENCE IN SOVIET RUSSIA
THE SCIENCE OF PETROLEUM
THE A.B.C. OF CHEMISTRY
SCIENCE AND LIFE
SCIENCE FOR YOU
SHORT STORIES IN SCIENCE
OSIRIS AND THE ATOM
SIX GREAT SCIENTISTS
SIX GREAT INVENTORS
SIX GREAT DOCTORS
SIX GREAT ENGINEERS
SIX GREAT ASTRONOMERS
THE STORY OF AGRICULTURE
THE YOUNG MAN'S GUIDE TO CIVIL ENGINEERING
RADIOASTRONOMY AND RADAR
ELECTRICITY

LORD HALDANE AND PROFESSOR EINSTEIN
AT 28 QUEEN ANNE'S GATE IN 1921

J. G. CROWTHER

STATESMEN OF SCIENCE

HENRY BROUGHAM
WILLIAM ROBERT GROVE
LYON PLAYFAIR
THE PRINCE CONSORT
THE SEVENTH DUKE OF DEVONSHIRE
ALEXANDER STRANGE
RICHARD BURDON HALDANE
HENRY THOMAS TIZARD
FREDERICK ALEXANDER LINDEMANN

LONDON
THE CRESSET PRESS

First published in Great Britain in 1965
by the Cresset Press, 11 *Fitzroy Square, London, W.*1

Printed in Great Britain by
Western Printing Services Limited, Bristol

The interests of a nation extend much beyond the interests of the one generation which forms its present population, and the statesman will feel sure that the effects already in action will operate with a much increasing power in the future.

LYON PLAYFAIR

Lecture on Industrial Instruction on the Continent: 1852

Foreword

THE Industrial Revolution changed the general direction of science from astronomy and natural history to physics, chemistry and biology. It multiplied the quantity of science and the number of scientists, and made the problems of the place of science in the life of the nation, and of the government of science itself, more pressing.

The men who addressed themselves to these problems, and contributed to their solution may be regarded as Statesmen of Science. Such men are becoming more and more important in an increasingly scientific age.

This book is devoted to nine of the most eminent during the last century and a half. Lord Brougham sought to extend the knowledge and use of science from individuals and the ruling class to the whole people. Sir William Grove had the leading part in changing the character of the Royal Society to adopt it to the needs of science in the new industrial age. The level of scientific standards and qualifications for entry was raised, but it was done in such a way that it became stereotyped, and the Society was unable to expand with the expansion of science, for nearly a century.

Lord Playfair took the lead in introducing science into the activities of government, and contributed much to the development of the organization of science and technical education. The Prince Consort conceived and launched a plan for British science, through the Great Exhibition of 1851. He envisaged the complex of scientific institutions at South Kensington in London as a centre for British, and indeed, for international science.

The place left in British scientific development by the death of the Prince Consort was to a considerable extent filled by William Cavendish, the Seventh Duke of Devonshire. In addition, he personally founded the Cavendish Laboratory, and he presided over the Royal Commission on Scientific Instruction and the Advancement of Science, which thoroughly investigated the condition of British science in the middle of the nineteenth century and discussed what should be done to improve it.

The idea of the Commission had been inspired by the remarkable, almost forgotten scientist, Colonel Alexander Strange, who proposed a modern system of scientific organization, operating under a Minister of Science, with the advice of two councils, one for military and the other for civil science. It is substantially the scheme which has been adopted since the 1960's, a hundred years later.

The Devonshire Commission provided many valuable ideas, but these were acted upon sluggishly. British science in 1900 still remained inadequately reformed. This became painfully evident through the rise of German and American science. Lord Haldane was the promoter of action in this situation of increasing national danger and relative decline. He brought Brougham's vision of civic universities into being. He founded the Imperial College of Science and Technology on the Prince Consort's complex at South Kensington. He promoted the organization of research in the application of science to both military and civil purposes.

By the time of the First World War some scientific organization had come into existence. This provided the opportunity for Sir Henry Tizard and Lord Cherwell to gain their early experience of military science which helped to qualify them for their scientific statesmanship in the Second World War.

The present organization of British science was brought into being largely by the subjects of this book. In their work, its origins may be traced, and the perspective gained for its further development.

Acknowledgments

THE chief sources of information which have been drawn upon are given in the references at the end of the book.

I am grateful to Sir Patrick Linstead, F.R.S., for permission to quote from his Special Lecture on *The Prince Consort and the Founding of the Imperial College*; Miss Nora K. Strange for information on her grand-uncle Colonel Alexander Strange; Professor J. P. M. Tizard for permission to quote from certain of Sir Henry Tizard's addresses; Mr. Nigel Calder for permission to draw upon my article on the Prince Consort in the *New Scientist* of December 14th, 1961; Messrs. Cassell & Co. for permission to quote from *The Second World War* by Sir Winston Churchill; Messrs. Hodder & Stoughton from Lord Haldane's *Autobiography*; and Messrs. John Murray from Lord Haldane's *Reign of Relativity*.

I am particularly indebted to Mr. Graeme Mitchison for the loan of the print of his great-grand-uncle Lord Haldane and Professor Einstein. Mr. Ronald W. Clark and Messrs. Methuen kindly supplied the print of Lord Cherwell; the Royal Society kindly gave permission for the reproduction of the portrait of W. R. Grove from their *Record*; and the University of London for the reproduction of the Senate House portrait of Lord Brougham.

The print of the engraving of Colonel Alexander Strange was supplied by the *Illustrated London News*; and the prints of Lord Playfair, the Prince Consort, Sir William R. Grove, the Seventh Duke of Devonshire, and Sir Henry Tizard were supplied by the Radio Times Picture Library.

The captions of the portraits refer to their subjects by the titles by which they were known in their later years, not necessarily by those at the times when the original photographs were taken.

Mr. K. D. C. Vernon and Mr. M. R. Halliday gave me most kind assistance in using the library of the Royal Institution.

J. G. CROWTHER

Contents

Lyon Playfair

The Prince Consort

The Seventh Duke of Devonshire

Alexander Strange

List of Plates

STATESMEN OF SCIENCE

Introduction

BROADLY speaking, the statesmen of science at the beginning of the nineteenth century were concerned with the democratization of science, of making it a possession of the people.

Then came a period when the growing science required to be converted from an amateur into a professional activity.

This was followed later in the nineteenth century by much discussion on the problem of organization. By the middle of the twentieth century some organized science had been established, and statesmen of science became more concerned with operating it, or administration. This evolution can be seen in the activities of the successive subjects of this book.

The consideration of their lives and work shows that the leading ideas on the organization of science are old. Many of the principles being adopted today were conceived and expressed at least a hundred years ago.

Why has their adoption been so slow? It appears, from what these men said in the course of their efforts, that the chief obstacle was the nature of the social system. The comprehensive organization of science was incompatible with private enterprise.

Brougham and Playfair were the prisoners of their unquestioning belief in the political economy of Adam Smith. They would not propose action which ran contrary to its principles, and were thus crippled in their attempts to realize their excellent conceptions of how science should be incorporated in the national life.

The non-scientific politicians were in general almost inconceivably obtuse. From the point of view of science, Gladstone, the student of Homer, belonged technically, like Homer's heroes, to the Bronze Age.

Even Peel, who so intelligently grasped the significance of scientific ideas, believed that scientific organization belonged to the province of private initiative. He did not promote scientific projects which he saw were desirable, because he held on principle that they should not be carried out by the state.

The evidence of Lord Salisbury to the Devonshire Commission illustrates how a politician who understood science well was nevertheless prepared to inhibit the organization of science, because it was in conflict with the political principles to which he adhered. His advice was, that if the state was to give money for scientific research, it should do so by handing it to private bodies to spend. If a scientific activity would be profitable, it should be entrusted to private enterprise; if not, it should be undertaken by the state.

Such principles inherently prevented the creation of an effective state organization of science. They were held with equal tenacity by the leading Liberal and Conservative statesmen.

At the same time, most of the leading scientists held as tenaciously to the principle of the superiority of pure research.

The conceited complacency with which Playfair was treated, on the one hand, by purely political statesmen, was equalled by that with which, on the other, he was treated by purely research scientists.

The divorce of science and politics is the essence of reaction in the modern world. Today, science *is* politics; it determines the future of humanity.

In Playfair's day, and for long afterwards, scientists believed that it was more important to do science than to think about it. Now it is realized that it may be more important to think about science than to do it.

The technical specialist is under a strong temptation to believe that it is more important to solve technical problems than to live a civilized life.

The statesman of science has to guide science and scientists into a wiser course. He is one who has perceived the social implications of science, and striven to act on them, for the benefit of mankind and science itself. He works through the media of Parliament and politics, administration, education, communication and the Press. He may or he may not have been eminent as an original scientific investigator, but he has been concerned with science as a whole, and its interactions with society.

While most of the pure scientists of Playfair's time were rather satisfied with British science, foreigners did not share their opinion. To Liebig, England seemed to be about as backward as the United States then appeared to the English. It was a rich crude country, created for exploitation by the intelligent.

When Hofmann told Liebig in 1863 of his decision to leave England and return to Germany, he replied that he could not understand how he had come to such a decision. He believed it a great good fortune to belong to England, and enjoy a completely independent post, instead of suffering from the misery of German university conditions. Above all, the lack of intellectual competition was so attractive. 'England is so extraordinarily poor in truly scientific men that a man like you is a true blessing for the country; in no other can he hope to effect more; in none to gain greater influence. . . .'

That was how it appeared when Babbage and Faraday were still alive, and the *Origin of Species* had been published four years before.

Liebig was nevertheless correct. There was no adequate scientific organization, with full ranks of scientists of every grade. A handful of geniuses was no alternative.

It seems that the forces which built up the British Empire during the nineteenth century also contained the factors which prevented the construction of an adequate national system of science. This did not begin to take shape until the empire had disintegrated.

Capitalist industrialism was, on the whole, only interested in science which was immediately profitable. It regarded most science as in the same category as painting or poetry, which could be praiseworthily patronized by those wealthy men who chose to do so. It set the general direction in which science was to go, but it was not prepared to pay for its development unless the returns were quick and large.

The subjects of this book made outspoken criticisms of its lethargy in advancing and utilizing science.

The complacency derived from profits at home was increased by those from exploitation abroad, and paralysed the development of a scientific social order, both at home and abroad.

Comparison of the life and work of the nine subjects reveals certain features which have influenced the development of statesmanship in science.

Brougham and Haldane, like their great predecessor Bacon, combined their concern for science with the profession of law. They also became Lord Chancellors. Evidently, these men's constellation of interests was favourable to statesmanship in science. All of them, besides accomplishing great achievements, also suffered exceptional tribulations. Perhaps one cause of this was the strain of extending their grasp to science, in addition to law, philosophy, politics and literature.

Brougham, Playfair and Haldane were Scotsmen with Scottish educations. Their national characteristics appear to have aided them in promoting the organization of science.

Playfair and Strange had connections with India. British science appears to have gained something from the tradition of the British administrators of India. They dealt with large administrative problems, which were more detached from immediate commercial considerations than comparable problems in Britain. This is seen particularly in Strange, who directly applied his Indian administrative experience to the conception of an adequate scientific organization for Britain.

Playfair, the Prince Consort, Haldane, Tizard and Cherwell had part, or the whole, of their higher education in Germany. Their concern for the organization of science was influenced by their German experience.

Only Grove and the Duke of Devonshire had entirely English educations. It seems that men whose education was purely English did not make the greatest contributions to the organization of British science during the last hundred and fifty years. It is reasonable to conclude that English education was unsuited to the purpose, and that the Duke was an exception that proved the rule.

Military experience had its influence in stimulating an understanding for the organization of science, and the need for it to have the appropriate strategy and tactics. This is seen in the work of the Prince Consort, Strange, Haldane, Tizard and Cherwell. The intense pressure for scientific organization which has been exerted through military necessity is seen in the work of Tizard and Cherwell. At the same time, it illustrates the extreme importance of many-sidedness and balanced views in the statesmanship of science. Owing to limitations in various directions, these two masterful spirits came into collision. In the conflict, Tizard showed the better technical judgment, but less skill in politics; Cherwell was more skilful in making use of the political forces that could carry through the policies in which he believed, but he failed to submit his proposals to adequate technical criticism.

Their gifts were major, and so were some of their shortcomings.

To adopt a saying of Ben Jonson's in another connection, they were 'great but disproportion'd Muses'.

The belief that the kind of development of science which actually occurred was the only one possible is generally taken for granted. The careers of scientists are usually looked at as if they were fine plants which grew inevitably into the kind determined by their species. Babbage and Faraday would always have grown into a Babbage and a Faraday, irrespective of the social soil in which they were planted.

In fact, Babbage, Faraday and the rest were growing in an environment in which there were strong restrictive forces preventing the adequate organization of science. If these forces had been removed, the environment would have been different, and so would their achievements. Great though they were, under these conditions they would have been greater still. It might not have been necessary to wait for fifty years for the development of electrical engineering, or a hundred years for the computer.

If the British scientists of the last century and a half had been living within an adequate scientific order, Britain today might not have become a second-class power. The failure to create an appropriate scientific social order, which could have made full use of the national scientific talent, was due to the inhibiting effect of principles that are inherent in capitalist society.

Henry Brougham

1778–1868

I

Carrying Science into the Heart of the Nation

HENRY BROUGHAM initiated the first action by the British state for the education of the new population brought into existence by the industrial revolution. He became the most prominent promoter of the mechanics' institute movement, out of which organized technical education arose. He was the most influential founder of the University of London, and the proposer of a system of modern universities in the chief industrial cities, in which due weight was to be given to science.

He launched the *Society for the Diffusion of Useful Knowledge*, which was the first major effort to provide suitable scientific and technical literature for the new working and professional classes. It issued a large number of excellent works at a very reasonable price, in the form now known as paper-backs.

Besides acting politically and organizationally, Brougham wrote regularly on many aspects of science, especially in the earlier numbers of the *Edinburgh Review*, which he had helped to found. His scientific articles were one of its most original features. A running commentary on the progress of science had previously not been so clearly conceived and sustained in the intellectual journalism designed to influence governing opinion. This kind of journalism had hitherto been almost exclusively literary.

Brougham contributed by helping to change the public attitude to science, rather than by making scientific discoveries or teaching. This attitude, as in many other matters of public opinion in the period, was forcibly expressed by William Cobbett. In a lecture in 1830 he opposed the legalization of the sale of dead corpses for teaching and research: '. . . they tell us it was necessary for the purposes of science. Science! Why, who is science for? Not for poor people. Then if it be necessary for the purposes of science, let them have the bodies of the rich, for whose benefit science is cultivated! (Cheers.)'

Brougham's most recent biographer, Chester W. New, has claimed that he had a leading part in extending the democratization of science. He has suggested that by virtue of the number, variety and importance of his achievements, Brougham has had more influence on history than any other Englishman in the first half of the nineteenth century, and one of the reasons why this is not recognized is that the English believe that only prime ministers and party leaders can have major political importance.

Brougham was in office only four years, and was never prime minister, whereas a conventional statesman such as Palmerston held office for forty-six years, and that of prime minister for ten.

Brougham's difficulty in collaborating with colleagues was one of the causes of his exclusion from office. This had been attributed to his character and mental instability. The difficulty was exacerbated, however, by his education, which was both Scottish and scientific. His ideology was different from that of conventional English statesmen. His education had endowed him with a passion for improvement, and had helped him to understand and visualize what might be done.

It was hard to perceive at the beginning of the nineteenth century that the extension of scientific and technical education might be more immediately important for science than the discovery of particular facts and theories. In the second half of the twentieth century it is easier to see that progress depends as much on staff and equipment as on talent. A scientifically and technically educated population, provided with an adequate organization of research and development will in the long run be more fertile of discovery than occasional individual geniuses arising in a generally uneducated and unequipped population.

Brougham made his contribution through his combination of broad scientific knowledge with political achievement. He harnessed his political fame to his projects for scientific and technical education. The popular force of which he was the vehicle of expression became a motive power for advancing the democratization of science.

Physically, Brougham was a tall, ungainly man, with an ugly face and huge nose which continually twitched. Bagehot said that Brougham 'used to punctuate his sentences with his nose; just at the end of a long parenthesis he *could*, and did, turn up his nose, which served to note the change of subject as well, or better, than a printed mark'. He had great endurance, and 'the power of sleeping at any time'. The portrait painter B. R. Haydon wrote that 'His eye is as fine as any eye I ever saw. It is like a lion's watching for prey. It is a clear grey, the light vibrating at the bottom of the iris, and the cornea shining silvery and tense.'

He had a tremendous fund of knowledge, which he could draw upon instantly through a strong memory, with an accuracy which was sufficient to make it extremely formidable in debate, though not to make him a writer who can be relied upon without checking. His information, sarcasm, humour, pungent phrase, effective voice and tireless energy gave him great command over audiences. Intelligent opponents became wary of interrupting him, and he delighted or intimidated the majority of his hearers.

T. B. Macaulay, who was twenty-two years his junior and had suffered from his almost insane jealousy as a writer and polymath, referred to this power when Brougham was taunted in the House of Commons after he had become Lord Chancellor. Macaulay rose and asked: 'Was that a time for a member of that House, who would sooner have burned his tongue than have made such an attack in the presence of the noble person, thus to attack him behind his back?'

More than 50,000 Brougham papers of various kinds have survived, forming possibly the largest number left by any man. His activity and eccentricity showed symptoms of insanity. His most extraordinary efforts were carried out with manic intensity, and these were followed by periods of depression which were less concealed as he became more prominent. After painful aberrant behaviour to people, he frequently resumed relations with them most charmingly, as if nothing had happened. It often seemed that he had become really unconscious of his former actions.

He had delusions of grandeur, and tended to support his reputation for omniscience by exaggerating and embroidering his knowledge. He had an excessive self-confidence which prompted him to attempt anything. Once, when staying with Grey in the country, he was out riding, when they came to a river. As Grey led the way in fording it, he suddenly turned in his saddle and shouted: 'Brougham, can you swim?' 'I have never swum,' bawled Brougham, 'but I have no doubt I could if I tried.' When he was a student at Edinburgh he was challenged to solve a problem in chemistry before he had studied the subject. Nevertheless, he tackled it, and did better than others who had read chemistry. Later on, this attitude led to mistakes in technical matters.

Even in his old age he was in the habit of starting his annual vacation at Brougham Hall with mathematical and scientific studies. They served to keep him in touch with the life of science.

His opponents ridiculed the superficiality of his scientific knowledge. But statesmen should not be expected to make scientific discoveries. He could hardly do this without neglecting his work of government. But he should have a general knowledge of science and its implications, and a good way of acquiring this is to undertake regular exercises in science and mathematics.

Brougham in his earlier years rushed into print on every topic almost without correction. In his later years he was more careful. In 1855, at the age of seventy-seven, he published a treatise on an *Analytical View of Sir Isaac Newton's Principia*. He obtained the collaboration of the young E. J. Routh, who had just been Senior Wrangler in the year in which Clerk Maxwell was Second.

Besides promoting the social conditions in which science can develop, the statesman of science makes proper use of the expert knowledge and advice of the young scientists who are taking the lead in their own subjects.

II

Origins and Education

BROUGHAM'S father, Henry Brougham, was a minor Westmorland squire, who possessed the small estate of Brougham, near Penrith. After being educated at Eton, where he was a school-fellow of Joseph Banks, the future President of the Royal Society, he became engaged to the daughter of a neighbour. His fiancée died on the day before they were to have been married. He was sent to Edinburgh to recover from the shock, and thenceforth preferred Scotland to Westmorland, spending as much time there as he could. Neither he nor his ancestors were of much distinction, and there was mental instability in his family.

Henry Brougham senior was recommended to take lodgings with the widow of a clergyman, Mrs. Syme, who was the sister of

William Robertson, the eminent historian and Principal of Edinburgh University. Mrs. Syme had an attractive and able daughter with whom Brougham senior soon fell in love, and married. They moved into 21 St. Andrew's Square, where, on September 19th, 1778, Henry Peter Brougham was born.

Edinburgh was then at the height of its intellectual fame. Adam Smith had published *The Wealth of Nations* two years before, and Black was in his prime. Presiding over this cultural flowering was William Robertson, the infant Brougham's great-uncle.

The Robertson family superintended the education of the young Henry. He was given the best the world then had to offer. Brougham said that his maternal grandmother, the sister of Robertson, was 'remarkable for beauty, but far more for a masculine intellect and clear understanding. She instilled into me from my cradle the strongest desire for information, and the first principles of that persevering energy in the pursuit of every kind of knowledge which, more than any natural talents I may possess, has enabled me to stick to, and to accomplish, how far successfully it is not for me to say, every task I ever undertook.'

His grandmother worked with him at his lessons from day to day, so that at the age of seven he was ready to enter the Edinburgh High School. During the period that he was attending the school, his grandmother was also his daily help and instructress. Under her careful tuition he kept a good place in his class, and, 'with a perseverance that almost amounted to obstinacy', on one occasion made his teacher 'confess he had been wrong and I right, in some disputed bit of Latinity for which he had the day before punished me. My victory gained me immense credit with all my school fellows, and I was called "the boy that had licked the master".'

Brougham went into the class of the Rector, Dr. Alexander Adam, a noted teacher, in 1789, three months before the outbreak of the French Revolution. Dr. Adam was 'a zealous friend of liberty, and in those times and in that place was termed a democrat'. He illustrated his teaching and interpretation of the classics by allusions to 'the great events then engrossing the attention of the world'. His reputation and position were such that no exception was then taken to his comments. 'Three or four years later, when party violence was at its height, but when the crimes of the French mob had alienated many admirers of the Revolution, he carefully abstained from such subjects, though he still continued of that class which clung to the Revolution more or less, in spite of its crimes.'

Adam was deeply interested in public speaking, and encouraged his pupils to study and practise this art. Brougham says that his grandmother advised him to model his style on Chatham, and his father took him to hear famous orators. Brougham himself learned from a preacher with a weak voice the art of whispering. He developed his famous 'Brougham's whispers', that could penetrate to every nook and cranny of a silent, spellbound House of Commons.

Brougham says that at the age of ten, he heard his great-uncle, the Principal, forecast the French Revolution, in a sermon in 1788. Robertson's son did not publish it, to avoid his father being described as a Jacobin. His grandmother was the Principal's favourite sister, and presided over his household for eight years before she married. The Principal's sisters always respectfully addressed him as 'Sir'.

Adam was a first cousin of the Principal. Another first cousin, who was particularly close to him and his sister was John Clerk, the noted theorist of naval tactics, geologist and great-granduncle of James Clerk Maxwell.

Soon after entering the High School, Brougham had a serious illness. His father took him to his Westmorland house, with a tutor, Dr. Mitchell, who later became chief physician to the Rajah of Travancore.

Brougham's interest in science and mathematics was evident early. When he was about twelve, a relative who happened to meet him on a bridge in Edinburgh, noticed that he was carrying under his arm a volume of Laplace in French.

Among his playmates and school-fellows was Francis Horner, who later was to become a noted economist, and introduced Brougham to Holland House.

By the age of sixteen Brougham organized a Juvenile Literary Society, which debated such questions as the existence of innate ideas in the human mind, and whether the philosophy of Aristotle had been of ultimate advantage to the human mind.

Brougham entered Edinburgh University in 1792. He came especially under the influence of John Playfair the mathematician, and of Joseph Black, whose last course of lectures he attended. He also attended the lectures of Robison and Dugald Stewart. Brougham rarely spoke of Stewart, while Stewart is reported to have said that Brougham was the most brilliant student he had ever had, but was always verging on insanity. Robison greatly esteemed Brougham's brilliance, and may have given him too uncritical encouragement.

Playfair combated the contemporary British backwardness in mathematics, and stimulated the study of Continental mathematics, which had overtaken the British school in the hundred years since Newton was at his zenith. He learned geology in his later years to expound the revolutionary geological theories of his friend James Hutton. He was interested in Oriental studies, and the master of an expository prose style which has never been surpassed. He was the profoundest authority of the period on Bacon's philosophy of science. In addition, he was a man of the world. He was a candidate for the hand of the rich and fascinating widow, Mrs. Apreece. Fortunately for him, she chose to accept Humphry Davy instead. In spite of her attractions, she was a self-centred person, and the marriage with Davy was unhappy.

Playfair could understand many sides of Brougham's nature. Brougham had two sorts of friends, intellectuals such as Jeffrey and Cockburn, one to become the editor of the *Edinburgh Review* and the other a distinguished lawyer and author; and roistering students described as 'fellows of dissipation, fun, and frolick'. After wild suppers, Brougham and the latter sallied out into the Edinburgh streets, where they wrenched off brass knockers and door handles, especially in the New Town, which 'abounded in sea-green doors and huge brazen devices, which were more than youthful hands could resist'. Their spoils filled 'a large dark closet' in his father's house. 'Writing at nearly ninety years of age, I can recall those, not boys' but young men's freaks with pleasure and even exultation.'

In letters at the time, Brougham gave advice to friends, apparently based on his own experience, on the medical treatment of venereal disease.

Walter Scott founded the Friday Club in 1803, of which Brougham, Playfair, Jeffrey, Sydney Smith, Cockburn and Dugald Stewart were original members. After a discussion on Greek medicine and Galen at one of their suppers, Brougham, Professor Playfair, the Rev. Sydney Smith and Mr. Thomas Thomson (Clerk of Sessions) went into the streets, primed with Brougham's own special punch made of 'rum, sugar, lemons, marmalade, calves foot jelly, water and more rum', with the intention of securing a bronze head of Galen, erected high over the door of an apothecary's shop. The professor tried to hold Sydney Smith steady, while Thomson climbed on his shoulders to reach the head. When he had almost got it, they suddenly observed the police watch approaching. They took to their heels, while Brougham looked on with a grin. He was suspected of having tipped off the watch.

Brougham had a lively correspondence with his cousin Francis Horner, in which they discussed science, politics, and their aims in life. Before he was eighteen he sent Francis a long mock heroic poem, which he called the *Bankiad*, and begged him to *burn* after reading it. In the accompanying letter he said that Sir Joseph Banks had courted a young lady called Blosset, before he sailed in the *Endeavour* with Captain Cook. Banks had given her a bond for £10,000, if on his return he did not marry her, and he actually incurred the forfeiture. He had this story from his father, who was a school-fellow of Banks, and knew both parties well. Passages in the *Bankiad* ran:

Otaheite: a night scene

And now at rest from boistrous waves and winds
The Good Endeavour, peaceful mooring finds,

. . .

Brave Cook fatigued, in hammock courts repose
Nor dreams of falling mid new South Sea foes:
The Lincoln Hero, *too at full length laid,*
His mighty carcase is by Morpheus sway'd.
When Lo! in dreams a lovely form appears,
In her right hand a Parchment bond she rears.
Canst thou forsake me for that tawny jade
In whose canoe so oft thou seekst the shade?
Arise, arise, thy dear first love complains
Ah leave Oberea, to her South Sea swains.
See here this bond (ten thousand pounds of gold)
Shall from thy coffers into mine be told.
Accents of these, of mingled grief and rage,
Awake the man of plants, *the grazing sage.*
'By God tis true—damme, tis very true.
Give up the jade—then lose the money too.—
But still a wife—be saddled with a wife—

Perchance a family—a BORE *for life—*
What then becomes of all my plants and STONES
In gathering which, so oft I've risked my bones?
'No, no—by God! I vow it shall not be—
Cost what it will—I must; I shall be free.
What might I not buy with ten thousand pound
What charming, rare museums, second hand?
Books, Ribbons, ROTTEN BIRDS *and* boroughs, *Land?*

. . .

Not long afterwards Brougham was seeking Banks' influence in securing permits for freedom from being pressed into the Navy, and trying to get diplomatic appointments.

At about this time, Brougham remarked in a letter to Francis on the bad effects of 'close mathematical labours' on his 'fluency of speech'. After working on a problem he found he was unable to shine in company afterwards. With regard to his future he told Francis: 'Science is unquestionably a far finer field for mental exertion than *Law* or even *politics*: but worldly things have their weight and their sweets: an independent spirit revolts from the idea of subsisting wholly on any man's bounty, even on a father's.'

Brougham eagerly studied Newton's *Optics*, which was particularly highly esteemed by the Edinburgh school as the best example of experimental physics. He thought he had been able to add something to Newton's work on interference and diffraction, and at the age of sixteen wrote a paper on his investigations with the title: *Experiments and Observations on the Inflection, Reflection, and Colours of Light.* It was communicated to the Royal Society of London by the Secretary, Sir Charles Blagden, and read when he was seventeen. The paper exhibited some originality and great industry. Brougham followed this paper, published in the *Philosophical Transactions* for 1796, with a second under the title *Further Experiments and Observations on the Affections and Properties of Light*, which appeared in the *Transactions* for 1797. The Swiss physicist Prévost subsequently drew attention in the *Transactions* to faults in these two papers. They had not been thoroughly refereed, and it also seems probable that Robison had passed them without perceiving their shortcomings.

Brougham sent a third paper to the Royal Society. This was on the geometrical subject of *Porisms*, and was published in the

Transactions of the Royal Society in 1798. Porisms are a kind of proposition which deals with the conditions which render a given problem capable of an indefinite number of solutions. Playfair had recently contributed to this subject, and his pupil began by saying that it was to this mathematician that 'we owe the first distinct and popular account of this formerly mysterious but most interesting subject'. Porisms had been discussed by Euclid, and in the third century A.D. by Pappus of Alexandria. They had used classical geometrical methods, whereas Brougham used modern analytical methods.

While Brougham was a student at Edinburgh, George Birkbeck and Thomas Young were among those who were attending some of the same lectures, including those of Black. Birkbeck was two years older than Brougham, and Young, already an accomplished scientist and scholar, was five years older. Young never had a systematic university education, but attended some lectures to extend his knowledge. There does not seem to be any evidence that Brougham had much to do with them as a student, though his subsequent relations with both had important effects.

Young was attending the Edinburgh courses to extend his training for the medical profession. He was a profound scientist, but of an introspective, intellectually self-contained nature. These characteristics were probably intensified by his Quaker origin. He wrote in a heavy style, with long sentences and many qualifications, like a German professor. The future founder of the wave-theory of light and decipherer of the Egyptian hieroglyphics had already progressed far in the knowledge of science and languages, which was to earn for him the reputation of being the most learned Englishman who ever lived.

Brougham and Young were separated by age, training, and development. Brougham was still the precocious student, Young the adult scholar widening his reading. Besides this, they were extremely different in temperament and opinions. It is possible that they did notice each other, and mutually formed an instinctive dislike. Brougham was inspired by Black, whereas Young only derived 'some little information on chemistry' from his 'copious course'. In Greek he found only 'many well-informed men, but hardly any deep scholars'. He had an aristocratic view of learning, exactly the contrary of Brougham's. Years later, Brougham remarked that whereas Cambridge produced a few profound scientists, and a large number of graduates unversed in modern knowledge, Edinburgh produced a large number of men who had a useful knowledge of contemporary science.

In 1800 Young published an article in the *British Magazine* in which he expressed his belief in the inferiority of analytical to geometrical methods of investigation, and referred to Brougham's paper on *Porisms* as an example. Young's opinions on method, and his literary style, are well illustrated in the following sentence: 'the strong inclination which has been shown, especially on the continent, to prefer the algebraical to the geometrical form of representation, is a sufficient proof, that, instead of endeavouring to strengthen and enlighten the reasoning faculties, by accustoming them to such a consecutive train of argument as can be fully conceived by the mind, and represented with all its links by the recollection, they have only been desirous of sparing themselves as much as possible the pains of thought and labour by a kind of mechanical abridgment, which at best only serves the office of a book of tables in facilitating computations, but which very often fails even of this end, and is at the same time the most circuitous and the least intelligible'.

He proposed the collection of a 'complete system' or index of mathematics, which would provide an easily accessible record of what has already been discovered. This would help the mathematician, who 'may very easily fancy he has made discoveries, when the same facts had been known and forgotten long before he existed. An instance of this has lately occurred to a young gentleman in Edinburgh, a man who certainly promises, in the course of time, to add considerably to our knowledge of the laws of nature. . . .' Young pointed out that some of Brougham's results were variations, or rediscoveries, of properties of curves already obtained by Huyghens and Newton. Indeed, the equation for one of those curves 'is to be found in a work no less common than Emerson's *Fluxions*, nearly in the same form as it is published as new in the *Philosophical Transactions* for 1798. We find in the same paper a new method of dividing an elliptic area in a given ratio; but the curve which the author calls a cycloid is the companion of a trochoid, and is only a distortion of the figure by which Newton had very simply and elegantly solved the same problem. . . .'

Young was right in pointing out that several of Brougham's results were only variations of previous discoveries, but he ignored the original features of his paper, and was wrong in his opinion of method. Brougham was right in advocating the use of analytical methods, besides obtaining some new results.

Brougham was deeply angered by Young's criticism; nor was he alone in his anger. Young had dismissed Dr. Robert Smith's *Harmonics* as 'a large and obscure volume, which, for every purpose but for the use of an impracticable instrument, leaves the subject precisely where it found it'.

Robert Smith, who was born in 1689 and died in 1768, was a cousin of Roger Cotes, and a follower and friend of Isaac Newton. He wrote a treatise in *Optics*, which was also severely criticized by Young. He became Plumian professor of astronomy, and Master of Trinity College. Because of his *Optics* he was known to his students as 'Old Focus'. He was the founder of the Smith's Prizes, the most famous of Cambridge mathematical prizes. Young's strictures provoked Robison, a reverential admirer of Newton, and Brougham's teacher of physics, to write that he was 'sorry to see this', because he had great expectations from the future labours of Young 'in the field of harmonics'. Young's late work in the subject was 'rich in refined and valuable matter. We presume humbly to recommend to him attention to his own admonitions to a very young and ingenious gentleman who he thinks, proceeded too far in animadverting on the writings of Newton, Barrow and other mathematicians.'

Young's criticism was regarded in Edinburgh circles as conceited. Brougham considered that an unprovoked attack had been made on himself. Peacock, the biographer of Young, was particularly well qualified to express an opinion on this matter as a friend of Young and an eminent mathematician, and a reformer who had assisted in some of Brougham's activities. Referring to the paper on *Porisms*, he said: 'The author of this paper, which contains several porismatic propositions, which are curious and original, was Mr. Brougham, then a very young man, whose enterprising genius seems to have prepared him to grapple with every branch of human knowledge; and though the particular criticism referred to was just, it was somewhat flippant and ungracious, and was probably not without its influence in provoking the severe retaliatory treatment which Young's own Memoirs shortly afterwards experienced at the hands of one who, not himself invulnerable, was armed at all points, and always prepared to come to close quarters with his enemies.'

While this controversy was simmering, Brougham was very active in many other things.

The Scottish attitude to education sprang from complex and profound causes. In the first place, it arose out of the Scottish attitude to religion. The priest was the spiritual leader, whom the local population had chosen by election; there was a democratic element in his appointment. He was expected to give leadership through the medium of preaching. Consequently, rhetoric, the technique of persuasion and the communication of information through speech, became highly esteemed.

The Scottish religious organization had a very important rôle in the struggles with the English for national independence.

The Scottish universities were initially training colleges for priests, and reflected the characteristics of the Scottish religious system. Their professors were secular priests who lectured to assemblies of students. They were expected to expound knowledge by the same technique by which the priests expounded religion.

In England, the attitude in the ancient universities was different. A professor was a gentleman imparting knowledge rather than an authoritative spiritual guide. He even preferred to be known as 'Mr.' rather than by his academic title.

The differences between the Scottish and the English attitudes to education had deep historical and social roots, and mutual understanding between them was not easy. The difference was deepened by the transfer of the Scottish Court from Edinburgh to London, when James I ascended the English throne. This reduced the direct influence of aristocratic ideas in Scottish education, and left the democratic tradition more in possession.

Brougham, with his rhetoric, democracy and mixture of natural science with the rest of knowledge, was a spectacular product of the Scottish educational tradition. As such, he was unintelligible and distasteful to many Oxford and Cambridge men who, however profound they might be, generally preferred to be known as gentlemen rather than informed and practical men.

III

Finding a Profession

HENRY BROUGHAM senior had six children and only a small income, so he could not allow them much. His eldest son had definitely before him the necessity for earning a living. Henry Peter Brougham's first publications were scientific, but there was no scientific profession which he could enter. Many of the keen Edinburgh students of science went into medicine, and an increasing number into industry. As the son of an English squire, Brougham was not orientated in these directions. Like other Edinburgh graduates of gentlemanly descent, energetic intellectual interests, and little money, he was encouraged to enter the law. His teacher Dr. Adam, his father, and the exciting atmosphere of intellectual debate in the numerous Edinburgh societies and clubs, all impelled him in this direction. As a boy he had lived in St. Andrew's Square next door to Lord Buchan, the brother of the great Scottish lawyer Lord Erskine. In this atmosphere, Brougham deliberately developed his technique of speaking.

Like most of the able Edinburgh students of the period he was well acquainted with the philosophy and career of Francis Bacon. Dugald Stewart and Robison had a thorough knowledge of Baconian philosophy, and Playfair was the great living authority on it. Brougham himself said that one of the first things he did after entering the University was to join in a debate in a society on Liberty and Necessity, in which he exposed the mistakes of other speakers in terms of Bacon's theory of idols, or errors which arise from the nature of the mind.

New says that Brougham gave much attention to Bacon at this time, whose example of a combined career in law, politics, literature and science may have influenced him. Brougham was inclined to take 'all knowledge for his province' then, and for the rest of his long life. As the number and variety of his activities multiplied, this thread helped to hold them together in a whole, the rationality of which was often not evident to observers. In spite of his aberrations and failures, Brougham succeeded in following Bacon as a statesman who combined initiative with regard to science, law and literature.

During vacations Brougham explored Scotland in walking tours with some of his student friends. In the west of Scotland, 'the evenings (if sober) were diversified by visits to the Glasgow natives, whose golden brutality served to render our private society doubly agreeable'. He broadened his education by tours in the Scottish islands, and in Scandinavia. It was for these tours, which involved travel at sea, that he secured protection through Sir Joseph Banks, against being pressed as a young man for service in the Navy.

He found Denmark in the grip of a despotism which, 'execrable as its theory, is in practice mild and gentle. Every liberty of speech and writing is practised, to a degree of licentiousness unknown in England, or known only to be severely punished. Of this the natives seem perfectly conscious, and laugh at English liberty, which they call a mere name.' The Swedes already had houses 'all good and clean—magnificent compared to those of the English peasantry'. The learned Swedes were stigmatized as Jacobinical, and were great readers of *The Wealth of Nations*. All of them were freethinkers. But the manners of the people in Stockholm were 'extremely dissolute'.

After he had returned to the grind of learning law at Edinburgh, he wrote to his companion Charles Stuart, who later became Lord Stuart de Rothesay and an ambassador: 'I still continue more and more to detest this place, and this cursedest of cursed professions.' He appeared to be giving too much time to chemistry, physics and mathematics. The aunt of one of his friends wrote that she hoped 'he will now settle to Business', and reported that Stuart had said that 'he is the cleverest man he ever knew, but the least steady'. He was, however, now 'applying very close'.

Brougham explored the possibility of escaping from the detested profession indirectly through science. 'It had occurred to me that my father's old friend and schoolfellow, Sir Joseph Banks, who had on several occasions expressed an interest in my welfare, might have it in his power to help me.' This time he asked Banks for aid in securing a diplomatic post, but it was not effective.

Brougham set out to qualify himself for some kind of public position by writing an authoritative book on *The Colonial Policy of the European Powers*. He published a large work on that subject, containing 1,176 pages, divided into four books, in 1803.

One of his aims was to combat the current propaganda against colonization, on the ground that it was economically unprofitable. He considered that he had shown 'how completely erroneous those vague assertions are, which ascribe nothing but expense to the maintenance of colonial relations', and that 'even the colonies which bring the smallest direct revenue into the coffers of the mother country, contribute much more to their own separate government and defence, than many of the contiguous districts'.

The most striking part of the work was the fourth book, which dealt in particular with Negro Slavery. He gave a trenchant well-informed account both of negro slavery and the slave trade, with the aim of finding a suitable policy for dealing with 'the complicated iniquities and the manifold disadvantages of the slave system'.

He started by making very clear that he did not propose immediate emancipation. 'Some zealots have contended, with an inexcusable thoughtlessness, that the crimes of those whose avarice has transferred the population of Africa to the West Indies can only be expiated by immediate emancipation of the slaves. The councils of such fanatics have unhappily been adopted and carried into effect by one of the most enlightened nations in the world; and we have frequently had occasion to view the consequences of those insane measures in the course of this Inquiry.'

The only plan for dealing with the situation 'must proceed upon the principle of new-modelling the present structure of society, and retaining at the same time all the parts of which it is composed'.

The first step was the Total Abolition of the Slave Trade, which he sharply distinguished from the system of slavery already established in the colonies. He argued that effective action could best begin from outside the colonies, by stopping the slave-trade at sea. 'No assembly composed of planters, and sitting in a slave colony, will ever, to the end of time, think for one moment of abolishing the trade.'

'The mother country alone is competent to effect the abolition of the slave trade,' because action could be taken by the Government in London to suppress the slave-trade at sea. When the import of fresh slaves was cut off, the planters would be forced to ameliorate the condition of their slaves. This would set in motion the same train of social forces which gradually changed the slave system of the ancient world into feudalism, and of feudalism into capitalism.

'We meet with many very singular analogies between the history of the negroes in South America, and that of the villeins or bondsmen of Europe, in the earlier feudal times.'

Besides giving a vivid and compact account of negro slavery, Brougham interpreted its future in terms of social dynamics. He concluded his book with the observation: 'It seems to be the lot of nations to derive instruction from experience, rather than example; and however acutely they may discern the consequences of folly in the conduct of their neighbours, no sooner has the case become their own, than indolence, or timidity, or a senseless confidence in good fortune, blinds them to the most obvious applications of the lessons before their eyes; discourages all ideas of reformation; and gives birth to the same strange delusion, so often fatal to individuals, that the circumstances and the conduct which have ruined others, may prove harmless or beneficial to themselves.'

The book achieved its aim. When Brougham toured Holland in 1804, furnished with an American passport and papers because of the Napoleonic Wars, he found it already well known. In London it secured for him the lasting regard and friendship of Wilberforce. Later on, the book attracted the attention of Karl Marx.

Brougham had not yet clearly perceived where his political future lay. He appears to have asked Wilberforce, William Pitt's close friend, whether there was any chance of his being found a Tory seat in the House of Commons. Nothing came of this.

While the book was in the press a great deal more was happening to Brougham. He was elected a fellow of the Royal Society of London in 1803. He had been born in 1778, the same year as Humphry Davy, and he became a fellow of the Royal Society in the same year.

Besides this, in 1802, Brougham had been associated with the foundation of the *Edinburgh Review*, an event of great intellectual and political importance.

IV

The Edinburgh Review

THE intense intellectual activity in Edinburgh during the last years of the eighteenth century grew under a crust of political dictatorship exercised by Dundas, on behalf of the Tories and William Pitt. There were only four thousand voters in the whole of Scotland, and it was not difficult to control so small a number by bribery. Dundas was smilingly relentless rather than brutal; educated people simply just did not get the better jobs unless they entirely engaged themselves to the Tories.

The new type of middle-class student, trained in the new political economy and science arising out of the Industrial Revolution, was in sharp conflict with the Dundas régime. Their ideas were so different that they could not cooperate with it, even when they tried.

In this atmosphere of frustration, Francis Jeffrey, Sydney Smith, Francis Horner and some others conceived the idea of starting a review to provide a medium of expression for their pent-up aspirations. They thought of asking Brougham to join them, but Sydney Smith objected on the ground that he was too rash and indiscreet. Smith was persuaded to withdraw his objection, and Brougham was invited to come in. Jeffrey was to be the editor. He was twenty-nine years old, and Brougham, the youngest of the founders, twenty-three.

The new journal was published by Constable on a thoroughly middle-class businesslike basis. The editor was to be paid the then handsome salary of £300 a year, and contributors were to be paid for at the then high rate of £10 per sheet.

Articles were to be fearlessly critical and anonymous, and there were to be no concessions to the public in intellectual standards. The journal was conceived almost in a spirit of intellectual defiance to what is nowadays called the middlebrow.

To the surprise of the founders, the new review went off like an intellectual explosion. They were astonished by the circulation, which swiftly rose to the unheard-of number of 3,000. The quality, pay and success brought a stream of able contributions from others besides the founders. The review immediately became the most influential journal in the English-speaking world on the intellectual aspects of the formation of governing opinion.

The first number, which appeared in October 1802, contained twenty-nine articles. Seven of them were by Brougham. Three of these were on books of travels, one on his special subject of negro slavery, and three on science. One of these consists of a detailed review, more than six thousand words long, of Playfair's expository masterpiece: *Illustrations of the Huttonian Theory of the Earth*, which had been published earlier in the year.

Brougham took a detached view of the work of his own teacher. He dwelt on the difficulties of the study of the history of the earth, on the number and diversity of the facts necessary for such an inquiry. 'To so short a distance are we yet removed from the period when mineralogical phenomena first derived explication from chemistry, that attempts to form a theory of the earth may be considered rather as exercises for fanciful and speculative minds, than as sources of improvement to useful science. It cannot be denied, however, that observations accumulate but slowly when unassisted by the influence of system.'

The theory depended on the startling 'supposition of a perpetual central heat, capable of melting limestone by its intensity, and of elevating continents by its expansion'. The origin of this heat posed a very difficult question. As Playfair had explained, it could not be maintained 'either by combustion, by friction, by the absorption of the solar rays, or by any of the other causes from which heat is known to be derived. . . . Heat generated and supported without combustion, and at a distance from all the other sources from which heat is found to proceed, is a substance with which we have no acquaintance, and which we cannot admit to exist, merely because such a supposition would enable us to account for certain appearances.'

The adequate answer to this question came exactly one hundred years later, when, in 1902, Rutherford explained the internal heat as a result of the spontaneous disintegration of radioactive atoms in the earth's material.

Brougham proceeded to discuss the Huttonian theory of the formation of stratified rocks, of mountain-building, and the scientific explanation of the numerous mechanical, physical and chemical processes involved. He concluded that the ability with which Playfair 'has combined the complicated materials of his subject, and the correct and luminous order he has observed in the statement of a loose and analytical argument, have given a precision and scientific unity to the system of Dr. Hutton, in which it was formerly deficient. . . . The work is therefore highly worthy of perusal, and deserved to be considered as by far the most able elucidation and vindication of the Huttonian theory, that has yet been presented to the public.'

This view of Playfair's book has been generally accepted ever since.

The other substantial scientific article by Brougham in this first volume was a review of Wood's *Elements of Optics*. Brougham commented that the subject appeared to have been treated mainly from the mathematical point of view for the benefit of astronomers, and not in the inductive, or what we should call the experimental, physical style of Newton's *Optics*. He thought that the work succeeded very well as a textbook. 'The parts are digested and arranged with great perspicuity; the order in which they succeed each other is, for the most part, natural and easy; the demonstrations are sufficiently neat and concise; and yet the steps of the reasoning are given with such fullness, that any learner may readily follow them, provided he is prepared by a previous acquaintance with the elements of mathematics.' He considered, however, that the author's references to the experimental branch of the science contained inaccuracies, and his account of Newton's speculations on the nature of light was in some points completely mistaken.

Brougham shows himself preoccupied with the details of the question whether light consists of particles and waves. He concludes his review with the comment that failure to distinguish clearly between experiment and theory has in some other writers 'given birth to the most deformed and noxious productions of speculative imagination'.

Brougham's reviews on travels and slavery are what might be expected of an author about to publish an authoritative book on colonial policy. One work dealt with a survey of the Ottoman Empire, Egypt and Persia, carried out by the French in the early stages of their Revolution; another dealt with Scandinavia.

Brougham's contributions amounted to at least 25,000 words, forming about 55 pages out of 252, in the first volume.

In the second volume, published in January 1803, he had

another six articles, of which four were on science. The first of these was on a paper by Robert Woodhouse in the Transactions of the Royal Society, *On the Necessary Truth of certain Conclusions obtained by Means of Imaginary Expressions*. Woodhouse was one of the Cambridge mathematicians engaged in modernizing British mathematics at the beginning of the nineteenth century. He promoted the critical consideration of mathematical methods, which was part of the reform. For a hundred years after Descartes, Newton and Leibnitz had invented analytical geometry and the calculus, mathematicians had used and developed these methods, and had obtained with them a rich harvest of profound results.

As the new mathematical techniques were overwhelmingly fertile, mathematicians did not stop to bother about obscurities which occasionally arose in them. One of these was caused by the use of entities such as the square root of minus one. These evidently had no meaning in terms of analogy with ordinary numbers such as 1, 2 and 3. They were therefore described as *imaginary* numbers; nevertheless, these *imaginary* numbers, when handled according to the ordinary rules of calculation, could be used to obtain results which were found to be *real* in the actual world.

By the beginning of the nineteenth century, mathematicians were no longer satisfied with cheerfully accepting such entities as long as they led to useful results, without probing into their exact nature.

Brougham started with the comment that no small part of modern mathematics depended on the use of imaginary quantities. 'It is natural to expect that the grounds of a doctrine, on which rests so large a part of the analytical edifice, have been fully examined; that all objections have been successfully answered; and that no room is left for doubt or cavil. The contrary, however, will, in reality, be found to be the case. Mathematicians have been more attentive to improve and extend their methods than solicitous to examine the principles on which they are founded.' Men of a scientific turn could not be satisfied with this situation. He quoted Woodhouse's view that 'if operations with any characters or signs lead to just conclusions, such operations must be true by virtue of some principle or other; and the objections against imaginary quantities ought to be obviated upon the unsatisfactory explanation given of their nature and uses'.

Brougham said that this position could hardly be denied. But if it was intended to argue 'that every general method that uniformly leads to true conclusions, must therefore be regulated by the rules of sound logic', this could not be accepted. 'The differential calculus, as laid down by Leibnitz and his followers, is another example of a method, even more extensive than the imaginary arithmetic, always leading to truth, and yet founded in false and inconclusive reasoning.'

Brougham expressed the opinion, supplied by a quotation from Lagrange, that the paradox in the use of imaginary quantities and the calculus was in both cases solved in the same way. The false suppositions in the methods were 'obviated and corrected by the very operations which the rules of the calculus require to be performed'.

The elucidation of these problems, and the provision of an adequate logical basis for the new mathematics was to prove one of the greatest achievements of the nineteenth-century mathematicians.

Brougham was not a professional mathematician. His views on the logical problems of mathematics were not particularly accurate or technically far-seeing, but he understood the general character and importance of the subject.

His next article was on William Herschel's paper in the *Philosophical Transactions* on *Observations on the two lately discovered Celestial bodies*. These were the minor planets Ceres and Pallas, recently discovered by Piazzi and Olbers respectively. Brougham says that 'this excellent astronomer has given us a set of new and accurate observations, tending to establish some very singular and interesting facts. We hold it to be a duty indispensably incumbent on us to present our readers with a sketch of this very valuable paper.'

Herschel had shown that the new bodies were very much smaller than the planets, or even their satellites. They moved in eccentric orbits, and their motion might be in the same, or in the opposite, direction as that of the known planets revolving round the sun. He concluded that they were neither comets nor planets, and proposed the name of Asteroids.

Brougham said he had 'the most implicit confidence on the accuracy of his observations, from long experience of his general skill, patience and fidelity, and from our knowledge of the excellence of his instruments'. But with regard to his conclusions, 'with all possible deference, we hold ourselves as well qualified to judge of the truth of these, as if we had ourselves made or verified the observations upon which they are founded'.

Brougham objected to the introduction of the new term Asteroid, which implied that the solar system contained different kinds of bodies unconnected in their nature. He thought it would be more philosophical 'to consider that both planets and comets are bodies of the same nature, forming different parts of one great system'.

He criticized Herschel severely 'for coining words and idioms'. He objected to his new terms such as space-penetrating power, telescopic sweeps, construction of the heavens, quintuple and multiple stars, stellar nebulae, milky nebulosity, straight-line orbits, etc. He esteemed him almost entirely as an observer, and had little appreciation for the new concepts implied in Herschel's new terminology. He particularly objected to Herschel's 'hasty and erroneous theory concerning the influence of the solar spots on the price of grain: Since the publication of Gulliver's voyage to Laputa, nothing so ridiculous has ever been offered to the world. We heartily wish the Doctor had suppressed it. . . .'

Another of his articles was on Kepler's Problem; that is, how to calculate the true place of a planet at a given time. In it Brougham expounded the advantages of the new method of treating the problem, recently introduced by Ivory.

Two of his articles in the second number contained a savage attack on Thomas Young's Bakerian Lecture to the Royal Society on *The Theory of Light and Colours*. Brougham viewed Young's work in a very hostile spirit. Young had produced substantial new experimental and theoretical evidence for the wave-theory of light, and had thereby made the biggest contribution to the science of optics since Newton.

He was original and profound, but had less genius for systematization. He did not expound his work in a way which easily carried conviction to those who were not already disposed to accept it. He so qualified his account of crucial observations as to leave an element of doubt about some of them. Brougham quoted his description of an experiment exhibiting the interference of light waves, in which a drop of oil was interposed between a prism of flint glass and a lens of crown glass. On the prism and lens being pressed together, the central spot seen by reflected light was white, surrounded by a dark ring. Young characteristically went on to say that 'the white spot differed, even at last, in the same degree from perfect whiteness, as the black spot usually does from perfect blackness'. Brougham interpreted this as a doubt of the certainty of his observation.

Young showed how a number of the more refined properties of light could be explained by the wave-theory. He had not yet escaped from the influence of the analogy of light with sound, which was known to be propagated by waves in air. In sound waves the particles of air vibrate forwards and backwards, or longitudinally. Young was not clear at first whether the light waves vibrated forwards and backwards, or sideways, that is, transverse.

Besides this obscurity in the kind of wave-motion, Young supposed that there must be a medium, an ether, to carry the waves. Proposers of wave-theories naturally had in mind the analogy of air as a carrier of sound waves. Brougham contended that the hypothesis of an ether 'only removes all the difficulties under which the theory of light laboured, to the theory of this new medium'.

Brougham, who had been brought up in the Scottish school which particularly revered Newton's work on optics, regarded Young's proposal to replace Newton's theory of light by an etherial wave-theory as presumptuous as well as unconvincing. He said that his 'paper contains nothing which deserves the name, either of experiment or discovery', and 'it is in fact destitute of every species of merit'. It exhibited, moreover, 'dangerous relaxations in the principles of physical logic. We wish to raise our feeble voice against innovations, that can have no other effect than to check the progress of science, and renew all those phantasms of the imagination, which Bacon and Newton put to flight from her temple.'

Brougham recommended Young to spend the winter re-reading Newton's *Optics* and the *Principia*, and repeating Newton's experiments. 'If, after that, the making of discoveries and building of systems should appear as easy as he seems at present to think it, he may proceed to apply the skill he has learned, with that caution which becomes the true philosopher.' As for the Royal Society, which had printed Young's papers, it should not allow its *Transactions* to be 'degraded into the rank of a mere contrivance for the printing of miscellanies. . . . We implore the Council, therefore, if they will deign to cast their eyes upon our humble page, to prevent a degradation of the Institution which has so long held the first rank among scientific bodies.' Was it impossible for the Society 'to ward off the encroachments of time, and to renovate, in new achievements, the vigour of former years?'

Brougham's article was widely read. It delayed the acceptance of the wave-theory of light. This did not occur until the subject was clarified, systematized and mathematically developed by Fresnel. John Herschel described the respective contributions of Young and Fresnel as: 'early, acute, and pregnant suggestion characterizing the one; and maturity of thought, fulness of systematic development, and decisive experimental illustration, equally distinguishing the other'.

Some authorities have asserted that Brougham's article submerged Young's reputation. Tyndall said that 'For twenty years this man of genius was quenched—hidden from the appreciative intellect of his countrymen—deemed in fact a dreamer, through the vigorous sarcasm of a writer who had then possession of the public ear.'

The case was not so simple. The heavy and complacent tone of Young's composition, which contributed to the slow acceptance and misjudgment of his work, was connected with his educational background and his conception of the nature of scientific effort. De Morgan remarked that Newton had 'well-nigh strangled the undulatory theory in its cradle', and Young 'first played a part of power in its resuscitation'. Young's works were 'treasures to all who know what intellectual wealth is'. But he had not had a systematic university training. 'His early education was not, like that of Newton, conducted under a system which corrects the false impressions of green age.' He did not acquire a generally acceptable style of presentation.

He was a well-to-do man, who engaged in science as if it were a private work of art, or hobby. He was a great admirer of Cavendish, the enormously rich nobleman who did not bother to publish many of his greatest discoveries.

Young was hindered in his profession as a medical doctor by diagnosing his patients' illnesses according to a balance of probabilities; they wanted to be told definitely what was wrong with them, and what to do to get well. His detached attitude also led to unfortunate results in the Nautical Almanac compiled under his direction. It contained serious inaccuracies, even overlooking that a leap year contained a February 29th.

Young was deeply hurt by Brougham's attack. He wrote a detailed pamphlet in reply, for 'even a man's friends may be so far misled by a garbled extract from his own works, and by the specious mixture of partial truth with essential falsehood, that they may not only be unable to defend him from the unfavourable opinion of others, but may themselves be disposed to suspect, in spite of their partiality, that he has been hasty and inconsiderate at least, if not radically weak and mistaken'.

Young said that as a result of the attack, he would terminate his pursuit of science, and devote his efforts to medicine, 'the ultimate object of all my labours'. It seems that he feared the hostile publicity would affect his medical practice.

He said that only one copy of his reply was sold. The effect on the general public was therefore negligible. However, he did circulate it privately. Later on, his friend George Ellis showed it to Canning, who 'read it with great attention'. Canning said that it proved the 'malice and want of candour' of the Edinburgh Reviewer, and if Young was correct in believing it was Brougham he had been treated with rather too much lenity. Walter Scott also sympathized with Young.

The conflict between Brougham and Young was not purely scientific. Canning became Brougham's chief political opponent, the intellectual leader of the Tories and political reaction. Scott also was a Tory stalwart, to be defeated by one vote by Brougham in a contest for the Rectorship of Glasgow University. The Tories founded the *Quarterly Review* as a counter to the Whig *Edinburgh Review*, and Young became a copious contributor to it. Young's political outlook contributed to the delay in the acceptance of the wave-theory of light.

Brougham returned to the topic of optics fifty years later. He published papers in the *Philosophical Transactions* of the Royal Society, and in his collected *Tracts*, in which he described further experiments, carried out with more elaborate apparatus, in his château at Cannes, and at Brougham Hall, in the years 1848–9, on the lines of his papers of 1796 and 1797. In a note he says that in his 1796 manuscript there was 'a remark on the effect of exposing a plate of ivory, stained with nitrate of silver, to the rays of the spectrum, and also on the effect of exposing the plate to the rays passing through a very small hole into a dark room, and which form the image, more or less distinct, of external objects'. Brougham says that Blagden left this out, because he considered 'it referred rather to a subject of Art', and that if he had not done so 'it would have led to making trials which must have ended in the discovery of the photographic process many years before it was eventually introduced'.

In the third number of the *Review*, Brougham wrote on Wollaston's experimental work in optics with great enthusiasm, especially his observation of the effect of ultra-violet rays on silver nitrate. He says that he had made a similar observation himself some years before. He did 'not hesitate to pronounce' Wollaston's discovery the most important in physical science for many years; but in his next article, also on Wollaston, he said he was 'much disappointed to find, that so acute and ingenious an experimentalist had adopted the wild optical theory of vibrations'.

Brougham appreciated the chemical discovery of the element columbium by Charles Hatchett, and reviewed Joseph Black's posthumous *Lectures* in an article of twenty-five pages in the sixth number of the *Review*. Brougham reverenced his former teacher, whose qualities were the very reverse of his own. Black had published very little. He never even gave an account in print of his discovery of latent heat. Brougham attributed Black's behaviour to a 'want of passion' which was one of his conspicuous qualities. His mind was always 'unabsorbed by any predominant enthusiasm, and at leisure to regard the most trivial concerns. He was never, like Newton or Smith, known to be absent in society; or thoughtless and playful in his hours of relaxation, like Hutton and Hume. . . .'

In the sixth number he also contributed an article on meteorites. He criticized various theories which attributed them to processes on the earth. He was inclined to believe, on the basis of the low speed of escape of particles from the moon, that they might be produced by lunar volcanoes. 'A knowledge of the internal structure of the moon may be the splendid reward of our investigations' into the physical and chemical nature of these objects.

Among other subjects treated by Brougham in early numbers of the *Review* were Leslie and Rumford on Heat, and a series of articles on Davy's Bakerian Lectures, describing his discoveries in electro-chemistry.

Brougham wrote at least two hundred articles for the *Review*, of which about one-quarter were on science. The percentage of science articles decreased as he became more involved in politics and law, but his attention to science continued.

His articles on personalities became of particular interest. One of the most outstanding was in the July number of 1838. He was angered by a 'silly, dull, and disgraceful publication' on the *Times of George IV*. It stung him to sit down and write straight off in a white heat, in the intervals of a Judicial Committee of the Privy Council, a magnificent account of the affair of *George IV and Queen Caroline*. It contains remarkable depictions of the main characters, including George III, Eldon, Canning and others. In it, Brougham associates the reactionary tendencies of Eldon and Canning with their classical non-scientific education.

'Mr. Canning was, in all respects, one of the most remarkable persons who have lived in our times. Born with talents of the highest order, these had been cultivated with an assiduity and success which gave him a distinguished place among the scholars of his day; and he was only inferior to others in the walks of science, from the accident of the studies which Oxford cherished in his time being pointed almost exclusively to classical pursuits.'

He wrote a series of *Lives of Men of Letters and Science*, published in two volumes in 1846. These included accounts of Black, Watt, Priestley, Cavendish, Davy, Lavoisier, Banks and D'Alembert. They have two great merits. The first is that they conform to Clarendon's qualification for a historian: 'there was never yet a grand history written but by men conversant in business and of the best and most liberal education'; the other is that he was personally acquainted with several of the subjects.

Brougham's articles on matters other than science were also striking, and as controversial. In 1808 he reviewed Byron's first volume of poems, *Hours of Idleness*. Brougham quoted Johnson's saying that when a nobleman appears as an author, his merits should be handsomely acknowledged. 'It is this consideration only, that induces us to give Lord Byron's poems a place in our review, beside our desire to counsel him, that he do forthwith abandon poetry, and turn his talents, which are considerable, and his opportunities, which are great, to better account.'

He said that the author protested too much that his poems were only those of his minority. In fact, Byron was rather old for a prodigy; had not Cowley composed at ten, and Pope at twelve? Nine out of ten men who are educated in England write verse to their old school on leaving, 'and that tenth man writes better verse than Lord Byron'. Brougham quotes Byron's desperate verses 'on a distant view of the village and school of Harrow', and other echoes of Gray. 'But whatever judgment may be passed on the poems of this noble minor, it seems we must take them as we find them, and be content; for they are the last we shall ever have from him.'

The effect on Byron was salutary. He wrote *English Bards and Scotch Reviewers*, and became a great poet.

Brougham's article on Byron's *juvenilia* was better-tempered and better-natured than his article on Young's wave-theory of light. Both articles had one feature in common; they could not have been written by a 'gentleman' of the English type. Brougham saw the intellectual world of Young, and the social world of Byron from the outside. His consciousness of belonging to the Scottish middle-class tradition, rather than any stratum of English society was fundamental in shaping his personality and career.

Brougham used the *Review* for introducing his policies and projects to the world, especially in education, the abolition of slavery and law reform. He contributed to the development of the modern technique of propaganda, which he used in furthering his causes.

V

Education of the People

BROUGHAM began to take the political leadership of the movement for the education of the people about the year 1810. He became an active supporter of the development of primary schools for the working classes by Joseph Lancaster, Robert Owen, and other educational innovators, though his chief inspiration in this field came from his knowledge of the parish schools in Scotland. He worked also for technical, scientific and university education, and after nearly twenty years of propaganda, he began to salute education as a greater power than war. In 1828, when Wellington was prime minister, and the Napoleonic wars were still a vivid memory, he expressed this in a speech in the House of Commons. The passage was reported as follows:

'Let the soldier be ever so much abroad, in the present age he could do nothing. There was another person abroad. . . . The schoolmaster was abroad and he trusted to the schoolmaster armed with his primer more than he did to the soldier in full military array for upholding and extending the liberties of the country.'

His slogan *The School Master is Abroad* echoed through the world, from Germany to Canada.

Brougham outlined his policy on the *Scientific Education of the People* in an *Edinburgh Review* article in 1824. This contained the substance of his pamphlet on *Practical Observations upon the Education of the People*, which appeared in the following year, and went through twenty editions in a few months. He gave the profits from it to the recently founded London Mechanics' Institution.

In the article Brougham said that the *Review* had often dealt with the question of elementary education for the poor. He now proposed to discuss 'the manner in which the working classes of the community may be most effectually and safely assisted in improving their minds by scientific acquirements'. His first point was that one must not suppose that the provision for elementary education was adequate because one was starting to discuss higher education. 'There is no reason whatever for postponing the consideration of the latter until the former shall be completed.'

A fundamental part of his policy was that, while 'the interference of the Government may be not only safe but advantageous' in elementary education, 'no such interference can be tolerated . . . with the subsequent instruction of the people'. This was because the influence of those who teach advanced ideas is much more important than of those who teach merely reading and writing. The non-conformists, who were in general most interested in education in science, were opposed to the influence of the reactionary governments of the period, and feared the extension of their control over scientific and higher education.

This was one of the reasons why Brougham stressed the importance of the working class organizing their own system of higher education, independent of the government. Unfolding his ideas in the pamphlet following his article, he said: 'The people themselves must be the great agents in accomplishing the work of their own instruction.' They cannot, however, 'wait until the whole people with one accord take the determination to labour in this good work'. He therefore recommended individual self-improvement after the manner of Benjamin Franklin. Brougham's advice was subsequently vulgarized in Samuel Smiles's *Self Help* for personal profit.

The first need for promoting knowledge among the poor was cheap publications. In spite of British expertness in manufacture, English books were still double the price of those in other countries. The method of publishing works in parts was 'admirably suited to the circumstances of the classes whose income is derived from wages'. The *Mechanics Magazine*, 'most ably edited by Mr. Robertson', had a large circulation, and for three pence a week communicated 'more valuable information both scientific and practical, than was ever before placed within the reach of those who can afford to pay six times as much for it'.

Brougham proposed that circulating libraries, book clubs, cottage libraries, parish libraries, itinerant libraries and reading societies should be promoted. Books should be read to workers while at work in the workshop, a proposal considerably in advance of the modern 'Music while you Work'!

Authors who wrote 'elementary treatises on the Mathematics, sufficiently clear, and yet sufficiently compendious', would perform an essential service. Enough will have been accomplished if the student perceives the general nature of geometrical investigation.

The instruction of the people in the rudiments of knowledge is an object 'sufficiently brilliant to allure the noblest ambition; for what higher achievement did the most sublime philosophy ever aspire after, than to elevate the views and refine the character of the great mass of mankind. . . .?' In these times, 'science no longer looks down as of old upon the multitude, supercilious. . . .'

'If extending the bounds of science itself be the grand aim of all philosophers in all ages, they indirectly, but surely, accomplish this object, who enable thousands to speculate and experiment for one to whom the path of investigation is now open.' It was not necessary that all should proceed beyond the rudiments, but 'whoever feels within himself a desire and an aptitude to proceed further, will press forward; and the chances of discovery, both in the arts and in science itself, will be thus indefinitely multiplied.'

'Indeed, those discoveries immediately connected with experiment and observation, are most likely to be made by men, whose lives being spent in the midst of mechanical operations, are at the same time instructed in the general principles upon which these depend, and trained betimes to the habits of speculation.'

'He who shall prepare a treatise simply and concisely unfolding the doctrines of Algebra, Geometry, and Mechanics, and adding examples calculated to strike the imagination, of their connexion with other branches of knowledge, and with the arts of common life, may fairly claim a large share in that rich harvest of discovery and invention which must be reaped by the thousands of ingenious and active men, thus enabled to bend their faculties towards objects at once useful and sublime.'

He was not without hopes of seeing formed 'a Society for promoting the composition, publication, and distribution of cheap and useful works'.

Brougham went into the details of the cost of organizing scientific and technical lectures. He proposed the mass-production of cheap teaching apparatus, made with interchangeable parts. 'The simplification of apparatus for teaching physical science is an important object . . . a compendious set of machines may be constructed to illustrate at a very cheap price a whole course of lectures. Certain parts may be prepared capable of being formed into various combinations . . . where separate models are necessary, their construction may be greatly simplified by omitting parts which are not essential to explain the principle, and show the manner of working. . . .'

The price will be greatly reduced when they are 'prepared by wholesale'. A friend of his was already devising simple apparatus for illustrating mechanics, and after this, he will consider the production of 'cheap chemical laboratories'. One of the great engineering factories was considering the preparation of cheap apparatus for teaching, 'so that any Mechanics' Institution may on very moderate terms be furnished at least with what is necessary for carrying on a course of dynamics. The drawings may be multiplied by the polygraphic methods generally in use.'

Brougham attributed the founding of Mechanics' Institutions to Dr. George Birkbeck. 'That most learned and excellent person formed the design . . . of admitting the working classes of his fellow-countrymen to the knowledge of sciences, till then almost deemed the exclusive property of the higher ranks in society.' He gave details of the development of the Mechanics' Institutes, collected from different parts of the country.

The question was no longer whether or not the people should be instructed, but whether they should be well or ill-taught. They might become 'well-educated, and even well versed in the most devoted sciences'. If their superiors were to deserve to be called their *betters*, 'they too must devote themselves more to the pursuit of solid and refined learning; the present public seminaries must be enlarged; and some of the greater cities of the kingdom, especially the metropolis, must not be left destitute of the regular means within themselves of scientific education'.

Here Brougham conceived the system of new universities in London and the other great cities, which would provide advanced education in science. Through them the distance between the upper classes and the new educated working classes was to be preserved.

Brougham gave the statesman's lead to the realization of these proposals. He turned educational developments, which were arising spontaneously out of the social situation, into consciously understood and organized movements.

Professor John Anderson of Glasgow University, who had given the instrument-maker James Watt his model of a Newcomen engine to mend, and thus set Watt on the way to invent his improved steam-engine and start the modern mechanical age, was an admirer of the French Revolution, and a democrat; he had invited artisans in their working clothes to attend his university lectures on natural philosophy. He bequeathed his fortune for an institution for the education of mechanics and women. This became known as the Andersonian Institution. Out of it grew the Royal College of Science and Technology, and in 1964 the new University of Strathclyde.

Brougham's old fellow-student George Birkbeck became professor of natural philosophy at the Andersonian Institution in 1799. Birkbeck noticed the thirst of the mechanics in the Glasgow workshops for scientific knowledge, and following on the efforts of the founders of the Andersonian, he started free lectures on science for mechanics. By the time of his fourth course, he had a Mechanics' Class of five hundred.

In 1805, however, Birkbeck left Glasgow to start a medical

practice in London. His Mechanics' Class continued, and in 1823 was separately established as the Glasgow Mechanics' Institute.

In London, Robertson, the editor of the *Mechanics Magazine*, read of the founding of the Glasgow Mechanics' Institute, and proposed that one should be founded in London. Robertson and his assistant Hodgskins, together with Francis Place, the famous radical tailor, drew up a plan for a London institution. A private meeting was called, with Birkbeck in the chair, to consider the plan.

Brougham converted the proposals from a matter of discussion to one of action by entering the room, walking up to Place, and saying in his loud House of Commons voice, with the accents which were universally known to portend significant action: 'This matter will go on well, I see. You are always to be found where there are proceedings to be taken for the good of the people. Your presence is a guarantee that the society will go on well.'

The London Mechanics' Institute was duly founded, and later on evolved into Birkbeck College, one of the colleges of the University of London, which has provided particularly for adult students who work during the day and study in the evenings.

Brougham gave his energy and influence to the support of the Mechanics' Institute movement for the rest of his life, but he always described Birkbeck as the founder of the movement and the London Institute in particular, This annoyed Robertson, Hodgskins and their working-class friends, who had also contributed an essential part.

Brougham never gave a systematic exposition of his ideas on education. On the whole, however, he acted as if he regarded popular education as a means by which working-class men could rise into the middle and professional classes.

VI

London University

BROUGHAM supported the project for London University by action in the House of Commons and in the Press. He outlined his views on it in the *Edinburgh Review* for August 1825.

'We regard the event of a new University being founded, but more especially in the Capital of the British Empire, as, in every point of view, among the most important to which these times, so fruitful in improvement, have given birth.' Its influence on the advancement of knowledge, and the progress of the species would be very great, 'were it even to be established upon the same principles which have been adopted in the old collegiate institutions of England'. It would be a vast addition to England's means for 'literary and scientific education', and help her provisions for higher education to keep pace with her rapidly increasing population.

'Oxford and Cambridge teach no more than from three to four thousand young men, out of at least two hundred times that number, of an age fit for instruction.' Scotland had more students in her universities, though she had only about one-sixth of the population. Brougham then made a trenchant analysis of the history of Oxford and Cambridge, pointing out that they had evolved to educate 'the two classes, of Ecclesiastics and Patricians'.

The system was very costly, so that only the sons of the well-to-do could go there, and a small number of able poorer youths through scholarships. Entry was virtually restricted to members of the Established Church, and the monopoly of the right to grant degrees gave these universities comprehensive control over ideology. 'In a word, the real cause of the scantiness of education was the fundamental axiom, the first principle of English education, that actual education means Oxford and Cambridge!'

As the universities were so far distant, both in miles and socially, from the populations of the cities, the 'middle classes must let their sons grow up, with such learning as they could pick up at a grammar school, and, forthwith, plunge into business'.

Meanwhile, at the universities students were absorbed in literary exercises and mathematical problems or puzzle-solving. There was no medium between the almost entire idleness of dissipation, and 'such skill in making Greek and Latin verses as would astonish a first-rate German commentator, and such readiness in solving difficult problems as would surpass the belief—certainly far exceed the power of Sir Isaac Newton, were he again to visit the banks of the Granta'.

He thought the Scottish system of students living at home, or in the houses of other people, 'uniting domestic habits and parental superintendence with College study' accounted for 'the superiority of our youth in sober, prudent, and virtuous habits, as well as proficiency in their studies'. How Brougham must have been strengthened in these convictions, as he remembered with 'exultation' his own riotous behaviour, living at home as an Edinburgh student!

It was true that the Scottish system could not produce such 'rare expertness in verse-making and working analytical questions' as the handful of Wranglers and Medallists produced every year at Cambridge, 'yet, in a thousand young men attending the classes of Edinburgh or Glasgow, hardly fifty will be found who are not tolerably well versed in the branches of ornamental and useful knowledge'.

The absurdity of making the whole of England tributary to Oxford and Cambridge was glaring, especially with regard to the cities. 'Every place could not maintain a College: But towns of 80,000 or 100,000 inhabitants well might; and above all, . . . the Capital, with a population of twelve hundred thousand, as many as the whole kingdom had in the days when Oxford and Cambridge flourished most. . . .'

With his excellence in providing illustrative quantitative details, Brougham gave an analysis of the income and expenditure of an average London professional man, such as a lawyer or doctor, showing how he could not afford to educate his son at Oxford or Cambridge. Would it not be more sensible to create a university in London, where he could study while living at home?

Brougham then considered the possibilities of London as a university centre. 'It is the resort of the most celebrated persons of every description,' including those in the arts, sciences and letters. London contained a far larger number of eminent scientists than Oxford and Cambridge; the Royal Society was based there. London offered particular advantages for providing professors in those branches of knowledge in which eminence can be obtained only through great practice, 'as in law, anatomy, medicine, and all the fine arts'. London offered unique advantages for medical study, yet medicine was being taught at 'the London Hospitals without any regular course in medical study'.

The Mechanics' Institutions had recently been founded, 'which are a kind of College for those most numerous, poorer, and valuable part of the community'. They were rapidly improving themselves, and would in a very short time 'become greater proficients in science than ninety-nine in a hundred of the Doctors themselves at our antique Universities'.

The worthy citizens of London, the traders, and gentlemen of moderate fortune were becoming uneasy at this situation. They were not quite satisfied with the prospect of 'having their work-people far more knowing than themselves and their children'. As they could not afford to send their children to Oxford or Cambridge, they required institutions of higher education near their own homes.

Besides these, there were the Dissenters, who could not send their sons to Oxford or Cambridge because of exclusion on religious grounds. The Dissenters formed 'a very large, and a most wealthy, intelligent, and respectable class,' and they abounded particularly in and near the metropolis.

To meet this situation, theological studies were to be omitted from the curriculum of the New Institution which was to be founded. 'We profess to teach the sciences and literature. With religion we meddle not; but leave each student to learn it where he and his parents please, and from such persons, and in such shape as it suits them, and accords with their principles.'

Finally, he disposed of the belief that the Crown alone had the right to create a university; London as a city could do so. The idea was not new. He quoted a tract published in 1615, dedicated to Edward Coke, containing a proposal for 'The Third University of England, or a Treatise of the foundations of all the Colledges, auncient Schooles, &c., within and about the famous citie of London.' The author pointed out that in the city all the arts and sciences were taught, including geometry, astronomy, hydrography, geography, geodesy and optics; 'particularly and academically' at Gresham College. Besides this, theology, 'the chiefest science, the Science of Sciences', was taught through St. Paul's Cathedral and other churches.

All that was wanting was that these facilities should be under the supervision of a single authority, that is, 'an honourable chauncellor, which the King, my Master may easily at his Maiesties pleasure supply. . . '. Thus the nineteenth century was only being asked to meet a need which had been already perceived in the seventeenth.

When the movement for a London university had advanced to

the stage where decisive action was required, meetings of the leading sponsors were held in Brougham's chambers, under his chairmanship. The first public proposal was launched at a meeting with the Lord Mayor of London in the chair. After the project was proposed, Brougham rose. 'He commenced, all was stillness; he proceeded, all was satisfaction; he concluded, and all was applause; he entered into the merits of the question with his usual adroitness and skill.' Sir James Mackintosh, seconded by Thomas Campbell the poet, moved that the name of the new institution should be 'The London University'.

Brougham established the importance of the project in leading political circles. He was so active in forwarding it that the new university became identified with him. Grey used to refer to 'your university' when he mentioned it in his correspondence.

The strength of the obstruction to the project is illustrated by Peel's attitude as M.P. for Oxford University, and a member of the Cabinet. He wrote to Dr. Lloyd, the Dean of Christ Church, in May 1825, marking his letter private, and said:

'Brougham means to bring in a bill for forming a Joint Stock Company, capital £200,000, for the foundation of a London College.

'Professors, *Chancellor &c.* for it to be elected by subscribers. Religious education to be excluded from the scheme.

'This must be opposed and rejected, but I have hardly time, to give such an important subject all the attention which it deserves.'

He wondered whether there had been any public discussion on a London University, and whether the impolicy of educating students in a metropolis had been considered. Had not the Inns of Court been a centre of immorality when youths of 17 or 18 had studied there?

Could it be argued that because Westminster was as well-conducted as Eton, a London College would be as fit a place for the education of youth as Cambridge or Oxford?

He asked the Dean where he could find useful information dealing with these points.

Brougham and his fellow-founders had to overcome obstruction from within the Cabinet itself, led by so able a man as Peel.

VII

The Diffusion of Useful Knowledge

BROUGHAM guided the Society for the Diffusion of Useful Knowledge virtually through the whole of its existence. 'It owes its establishment to Lord Brougham, whose personal exertions first brought the Committee together, and who has continued in the office of Chairman throughout its existence, and not only in the office, but in the unremitting performance of its duties,' says the Address of the Committee in 1846, which was drawn up by Augustus de Morgan, and corrected in proof by Goldsmid and Brougham.

The Society was started in 1826, and continued effectively until 1846, and was dissolved in 1848. Brougham supervised its business, approached authorities for books and articles, wrote and read himself, and continued to work energetically for the Society, even during the period when he was Lord Chancellor.

He was very active in the autumn of 1826 with the preliminary organization, which arose out of his long campaign for the improvement of the education of the people. Among his original associates were James Mill and M. D. Hill. H. Hallam, S. Rogers, Rowland Hill, Lord Althorp, I. L. Goldsmid, J. Scarlett, H. Warburton, L. Horner, F. Jeffery and Jos. Wedgwood, junr., were among the members of the Committee, and T. Coates was Secretary.

A prospectus was prepared, in which the object of the Society was described as 'the imparting of useful information to all classes of the community, particularly to such as are unable to avail themselves of experienced teachers, or may prefer learning by themselves'. It was to be attained by the periodical publication of treatises on different branches of knowledge, with applications to practical uses. Each treatise was to contain thirty-two pages, and would be sold at sixpence. About 180 subjects were proposed, of which 70 dealt with natural science. Brougham used the word 'science' in the Baconian sense. They would deal with: 'science, which in its comprehensive sense means *knowledge*, and in its ordinary sense *knowledge reduced to a system*'.

His plans and programme were expounded in several articles in the contemporary numbers of the *Edinburgh Review*, according to his principle of advance propaganda for scientific, cultural and political projects. In these, it was pointed out that elementary books suitable for the Mechanics' Institutes were rare. It was 'a want felt not merely by the working classes, but by persons in every rank in society'. It was felt even by 'the young of the upper classes who are learners of any science'. Books were required 'embracing all knowledge', with 'the good, the highest good, the moral improvement of all classes, for its end'.

The executive of the Society had a far more democratic composition than was customary. There were no honorary patrons, and all members of the committee were expected to work. When Brougham subsequently tried to secure financial support from the Government when Peel was prime minister, Peel remarked that the committee included men of high distinction, 'but almost without exception they are of different connection from my own'.

The Society made arrangements with the bookseller Charles Knight to publish the works it had in mind. Knight had previously attempted to launch a series of cheap weekly books, but had not been successful. His descriptions of how the Society's projects were brought to life illustrates Brougham's creative influence and power.

Knight was taken by a friend to meet Brougham in his chambers. As they went on their way, 'there was an image in my mind of the Queen's Attorney-General, as I had often beheld him in the House of Lords, wielding a power in the proceedings on the Bill of Pains and Penalties which no other man seemed to possess. . . '. When he arrived, Brougham was seated among his briefs, and was evidently delighted to talk about something more interesting. He saluted their mutual friend with a joke, and cordially welcomed Knight. He at once went into the subject, and Knight's views, 'without the slightest attempt to be patronising'. He was 'the foremost advocate of education', but he did not indoctrinate or bore him, as so many educationists had done. He put Knight at ease, and inspired his confidence.

The *Library of Useful Knowledge* was launched in 1827, with sixpenny books issued fortnightly. Brougham wrote a preliminary booklet on *The Objects, Advantages and Pleasures of Science*. In it, he gave first place to the cultural values of science, the second to its usefulness, and the third as a source of pleasure and entertainment. He suggested, in the manner of Bacon, that the whole of knowledge: the arts, morality, political science, government and law, should be expounded from this point of view. The booklet attained a sale of more than 39,000 copies. It enabled the Society to set a new level in the sale of informative literature.

The large circulation gave courage to launch the *Penny Magazine*. This came out in weekly penny numbers, and a monthly supplement. It rapidly gained a regular circulation of 150,000 copies. Brougham perceived its propaganda possibilities, and it is said that *The Times* began to turn against him from fear of competition from this new mass publication.

The success of the magazine inspired the foundation later on of the *Penny Cyclopaedia*. The kind of material in it was read by hundreds of thousands, where previously it had been read by only thousands, and it could be obtained elsewhere only at ten or twenty times the price.

Knight suggested that the Society should issue a modern almanac, to replace the degraded publications appealing to superstition. He sketched a plan, and went to Westminster to consult Brougham.

'What an incalculable source of satisfaction to a projector, even of so apparently humble a work as an Almanac, to find a man of ardent and capacious mind, quick to comprehend, frank to approve, not deeming a difficult undertaking impossible, ready not only for counsel, but for action. "It is now the middle of November," said the rapid genius of unprocrastinating labour—"can you have your Almanac out before the end of the year?" "Yes; with a little help in the scientific matters." "Then tell Mr. Coates to call a meeting of the General Committee at my chambers, at half-past eight tomorrow morning. You shall have help enough. There's Lubbock and Wrottesley and Daniell and Beaufort—you may have your choice of good men for your astronomy and meteorology, your tides and your eclipses. Go to work, and never fear."'

When Knight set out again early on the next morning for Brougham's chambers he encountered the thickest fog he could remember, but when he arrived, he found a quorum of the Committee already there. 'The energy of the Chairman swept away every doubt.' An Admiralty astronomer was found to look over the astronomical tables. Wranglers were mobilized to read the mathematical proofs. The *British Almanac* duly appeared on the following January 1st. It had been written, printed and published within six weeks. It consisted of 60 pages of calendar, weather and astronomical facts; duration of sunlight and moonlight; useful remarks of practical importance on the management of a farm, garden or orchard; the preservation of health; and miscellaneous information.

The *Companion* followed later in the year. It contained 186 pages of information on the calendar, explanations of the celestial changes, chronology, geography, statistics, legislation, public improvements, and mechanical inventions brought forward in the previous year. With contributors such as Lubbock, Wrottesley, Daniell, Beaufort and de Morgan, the standard was very high, and effected a revolution in the quality of almanacs. Lubbock's work for the almanac led to the first reduction of tidal observations on an extensive scale, by himself and Whewell.

By 1843, seventy-two booklets on twenty-two branches of Natural Philosophy had been published, and were also available in four handsome volumes at about ten shillings a volume. Brougham had himself contributed the *Preliminary Discourse*. He heroically wrote the next booklet, on *Hydrostatics*. It contained some elementary errors, which were ridiculed by critics of the Society.

Thomas Love Peacock referred to it in his chapter on *The March of Mind*, one of Brougham's favourite slogans, in *Crotchet Castle*. ' "God bless my soul, Sir!" exclaimed the Reverend Dr. Folliott, bursting, one fine morning into the breakfast-room at Crotchet Castle. "I am out of all patience with this march of mind. Here has my house been nearly burned down, by my cook taking it into her head to study hydrostatics, in a sixpenny tract, published by the Steam Intellect Society, and written by a learned friend who is for doing all the world's business as well as his own, and is equally well qualified to handle every branch of human knowledge. . . . My cook must read his rubbish in bed; and as might naturally be expected, she dropped suddenly fast asleep, overturned the candle, and set the curtains in a blaze. Luckily, the footman went into the room at the moment, in time to tear down the curtains and throw them into the chimney, and a pitcher of water on her nightcap extinguishing her wick: she is a greasy subject, and would have burned. . . ."'

The first volume was completed with *Hydraulics* by J. Millington of the Royal Institution; *Pneumatics* and *Mechanics* by Dionysius Lardner of University College; *Heat* by Ogg; and *Optics* and *The Polarization of Light* by Sir David Brewster. On the latter subject Brewster was the leading authority of the day.

In the second volume there was a *Popular Introduction to Natural Philosophy* by Mrs. Marcet, with whose writings Faraday had educated himself when a youth; *An Account of Newton's Optics* by Lardner; *Optical Instruments* by Pritchard; *Thermometers and Pyrometers* by T. S. Traill; and four sections on *Electricity* and *Magnetism* by P. M. Roget, famous as the author of the *Thesaurus of English Words and Phrases.*

The third volume contained five parts. The first on *Astronomy* was by Sir B. Malkin, followed by a *History of Astronomy* by R. W. Rothman; *Mathematical Geography* by E. Lloyd; *Physical Geography* by H. J. Lloyd; and *Navigation* by Lord Wrottesley.

The fourth volume contained *Animal Physiology* by Southwood Smith; *Animal Mechanics* by Sir Charles Bell; *Chemistry* by J. F. Daniell, the inventor of the voltaic cell known by his name; and *Botany* by J. Lindley, professor at University College.

The two volumes on Mathematics were even more distinguished. Volume I contained five topics, issued originally in eleven parts. The subject was introduced by an essay on the *Study and Difficulties of Mathematics* by Augustus de Morgan. This was followed by *Arithmetic and Algebra* by James Parker; *Examples of the Processes* by de Morgan; *Algebraical Expressions* by J. Drinkwater-Bethune; and *Theory of Algebraical Equations* by Robert Murphy.

Volume II contained four topics, dealt with in twenty-two parts. *Geometry* was treated by Pierce Morton; *Trigonometry* by William Hopkins, the Cambridge coach who prepared James Clerk Maxwell and other Cambridge Wranglers; *Spherical Trigonometry* by de Morgan; and *Algebraical Geometry* by S. W. Waud.

Brougham said in his old age that he feared many of the books were too stiff for the readers for whom they were intended. In fact, many of them were much used as university textbooks, at University College and elsewhere.

Among other mathematical works published by the Society were de Morgan's famous *Differential and Integral Calculus*; G. B. Airy's classical exposition of *Gravitation; Projections of the*

Sphere especially with reference to maps of the stars, by de Morgan; and a *Treatise on Probability* by Lubbock and Drinkwater-Bethune. Barlow's *Tables* of logarithms, squares and square roots, etc., were also issued.

Sir John Lubbock edited a series of maps of *Stars on the Gnomonic Projection*, and Francis Baily supervised the preparation of Terrestrial and Celestial *Globes*.

A set of Lubbock's star maps was sent to Sir John Herschel at the Cape of Good Hope, who was engaged in surveying the Southern Heavens, to complete his fathers' project of surveying the whole sky. Herschel acknowledged them in a letter in December 1836 to de Morgan, in which he said: 'The maps of the Diffusion Society arrived safe—may I make you my medium for the communication of thanks, which are richly deserved as the maps are good. The Southern Circumpolar Map is very useful to me, as I am going over the stars (on nights of bad definition when nothing else can be done) with the naked eye, to settle comparative magnitudes, which are most woefully bungled in all the authorities. I think these maps, so far as I see at present, are preferable in that respect to Bode's, which are full of egregious errors.'

In a letter to John Herschel in 1862, de Morgan described how his connection with the Society led to his appointment to the chair of mathematics at University College. 'Did it chance to you that the first thing you wrote never was published? It did so to me. The first thing ever proposed to me was a treatise on mechanics for the U.K.S. I wrote a few chapters, and, chancing to become a candidate for what I now hold, I sent my MSS. in as a testimonial, and I believe it greatly helped me. At any rate, I was picked out of fifty candidates, being known to be only twenty-one last birthday. I think Brougham and Warburton were the people who dared a thing so bold. . . .'

While the Society's scientific and mathematical works were its most striking publications, the quantity in arts and miscellanies was even bigger. Works for engineers, such as Bradley's *Practical Geometry and Perspective*, and Henry Chapman's *Diagrams illustrating Mechanical Philosophy*, were included. The mathematics of insurance was expounded by D. Jones in *Annuities and Reversionary Payments*. Some works on crafts and industries were included, such as *The Art of Brewing* by D. Booth, which was rather popular, and Needham on *The Manufacture of Iron*.

M'Culloch wrote on *Commerce*, and produced his big *Statistical Account of the British Empire*, the first of its kind. It was published in two volumes at two guineas, Another particularly successful volume was an *Account of Bacon's Novum Organon* by J. Hoppus of University College. J. E. Drinkwater-Bethune and others compiled an excellent volume of *Lives of Eminent Persons*. Those of Galileo and Kepler, by Drinkwater himself, are particularly good. The *Farmers' Series* on the *Horse*, *Cattle*, *Sheep*, etc., was popular.

Besides these, there was the *Quarterly Journal of Education*, which ran for ten volumes, and became the source for information on the progress of education in the world during the first half of the nineteenth century.

The Society sponsored the *Penny Cyclopaedia*, which was completed in thirty volumes. It was, however, of too advanced a standard, and the heavy financial commitments in producing it were one of the causes of the Society's ultimate dissolution.

The high quality of the works was obtained by the devotion of the Committee of the Society. This contained about fifty members, who read and revised proofs of those topics of which they had special knowledge. The details of planning, consultation about authors and collection of expert opinion on manuscripts were carried out by an energetic Publications Committee. For example, in 1835 Lubbock revised proofs of Star Maps, a Scheme for the Microscope, the Almanac for 1836, and proofs of the *Penny Magazine* and *Cyclopaedia*. Brougham himself read proofs of *Criminal Trials*, a *Memoir of Romilly*, the *Journal of Education*, the *Magazine* and *Cyclopaedia*.

In her valuable *Thesis* on the Society, Miss Monica C. Grobel has demonstrated in detail how hard Brougham and his colleagues worked for the Society, and what a galaxy of conscientious and industrious scientific talent was mobilized to provide simple yet authoritative literature.

Brougham aimed to make science a possession of the people. This provided the foundation for the next advance: bringing quality as well as quantity of knowledge into the heart of the nation. Foremost in this second stage was Augustus de Morgan, whose unique career became possible through Brougham. De Morgan accomplished an immense work of intellectual democratization in mathematics and the history of science through the publications of the Society for the Diffusion of Useful

Knowledge. As the most eminent professor in the early University College, he had a profound influence on British mathematics. He was precluded by his views on religion from obtaining a professorship in Oxford or Cambridge. He owed to Brougham both his university and his chair.

His pupils Routh and Todhunter went to Cambridge, where they dominated Cambridge mathematical teaching. His own researches in mathematical logic inspired George Boole, and the modern development of the subject. This is now of great practical as well as intellectual importance, as it is the natural language of the computer.

His son George, together with a fellow-student, Ranyard, founded the London Mathematical Society in 1865. De Morgan was the first president of the Society, and defined the policy which has stimulated the development of British mathematics during the last hundred years.

Generally, the Society for the Diffusion of Useful Knowledge was much better at science than at social and political subjects. In its first *Companion to the Almanac*, under 'Advice to the Poor', the reader was told that 'the great mass of mankind are destined inevitably to live by labour; some are undoubtedly exempted from the necessity of working; they are few in comparison of the number who must submit to live by industry. But the wealth of the rich has arisen from labour. Capital, money, and property are no more than the savings made from the produce of labour, beyond the portion which was required for the preservation of the individuals who have worked to raise it. Upon these grounds, the rich are as justly entitled to their large possessions, as the cottager to his cottage. . . . Send your wife to market in preference to going yourself. Women are less subject to the temptation of drinking than men. They are better bargainers than men. . . . A woman is worth, on these occasions, from two shillings to five shillings in the pound more than a man. . . . The Poor rate is become the stumbling block to the independence and happiness of the labourers. . . .'

In 1837 Brougham 'called the attention of the Committee to the absence of all intellectual, ethical, or political subjects from the publications of the Society'. He began to write a series of volumes to remedy the deficiency. Two appeared, but by 1842 it became clear that they were not what the public wanted. They desired 'not knowledge of facts or lessons of experience, but only stimulus for party feeling, and materials for party discussions'.

Brougham was a middle-class reformist, who wanted to work for the working class. He was strongly opposed to organized political action by the working class on behalf of itself. He was Lord Chancellor in the Government which refused to intervene against the savage sentence of seven years' transportation passed on the six Dorchester labourers in 1834, for taking an oath of loyalty to their union of agricultural workers.

Thomas Coates in a report on Mechanics' Institutions for the Society in 1841 expressed the opinion that 'the exclusion of all discussion or even instruction concerning Politics and Political Economy is another cause of the indifference of artisans' towards the institutions. They preferred to go to taverns or political clubs where these topics were ardently discussed. He thought that nineteen-twentieths of the members were 'not of the class of mechanics, but are connected with the higher branches of handicraft trades, or are clerks in offices, and in many instances young men connected with liberal professions'.

'The Chartist and the Socialist zealously diffuse their opinions far and wide; they have erected halls, and established places of meeting in which they discourse to thousands; they invite persons of adverse opinion to listen to and freely discuss the exposition of their principles: the Socialists, especially, comprise in the plan of their societies some of the most useful and attractive objects of the Mechanics' Institutions. They have lectures on the sciences, they have music, and in some cases other classes, and they add to these the occasional attraction of tea-parties, accompanied by dancing.'

The number of their institutions was smaller, but the attendances were larger, because of the more lively free enquiry. In the Mechanics' Institutes, on the other hand, 'We explain to you the physical sciences; we demonstrate to you the atomic theory; we show you the orbits of the planets, but the nature and advantages of our political Constitution, a question which every newspaper more or less raises, and which is obtruded upon you and made a motive for your conduct at every election, shall not be taught or discussed here; nevertheless, the Chartists in the next street handle it quite freely, and will spare no pains to induce you to adopt their opinion.'

During the 1840's the working class had come to the conclusion that progress was to be found more through political than educational action. The Chartist campaign reached its height, and the pursuit of scientific and technical education became still more the preserve of the middle class, and those who aspired to rise into it.

In these conditions, the Society began to disintegrate, and in 1846 suspended its operations. Provision of scientific and technical education for the middle class was taken over by the municipalities and the state. In the Society's Address for 1846, it was said that the Society had arisen from the conditions of the nation in 1825. 'A spirit was awakened of which they have been the instruments—a spirit which led to the successive foundation of University College, King's College and the University of London, and which had previously established the Mechanics' Institutes; which overthrew the laws excluding Roman Catholics and Protestant Dissenters from the public service; which reformed the [parliamentary] representation in spite of the utmost efforts of wealth and power; which broke the chain of slavery throughout the British Empire, and is still at work in forwarding the best interests of the whole human race.'

Mass-education in science and technology, which was the aspiration of the working-class element in the Society for the Diffusion of Useful Knowledge at the beginning of its work, could only be realized after the working class had achieved political power.

In the U.S.S.R. and the People's Republic of China, Societies for the Dissemination of Scientific Knowledge have been created on an enormous scale. They form an essential part of the organization of a socialist state, in which their function is to pursue the continuous scientific and technical education of the population through the whole of their adult lives. In this way, the people are kept well-informed of the progress of science and technique, with the minimum of delay, to understand what action must be taken to promote science, and to utilize it, for the benefit of their country and themselves.

VIII

Acquiring and Losing Influence

THE young Brougham had acquired much knowledge in Edinburgh, but there was socially no scope for its exercise under Dundas's tight dominion. In 1803 he moved to London, and entered Lincoln's Inn.

The London world was much bigger than that of Edinburgh. Its complexities offered more opportunity, but it was also dominated by tough reaction. The French Revolution and the Napoleonic Wars had created an intense fear in the ruling classes of any social change. This paralysed rational political action to ameliorate the conditions of the working classes, worsened by the effects of the Industrial Revolution and the privations of war.

The old criminal law, derived from feudal times and values, was applied unchanged in the new society; a man could be hanged for stealing five shillings. The extent and complexity of the antiquated legal system hindered appeals. A rapidly increasing population intensified the effects of the harsh application of oppressive laws, and the ancient prisons became more overcrowded than ever, producing indescribable disease and corruption.

In the Army and Navy, discipline was preserved by floggings of a thousand lashes for trifling offences. The combination of workers to improve their lot was illegal, and there was no law to prevent the exploitation of child labour. The publication of books and newspapers was controlled, so that it was difficult to expose the full iniquity of the conditions. Education for the people was regarded as subversive, for it might equip them to challenge the ruling classes.

In this atmosphere, even Brougham's book on *Colonial Policy*, and the friendship of Wilberforce acquired through his criticism of the slave trade, were not sufficient to secure political promotion for him in Tory circles.

Brougham soon moved into the London circles of the Whigs, through the influence of Erskine, and the connections of his school and university friend, Francis Horner, who introduced him to Lord Holland, the nephew of Charles James Fox.

The Whigs regarded themselves as the heirs of the magnates of 1688, who had replaced James II with a monarch of their own choosing. They believed they were the legitimate rulers of the country, and resented the efforts of George III and his Tory friends to restore the governing authority of the Crown. They were even more aristocratic than the King and the Tories, but found themselves in opposition to them in defence of their own interests. Being in opposition, they fostered liberal ideas.

According to Brougham, George III had a 'firmness of purpose' combined with a 'contracted mind', which gave an appearance of inflexible consistency 'not seldom received as a substitute for honesty'. Where his prerogative was concerned, he exhibited 'the resources of a cunning which mental aberration is supposed to whet'.

George III believed that kings were entitled to rule, but he and his friends had not enough ability to rule by themselves. They had to secure the assistance of young men like William Pitt and George Canning, who had the knowledge and skill to govern a modern state; and the support of interests in the City of London, who were anxious about the safety of their wealth. While Pitt was virtually paid by the Tories to do their work for them, he was too intelligent to accept every piece of reactionary policy, such as support of the slave-trade. But he could not go so far against general Tory policy as to give such an anti-slave-trader as Brougham a Tory seat in Parliament.

Brougham decided to support the Whigs, and set out to make himself indispensable to Earl Grey, who had become their leader after the death of Fox. Grey was fourteen years older than Brougham. He had been known as the handsomest and proudest man in Europe. He was the essence of the Whig aristocracy, with a profound belief that they were the summit of social authority in the nation. Grey's estate was at Howick in Northumberland. He spent every moment there which he could tear away from London, absorbed in family affairs. He was indolent and sensitive, and yet, in spite of his absence and indolence, he exercised authority over his party, and over Brougham. He had a good judgment on what was politically possible, arising from his absolute confidence in his social position.

Grey and Brougham started on a collaboration which was to

last for many years, and culminated in the passing of the Reform Bill. The long correspondence between them, which Brougham published in his *Memoirs*, shows that while Brougham did the work, Grey made the decisions. Brougham was the Achilles who fought the battles of the Reformers, while Grey was the Agamemnon leading their hosts.

The correspondence reveals Brougham in a remarkably sensible light, in contrast with his reputation for incomprehensible aberrations. Grey instinctively made the decisions which were correct for the Whigs.

The contrast between the Whig aristocrat and the middle-class Scottish intellectual is noticeable in the correspondence, and it is evident that whatever Brougham had done, he never could have become assimilated into the Whig aristocracy. Grey's attitude to Brougham was a mixture of father to son with master to servant.

Brougham's first great service for the Whigs was the organization of the propaganda campaign in the General Election of 1807. His innovations in this campaign show him as one of the creators of modern methods of publicity.

While Brougham now looked to the Whigs to find a parliamentary seat for him, he had to make a living. He applied for admission to the English Bar, and on his first application the Tory Government sent both the Attorney- and the Solicitor-General to vote against him; he was defeated by one vote. After he was subsequently admitted, he decided to practise in the Northern Circuit. His middle-class competence and ideology qualified him to act for the increasingly wealthy and influential northern industrialists. Besides this, the Brougham seat was in Westmorland, and Grey's estate in Northumberland was only forty miles away.

Brougham was in no doubt of the attitude of the Whig leaders to lawyers. He wrote to Grey in 1808: 'From accidental circumstances I find myself placed in a situation which enables me to command a considerable degree of success in the profession of the law, and however odious that profession is (as God knows there are few things so hateful), I am quite clear that it would be utter folly in me to neglect so certain a prospect.'

Recent intercourse with people in the industrial North had impressed him with the possibilities. The traders and manufacturers were seething with discontent from the effects of the Orders in Council, begun by the coalition government of 1806, to counter Napoleon's European blockade of England. The Orders aimed at the suppression of all trade with France. This meant that the Navy was to prevent American sea trade with France. The Americans retaliated by suppressing British imports into the United States, and threatening war.

The manufacturers and traders of Liverpool, Birmingham, London and Manchester were in uproar, and briefed Brougham to present their case to Parliament for the repeal of the Orders.

He had to address members of both Houses at the Bar of the House of Lords, and contend with the opposition not only of the existing Tory Government, but also of the Whig ministers of the preceding coalition government who had begun the Orders. Brougham's brilliant presentation of the industrialists' case made him a national figure at the age of thirty.

The essence of his presentation was that 'one of the greatest, if not the very greatest, evil which can visit this country, a war with America' would be prevented by their repeal. Brougham ultimately succeeded, four years later, in winning their appeal. But in the days before the Atlantic cable it took weeks to convey news to America, so some days after the repeal, the Americans did in fact declare war. But the misunderstanding was presently resolved without too much difficulty.

Brougham said in his *Memoirs* that the repeal of the Orders was 'the first parliamentary victory for the new industrialists who were remaking England'. He regarded it as his 'greatest achievement'. In his leadership of other causes he 'had the sympathy and aid of others, but in the battle against the Orders in Council I fought alone'.

Brougham entered the House of Commons in 1810, when the Whigs found a pocket borough for him.

In the following year, he defended Leigh Hunt against a charge of criminal libel, for exposing the horrors of Army floggings. Though Ellenborough, the Lord Chief Justice, summed up against Hunt, the jury declared him not guilty. Brougham's success in this case earned him the regard of the many who were struggling against the social abuses of the period.

His achievements in the actions against the Orders in Council gave him a high reputation among Liverpool and northern merchants. He decided to stand for Liverpool in the election of 1812. There were two seats. The Tory candidates were Canning, the famous sitting member for Liverpool, and Gascoyne. Brougham and Creevy stood for the Whigs. After a tremendous contest, in which those most concerned with the exports of British manufactures to America supported Brougham, Canning and Gascoyne won by a small margin.

Brougham did not return to Parliament until 1816, when he was again provided with a Whig pocket borough. In this year, he proposed a Select Committee to enquire into the education of the Lower Orders. It revealed the facts of the situation, and was the beginning of modern British state action for education of the people.

Brougham was led to investigate the numerous charities which were supposed to be providing popular education. He discovered widespread misuses, as at Pocklington School. This school was supposed to be visited by fellows of St. John's College, Cambridge, to see that it was functioning properly. It had an income of £900 a year from endowments, but was educating only one pupil.

The unspeakable Scot even probed into the ambiguous uses of the charities from which some of the most ancient English public schools, and Oxford and Cambridge colleges, benefited. His activities were received with rage, and when he obtained an Act in 1818 for a commission to enquire into the use of educational charities, the House of Lords deprived it of its teeth.

Brougham introduced an Education Bill in 1820. In his speech he said that in England only about one child in sixteen was being educated. In Wales it was one in twenty. 'What a different picture was afforded by Scotland.' There it was about one in nine.

The money for building the required schools was to be provided by the manufacturers, and that for running them from the rates. The headmaster was to be a member of the Church of England.

Brougham's Bill was opposed by the Church, and especially by the Nonconformists, so he withdrew it. Nevertheless, and in spite of other absorbing tasks, he never ceased to work for a more modern educational system.

While Brougham was busy on the Northern Circuit as a practising lawyer, as well as in politics, he led a most active social life. His liveliness and humour, as well as his literary and scientific standing, made him welcome almost everywhere. Soon after he first came to London, the Prince of Wales heard of him, and had him introduced. He kept up his attendances at Royal Society meetings for practical as well as scientific reasons. He reported to Grey in 1809: 'I was at the annual election of the Royal Society today, which generally brings together a very courtly set. The alteration of tone was very striking. Everyone talked of the new ministry as mere shift, and it is hard to say whether Canning or his late colleagues were most blamed.'

Later in that year, Brougham first entered the social circle of the unfortunate Princess Caroline. In 1785 the Prince of Wales, the future Prince Regent and George IV, had married the Roman Catholic Mrs. Fitzherbert. Constitutionally, the marriage was invalid, and debarred him from succeeding to the Crown, so it was kept secret. After about ten years, the Prince's affections strayed to Lady Jersey, and his debts grew out of hand. The King offered to marry on condition that Parliament paid his debts. His niece, Caroline of Brunswick, was one of the ladies recommended for his consideration. Lady Jersey favoured her, because she was the least attractive candidate.

The Prince could not escape accepting her, and she was sent for from Germany. When he first saw her, he retreated at once to the far end of the room and called for a glass of brandy. Caroline was twenty-six; she was not beautiful, her teeth were already decaying, and she was badly dressed.

Caroline and the Prince were married, and in 1796 she gave birth to the Princess Charlotte, an heir to the throne. The Prince considered he had done his duty, and refused to continue to live with her.

Caroline was provided with her own establishment, which her liveliness and rank made a fashionable centre. Like other brilliant young men, Brougham found his way there; Canning was already a habitué.

Caroline was hearty, coarse and so indiscreet that it seemed highly improbable that she could be very immoral. She liked listening to clever men, who found her circle entertaining. The more she held a position of her own, the more the Prince hated her. She adopted the child of a docker, and the Prince instigated a 'Delicate Investigation', which he hoped would provide evidence on which he could divorce her. Ellenborough, Erskine and other eminent lawyers conducted the investigation, which acquitted her on the main allegation.

In his earlier years, the Prince was a Whig, in opposition to his Tory father. After he was appointed Prince Regent, he became converted to the principle of the supreme authority of the Crown, and consorted with the Tories. The Whigs, who had formerly helped him against Caroline, now helped her against him.

The Prince Regent's conversion to Toryism, arising out of his extreme selfishness, was a very serious political development in the conditions of 1809. The struggle against Napoleon was made the excuse for suppressing the reform and modernization of an out-of-date social structure. There was grave danger of a political dictatorship being established through Royal Tory authoritarianism.

Brougham sympathized with Caroline, in spite of her outrageousness, because she was so disgracefully persecuted. He also saw in her a means for attacking the Prince Regent and the Tories. As her legal adviser, he could help the Whig cause.

Brougham perceived even greater possibilities as adviser to her daughter. Charlotte was, after her father, heir to the Throne. If he could gain her confidence, he could look forward to being the established personal adviser to a future Queen of England. This might be of decisive importance in the choice of a future prime minister. In the event, Charlotte died early and the crown passed to Victoria, so nothing came of the calculation.

Before this, however, the Prince became as jealous of his daughter as he hated his wife. He feared he might die, and she become Queen without his ever having been King. When he became King as George IV in 1820, new features arose in the situation. George IV determined to use his kingly power to force the divorce. At the same time, Caroline acquired legal rights as Queen. She could have her own Attorney-General, and naturally appointed Brougham to that position.

Caroline had been very badly treated in England, so she longed to settle abroad. She was advised not to do this because it might weaken her position, but after years of fretting, she set up a ménage in Italy. She had an Italian servant with whom she appeared to be living, and her house was infested with third-rate Italian spies in the pay of the British Government.

She announced that she would return to England, and demand her rights as Queen. Her name, on the action of the King, had been excluded from the Liturgy, and she was denied access to the Coronation Service in Westminster Abbey. She tried to enter at one door of the Abbey, and then at another, but was kept out.

The British people were profoundly shocked by the exclusion of the Queen's name from the Liturgy. They were outraged by her ungallant treatment on the orders of a profligate king who dare not venture among them for fear of being stoned. Eight years before, in 1812, while Prince Regent, George had already utilized Congreve's rockets to fortify Windsor Castle against them. Grey had reported to Brougham: 'You know the drawbridge and the rockets were to be the great instruments of security in the new park against the mob.'

The people were passionately on the side of the ill-treated Queen. Nevertheless, George IV blindly insisted on the pursuit of an action for divorce. As the Queen's Attorney-General, Brougham led her defence. He was summoned to the House of Lords, and required to address the assembled peers on the principle of the action.

The spectacle produced a deep impression, both politically and socially, on foreign observers. The Russian Ambassadress, Princess Lieven, described how 'a lawyer sprung from the lowest ranks of society' inveighed against the Cabinet, and ridiculed ministers. 'Brougham has an astonishing facility; he did not correct himself once during a two-hours' speech, and a speech which could not be prepared, for it was only when they summoned him to appear that the House let him know the points on which he was allowed to argue.'

In an adroit cross-examination he destroyed the credibility of the Crown's series of seedy Italian spies. He reduced them to admitting that they could not recall the true facts of what had happened. He led them into a continual repetition of the phrase 'non mi ricordo', until their evidence dissolved in ridiculous laughter. The phrase became one of the catchwords of the day. Brougham's speech so held the peers that they even cut dinner engagements with their wives. His masterly certainty in his conduct of the defence, which was concerned with the assertion of the rights of the individual against a growing Royal authoritarianism, probably arose from his knowledge that in the last resort, the full facts about Mrs. Fitzherbert could be published. If this had been done, the monarchy might have been destroyed.

Brougham was a moderate Whig, not a revolutionary. The effect of his success was to make the King and the Tories retreat.

LORD BROUGHAM

This prevented the establishment of absolutism, but it also saved the monarchy.

After his gallant defence of the ill-used Queen, Brougham was a popular hero, and people became more willing to open at least one ear to what he had to say about education and science. He continued his campaigns for education, science, the suppression of slavery and the reform of the law with unabated intensity, and he also showed more frequent signs of overstrain.

In the House of Commons, he denounced ministers as 'mean fawning parasites of the Duke of Wellington', then prime minister. Grey informed Princess Lieven that he believed Brougham 'to be mad'. The Whigs would not make him their leader in the Commons, in spite of his immense services.

He made a prodigious speech in 1828 on a motion for a commission on law reform. It lasted more than six hours, and dealt with 120 topics. In it, he collected ideas from many quarters, including Bentham, who was infuriated at not being mentioned by name.

Most of Brougham's proposals for reform were carried out in the next ten years, and one, on the equality of Crown and subject, was achieved only by the Crown Proceedings Act of 1947.

Holdsworth has said that 'there is no doubt that his speech was the most learned and thorough criticism of the many defects of the common law that had ever been made since the Commonwealth period'.

George IV died in 1830. Reform could no longer be delayed, and a General Election took place later in the year. Brougham was invited by the Yorkshire industrialists to stand for the county, in succession to Wilberforce, who had retired. Under unreformed conditions, it was a very expensive constituency to contest. The Duke of Wellington said no gentleman could afford it. Brougham said he could contribute nothing, but the necessary funds were collected by his industrial sponsors. After a campaign in the Yorkshire towns, where he had audiences of up to 20,000, he was elected. He became the first non-Yorkshireman since the Reformation to represent Yorkshire. Lord Althorp, a Yorkshire peer, and one of the Whig leaders, described it as 'the highest honour and the greatest reward that ever was bestowed upon a public man'.

The Whigs had swept the country, and Brougham returned to the House of Commons as their outstanding member. Grey was called by William IV to form an administration. Brougham desired to be made Master of the Rolls, the second place in the legal hierarchy, a highly-paid post for life, which would allow him to remain in the Commons, where he was supreme. His mother, who was his closest personal counsellor, advised him to remain there at all costs. 'If, as is probable, office is offered you in the new Government, pause before you accept it, do not be tempted to leave the House of Commons. As member for Yorkshire, backed by all you have done for the country, you are more powerful than any official that ever existed, however high in station or rank. Throw not away the great position you have raised yourself to—a position greater than any that could be bestowed by king or minister.'

William IV, the Tories, and even some of the Whigs, were, however, determined to get Brougham out of the Commons. William IV indicated to Grey that he would not agree to make Brougham Master of the Rolls, but would agree to his being Lord Chancellor. Grey offered Brougham the Chancellorship, which he at first refused. He was then told that if he continued to refuse, an administration could not be formed, and the Whig party would be out of office for another 25 years. Brougham said he wanted time to consider the offer, and was given a few hours to make up his mind.

The lord chancellorship carried a salary of £14,000 a year, and a life pension of £5,000 a year. The combination of the appeal to his ambition, the fortunes of his family and his party loyalty overcame his reluctance, and he accepted. William IV claimed the credit for getting rid of Brougham. He told Lord Holland: 'You are all under great obligations to me. I have settled Brougham; he will not be dangerous any more.'

Thomas Love Peacock forecast what would happen in his poem on *The Fate of a Broom: An Anticipation*, published in 1831.

Lo! in Corruption's lumber-room,
The remnants of a wondrous broom;
That walking, talking, oft was seen,
Making stout promise to sweep clean;
But evermore, at every push,
Proved but a stump without a brush.
Upon its handle-top, a sconce,
Like Brahma's, looked four ways at once

Pouring on kings, lords, church, and rabble
Long floods of favour-currying gabble;
From four-fold mouth-piece always spinning
Projects of plausible beginning,
Whereof said sconce did ne'er intend
That any one should have an end;
Yet still, by shifts and quaint inventions,
Got credit for its good intentions,
Adding no trifle to the store,
Wherewith the devil paves his floor.
Worn out at last, found bare and scrubbish,
And thrown aside with other rubbish,
We'll e'en hand o'er the enchanted stick,
As a choice present for Old Nick,
To sweep, beyond the Stygian lake,
The pavement it has helped to make.

The historian of *The Times* (1785–1841) has described very well how Brougham was viewed by his opponents at this period: 'Brougham during the years 1825–1830 was at his best. He was recognized as insatiably ambitious, and men knew him to be unconscientious, but all listened to him with pleasure. His gaiety was not yet spoilt by ill-humour nor his enormous range of knowledge too deeply compromised with charlatanry.'

Brougham understood what had happened to himself, and was profoundly disturbed. At first he tried to put the best face on his position as Lord Chancellor. He busied himself with the duties, which he carried out efficiently. Like Bacon, he took pride in bringing the business of the Court of Chancery up to date; he performed with gusto the political tasks of the lord chancellorship, and continued to be very active in his causes of education and science.

He seemed to behave at times as if he again saw visions of the premiership, and started fitful intrigues in that direction. These faded out as soon as he recovered his clearsightedness. His political frustration increased his inner psychological conflict, but there was nothing to curb the personal behaviour of a Lord Chancellor. He became more eccentric, and personally difficult.

When Melbourne succeeded Grey as prime minister, he did not re-appoint Brougham as Lord Chancellor. Brougham became almost insane with mortification, and asked Melbourne whether he thought he was mad. Melbourne presently wrote to him: 'I will, however, tell you fairly that, in my opinion, you domineered too much with other departments, you encroached upon the province of the Prime Minister, you worked, as I believe, with the press in a manner unbecoming the dignity of your station, and you formed political views of your own and pursued them by means which were unfair to your colleagues.'

In 1837 Peacock wrote that he could fairly claim that his *Anticipation* had become *A Prophecy Fulfilled*.

Brougham fled to the South of France to nurse his wounds. He discovered a pleasant little fishing village called Cannes, and decided to build a house there for his delicate daughter Eleanor. Cannes became a fashionable watering place through Brougham's patronage. After his death the municipality erected a monument to the memory of the founder of its fortunes.

Brougham grew passionately interested in France. He was elected a member of the Institute. He convinced himself that he was Britain's best ambassador, and tried to act as such in the presence of the official British Ambassador. His behaviour was sometimes so ridiculous that people laughed in his face.

In England, he attended committees, wrote articles and books, and delivered addresses. He introduced the *brougham*, 'a garden-chair on wheels', in 1838. More than half a century later, it became the pattern for the coachwork for the first Rolls-Royces.

As Grey and Melbourne grew older and lonelier, they resumed friendly relations with Brougham, and in the end, Melbourne made him one of his executors. This would have been inconceivable if Brougham had not had a fundamentally good character, in spite of his mental instability and frequent aberrant behaviour.

IX

Life without Place

BROUGHAM was rejected from office in his fifty-sixth year, and died in his ninetieth. He lived for his last thirty-four years without any of the power which derives from political place. In this situation, the party discipline which had helped him to control his inborn genius and mental instability was weakened. He lashed about like a giant, trying to escape from social chains in which he was fettered. Cartoonists portrayed him as Samson, whose hair had been cut by Delilah, in the shape of Lady Holland. In his early days, he had failed to invite her and her husband into his house when they called at Brougham Hall, because his mother disapproved of her private life, and refused to meet her.

Brougham's political isolation threw him more on himself and his domestic life. He had married Mrs. Spalding, a lady of the Eden family, and a widow with two children. She had a considerable income. She did not participate much in his affairs, and presently became delicate. She bore him two daughters; the first died before she was two years old, and the second, Eleanor Louisa, lived only until she was eighteen.

Brougham was profoundly attached to his mother and brothers. He looked after them devotedly, and his brothers worked for him.

He became deeply devoted to Eleanor. She had weak health, and in his isolation he gave more and more attention to her. He kept her as much as possible at Cannes, and named his house *Château Eleanor Louise*. When she died in 1839, he was distraught. He wrote a novel to commemorate her, called *Albert Lunel*. It is impossible as a novel, but contains descriptions of the mental states of his characters, which seem to be introspective revelations of Brougham to himself. The passages are acute and graphic. In his other innumerable activities, Brougham was always extrovert, concealing his inner life. Nearly all copies of the book disappeared shortly after it was printed, but it was published after Brougham's death.

He continued his long friendship with Robert Owen, who, at the age of eighty-two, became a convert to spiritualism. The two retired creative reformers took part in séances, in which Owen claimed to receive communications from the spirit of the late Duke of Kent, Queen Victoria's father. The Duke had been one of the earliest and most appreciative admirers of Owen's work on children's education.

As Brougham's political ties were loosened, he veered in various directions, at times towards the Radicals, and at others, the Tories. He was active as a private member in the House of

Lords. Macaulay remarked that 'he has done wonders this session. A mere tongue, without a party and without a character, in an unfriendly audience, and with an unfriendly press, never did half so much before.' He tried to prove the truth of what he had asserted about Canning, that the 'distinguishing error of his life' was his belief 'that no one can usefully serve his country, or effectually further his principles, unless he possesses the power which place alone bestows'.

From his private position, he prosecuted the policies for which he had done more than anyone: the abolition of slavery, which he pursued after the slave-trade had been suppressed by his own and other efforts, and the evolution towards a ministry of education and an educational system.

He urged the implementation of the law reforms he had proposed. Through his efforts the law became simpler, quicker and cheaper. Prisoners charged with serious crimes were enabled to have counsel and give evidence in their own defence.

In 1847 he was chairman of a committee on juvenile offenders. He said: 'I regard the culprit as our patient . . . the state as the superintendent of the Infirmary . . . the governor with his assistants, as the physicians. . . .'

As late as 1857, he was active on a *Married Woman's Property Act*. He supported the Congress of Social Science at Birmingham in the same year. This was the first public congress in England at which a woman was invited to speak.

Robert Owen was enthusiastically interested in it, but was too ill to attend. He insisted on going to the meeting of the association at Liverpool in 1858, when he was eighty-seven years old. He was carried onto the platform by four policemen. 'It is now a matter of public history,' wrote Holyoake, 'how kindly Lord Brougham, as soon as he saw his old friend, took him by the arm, led him forward and obtained a hearing for him.' Owen 'in his grand manner, proclaimed his ancient message of science, competence and good will to the world'. When he had completed his first period, Brougham, out of regard for his failing strength, terminated his speech by clapping and starting applause. 'Capital, very good, can't be better, Mr. Owen! There! that will do.' Then Brougham whispered to a colleague: 'Convey the old gentleman to his bed.' As soon as Owen was put in bed, he became unconscious. He rallied for a short time, visited the house where he was born, and died later in the year.

X

Homage to Newton

BROUGHAM continued active efforts in science almost to the end of his life. He published experimental and theoretical papers on light in 1852 and 1853, in the *Proceedings* of the Royal Society and the *Comptes Rendus* of the French Academy of Sciences, pursuing the problems he had investigated in his youth. He published papers on the structure of the cells of beehives.

His treatise, with E. J. Routh, on *An Analytical View of Newton's Principia* was published in 1855, and dedicated to the Italian astronomer Plana, the nephew of Lagrange. This substantial work of 442 pages consists of an exposition of the *Principia*, using algebra as far as possible, to avoid the difficulties of Newton's geometrical methods. It was designed for two classes of readers: 'those who only desire to become acquainted with the discoveries of Newton, and the history of the science, but without examining the reasoning, and those who would follow the reasoning to a certain extent, and so far as a knowledge of the most elementary parts of geometrical and analytical science may enable them to go. It has been found upon trial that readers of both descriptions have been able to peruse the work with advantage, even readers of the second description.' Brougham regarded it as a contribution in his ceaseless campaign for the diffusion of knowledge.

He was particularly proud of being invited to deliver the address on the unveiling of the monument to Isaac Newton at Grantham, on September 21st, 1858, two days after his eightieth birthday. His address was based on the *Analytical View*, and shows him well-versed in the history of science and mathematics, with due notice of Cavalieri and Fermat as precursors in the invention of the calculus, and a judicious statement of the respective contributions of Newton and Leibniz. He mentioned Borelli's approach to the concept of gravitation in his ascription of the motion of satellites to the attraction of the planets, and thus being prevented from being carried off by centrifugal force.

He refers to the conjecture of de Dominis in 1611 on the possibility of the decomposition of white light, and the observation of Marcus of Prague in 1648, that a coloured ray is not changed by a second refraction. 'All this only shows that the discoveries of Newton, great and rapid as were the steps by which they advanced our knowledge, yet obeyed the law of continuity, which governs all human approaches towards perfection.'

The history of chemistry and biology showed the same features. These reflections on progressive development in science and life were expressed in the year before the publication of the *Origin of Species*.

Bacon's claim to be regarded as the father of modern philosophy 'rests upon the important, the truly invaluable step of reducing to a system the method of investigation' adopted by the ancient natural philosophers, Roger Bacon, Leonardo da Vinci, Gilbert and other eminent predecessors. He generalized it, and extended 'its application to all matters of contingent truth, exploding the errors, the absurd dogmas and fantastic subtleties of the ancient schools—above all, confining the subject of our inquiry, and the manner of conducting it, within the limits which our faculties prescribe'. He mentioned that Newton never refers to Bacon in his works, and says that 'it is certain that neither he, nor indeed anyone but Bacon himself, ever followed in detail the rules prescribed in the *Novum Organum*'.

Brougham comments that the same law of Gradual Progress is to be seen in the development of political economy. 'The great discovery of modern times in the Science of practical politics' is the 'Mixed Monarchy'. This allows freedom to be combined with order. 'The globe itself as well as the science of its inhabitants has been explored according to the law which forbids a sudden and rapid leaping forward.'

The same was true in the arts and mathematics, in oratory, painting and military tactics. The invention of logarithms was a notable example of gradual development. So was the invention of the steam engine. Causs and Papin, Worcester and Newcomen were eminent predecessors in its development. Brougham most esteemed the invention of the governor, 'perhaps the most exquisite of mechanical inventions; and now we have those here present who apply the like principle to the diffusion of knowledge, aware as they must be, that its expansion has the same happy effect naturally of preventing mischief from its excess, which the skill of the great mechanist gave artificially to steam, thus rendering his engine as safe as it is powerful'.

Brougham saw in what is now called feed-back the principle which will save science from itself, or in the conditions of today, save mankind from exterminating itself by the uncontrolled development of science.

In his comments on the prodigious nature of Newton's achievements he dwelt on his having discovered the Calculus of Variations before Euler and Lagrange, and the method of Partial Differences before D'Alembert. The first was shown by his discovery of the shape of the figure of least resistance to passage through a fluid.

He emphasized Newton's boldness in 'never shrinking from a conclusion that seemed the legitimate result of his investigations'. Instances of this were his discovery of the nutation, or to-and-fro movement of the earth's axis, owing to the combined action of the sun and moon on the earth: an effect not observed until sixty years later. Newton's estimate of the earth's density as between five and six times that of water, and his conjecture that the diamond consisted of an 'unctuous coagulated substance' were examples of his extraordinary speculative insight.

His calculation that the earth must depart from the shape of a perfect sphere by 1 part in 229 to 230, owing to the effects of its axial rotation, leaves us 'amazed, if not awestruck'. A century of research by Euler, Clairant, D'Alembert, Lagrange and Laplace did not substantially improve on it.

'When we recollect the Greek orator's exclamation, "the whole earth is the monument of illustrious men," can we stop short of declaring that the whole universe is Newton's?'

Even this was not Brougham's last scientific effort. In 1860 he published a collection of his *Tracts* on mathematical and physical subjects. He completed the three volumes of his *Memoirs* in his ninetieth year. He died shortly after, on May 7th, 1868, in Cannes, and was buried there.

The example of Brougham, like that of Bacon, is that his work in and for science was an integral part of his whole effort in life. Politics, science, law and literature were pursued together, and gave each other mutual inspiration and support, in his effort to play an adequate rôle in life, and improve the human condition.

William Robert Grove

1811–1896

I

Amateurs and Professionals

THE spread of scientific knowledge among the middle and the working classes as a result of the Industrial Revolution altered the social character of scientific activity. In the previous mercantile age, dominated by landlords and city merchants, in which the profits of overseas trade were often invested in country estates, science was still largely an individual activity. It was pursued by intellectual men of leisure for its own sake. Improving landlords were interested in natural history as an agreeable way of taking an intellectual interest in country life. Some of them pursued botany and zoology in search of improvements in agriculture and husbandry.

Successful doctors studied science in their leisure, and also with the hope of improving the technique of medicine. As a whole, however, medicine was still far from being scientific.

These scientists were predominantly amateur in their attitude to science. They formed the bulk of the members of the Royal Society for the first century and a half of its existence.

The development of industrialism in the second half of the eighteenth century changed this situation. The increasingly scientific and technical new industry produced new classes of scientists and technologists, who were not primarily amateur in their interests, but required scientific and technical knowledge in their trades and professions. A new scientific and technical professionalism arose. Men like Davy and Faraday, who had had no university education, became professional scientists. They brought the attitude of the craftsman into the research laboratory.

When they started work in London, they found science ruled by the old amateurs, at the head of which was the formidable Sir Joseph Banks, the improving landlord and founder of the development of Australia, who had inspired the scouring of the world for botanical and zoological materials, in the shape of plants and animals to be cultivated in the expanding British Empire.

Sir Joseph had ruled the Society since 1778. By the beginning of the nineteenth century his régime, which had done so much for Britain in the previous forty years, had become unsuited to the scientific needs of the new age.

Davy, Faraday, and men like them had little scientific interest in common with Banks and his class. After his swift and great success Davy formed the ambition of superseding, or at least succeeding Banks, as President of the Royal Society, and reforming it according to the ideas and needs of the post-industrial revolution scientists.

He was successful in following Banks as President, but he remained overawed by his powerful and exalted personality. He and his ambitious wife hankered after the kind of social position and authority which Banks had possessed. This prevented Davy from being more than half successful in reforming the Royal Society, and changing it from an organization of amateurs into one of professionals.

The Davy and Faraday type, the craftsmen transmuted into professional experimental investigators, were representative of only what might be called the working-class section of the new scientific research profession. An equally powerful section came from another product of the Industrial Revolution, the managing and commercial side of the new industry. Sons of bankers and industrial magnates began to bring the outlook of their class into science. Most of them were fanatical adherents of Adam Smith's political philosophy, and they desired to see science conducted in a business-like professional manner, like their father's offices in the City. Unlike Davy and Faraday, many of these young men had had the best education that money could buy. They had arrived at the frontiers of the most modern knowledge while still students.

When they came in contact with the Banks regime and its aftermath, they were as disgusted with it as Davy and Faraday. But unlike them, with their wealthy background, they were not intimidated like Davy, or, as Faraday at first, simply ignored. They came into the Society without any social inferiority complex, and angrily pressed for professionalization, which they described as being businesslike.

The most gifted and violent of this new class of scientist was Charles Babbage. He and his friends pressed for reforms, and when these were not immediately forthcoming, he caused uproar. Babbage exploded an intellectual bomb under the old Royal Society régime. This cleared the ground for reform. As the dust settled, and the way was cleared, men of tact and persuasion carried out the necessary changes, which converted the Royal Society from a body of talented amateurs into a society of professional experts. This change gave social recognition and status to the leaders of the new scientific profession.

Among the scientists who carried through this change in the character of the Royal Society, the leading part was taken by the scientist-lawyer, William Robert Grove. The scene on which he entered, and in which he operated so skilfully, was to a large extent the result of Babbage's explosive genius. It will be useful to look at this first.

II

Charles Babbage

BABBAGE was born in Devonshire in 1791, the son of Benjamin Babbage, the progressive manager of the banking firm of Praed, Mackworth and Babbage. The poet and political satirist Winthrop Mackworth Praed belonged to the family of his father's partners.

Babbage was a delicate child, and after a careful education was sent to Trinity College, Cambridge. He had a comfortable allowance, and made friends with other talented young men; in particular, John Herschel and George Peacock. In the isolation of the Napoleonic Wars, Cambridge had slipped further than ever behind Europe in mathematics. The three young men got little help from their tutors, so as students they began, and succeeded, in reforming Cambridge mathematics.

The young men gained their new mathematical ideas from Revolutionary France, who had mobilized her mathematicians and scientists to rationalize their mathematics and science. As part of their rationalization they introduced the metric system. This involved the calculation of new mathematical tables. Prony, the mathematician charged with this task, while reading

Adam Smith's *Wealth of Nations*, perceived that it should be possible to apply the principle of the division of labour to facilitate the calculations.

Young Babbage, brought up on Adam Smith, was fascinated by this development. It occurred to him that it ought to be possible to mechanize the elementary processes to which the French mathematicians had reduced the calculations. There is no definite account of when Babbage conceived this. It is variously ascribed to the years 1812–13, 1819, or 1820–1, when he was stimulated, or re-stimulated, to take up the idea by John Herschel.

Babbage and his friends applied to the Royal Society for a recommendation to the Government for the development of a machine for this purpose, based on a model which he had constructed and demonstrated. Only one member of the committee of the Royal Society which considered the matter was against it. This was Thomas Young, who had earlier been discouraging to Brougham.

Babbage considered that his great invention ought to have received one of the first two Royal Medals awarded by the Royal Society. It conformed more closely with the regulations for the medal than the researches of Dalton and Ivory which, strictly speaking, fell outside its period of reference; the medals were for recent work, not that done years ago.

Then he believed Davy had promised to support his election to one of the Secretaryships. When this did not materialize, he became further enraged.

Up to the year 1826, when his father died, Babbage, though the son of a rich man, had no income of his own, and had a large and growing family. He became extremely anxious to secure funds for developing his machine, and salaried positions to provide him with financial and filial independence.

At the same time, he worked on his machine with extraordinary intensity. He ransacked the mechanical engineering of England for ideas, and in the process conceived the notion of applying science to improving the operation of machinery. This is what is now called operational research.

Babbage was very anxious to secure the approbation of his father, and apparently showed parts of the manuscript of his book on the *Economy of Machinery* to him before he died. This work contains the germ of modern scientific industrialization, and was published in 1828.

As scientist

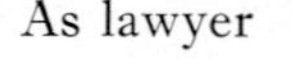

As lawyer

SIR WILLIAM GROVE

Unfortunately, Babbage suffered severe personal disasters in the midst of his intense creative labours. His father, his wife and two of his children died in the period 1826–7. The shock left his personality permanently impaired, though he inherited £100,000 from his father, which left him with independence.

He had a nervous breakdown, and in 1827 went on a continental tour to recover his health. This brought him in touch with Alexander von Humboldt, and through him he attended the first international congress of scientists, held in Berlin in 1828. Babbage returned with reinforced enthusiasm for the reform of the Royal Society, the reform of British science, and the foundation of new scientific organizations.

He expressed his views in the *Decline of Science in England* in 1830. In the following year, the British Association for the Advancement of Science was founded, with Babbage as one of the trustees.

Babbage was now personally a rich man, and engaged in a long battle with the Government over support for the development of his calculating machine. While waiting for the Government to increase its support, he continuously thought of improvements, and gradually conceived the complete principles of the computer, and even invented the vocabulary for describing its processes, which is in universal use today.

He was a genius of the first order, who saw how to make industry scientific, and mechanize science. He provided the ideas for the second half of the twentieth century, but he was too impatient to attend to the more modest needs of the science and industry of his own day. When he had discovered all the principles of the computer, he immediately planned a machine which could theoretically do everything that the biggest computer of 1964 could do. The construction of such a machine was beyond the powers of the engineering of his day.

In this situation, conscious of the magnitude of his own genius, and the limited understanding of the contemporary authorities, he grew more and more difficult. Many people regarded him as slightly deranged. The most intelligent scientists of the period understood the importance of what he had achieved, but were unable to persuade the Government to provide the kind of aid that he needed. This was development engineering, which had scarcely yet been conceived.

Thus there was discontent in the scientific world, on the one hand from men like Faraday, and on the other from those like Babbage. Yet Faraday and Babbage, for different reasons, were unable personally to lead the reform. Faraday was inhibited by his peculiar religious and his social background; Babbage by his overstrained personality. Men more at home in affairs were needed.

III

Lubbock and Herschel

THE reformers attempted to capture the leadership of the Royal Society by nominating John Herschel for the Presidency and J. W. Lubbock for the Treasurership in 1830. The traditionalists nominated the Duke of Sussex, the youngest son of George III, for the Presidency. After a tremendous contest, Herschel was beaten by eight votes, but Lubbock was elected.

Lubbock, like Babbage, was a mathematician and belonged to a banking family. While continuing in the family business, he devoted his leisure to research on the theory of the tides, and to scientific affairs. As has already been mentioned, he was active in the Society for the Diffusion of Useful Knowledge.

After his election to the Treasurership, he scrutinized the conduct of the Society's affairs with the eye of a banker. He caused the financial accounts to be drawn up in a businesslike manner, and to be circulated in printed form to the fellows. Previously, the ordinary fellows had not been informed of the details of the Society's management. In this way he provided the concrete data which were evidence to the professional mind, that the Society's affairs were not being properly conducted.

Besides exposing the former conduct of the Society as unbusinesslike, he acquired extra influence through the accident that the President, the Duke of Sussex, became more and more frequently absent through ill-health. On these occasions, Lubbock generally deputized in his chair. So, to a considerable extent, during the Duke's Presidency, one of the leading reformers was *de facto* president.

But progress in completing the reform did not proceed quickly.

Nearly twenty years passed before the Presidency, and election to the Society, were virtually restricted to professional scientists. When the Duke resigned in 1838, the Marquis of Northampton was elected as his successor. He was a noted antiquary and active geologist. He successfully followed a cautious policy, not offending either the professionals or amateurs.

Meanwhile, further improvements had been made in the Society's organization. The Committee on Papers, which decided whether papers should be accepted for publication, included a considerable number of members who were not active scientists, and therefore not experts on any branch of science. Papers of poor quality were sometimes passed because the referees were not expert. This situation was improved in 1838 by the appointment of eight specialist committees on various branches of science, for considering matters in their respective domains. Though these were the forerunners of the Sectional Committees which function today, they were not immediately successful; they lapsed in 1849, and were not revived on the lines of the present Sectional Committees until 1896.

In spite of the efforts of the reformers, the case for a Royal Society whose president and members were restricted, apart from a small special class, to practising or professional scientists, was not entirely convincing. The case against professionalization was well-expressed by Richard Sheepshanks, the leisured son of a Yorkshire woollen manufacturer, who had never had to earn a living, in a controversy with Babbage.

'There is a point of view in which the *mixed* nature of the Royal Society may be considered, which seems to have escaped most of our grumblers; it is that the union of so much rank, wealth, talent, and even of numbers, gives it great and appropriate weight in such a country as England. The Royal Society provides a competent body to inquire into every discovery and gives immediate and extensive publication to whatever is found of value. It is no slight advantage to be backed by the goodwill of 800 gentlemen, who comprehend almost all the scientific talent of the empire; and if national aid should be required, the influence of the Royal Society, with a good cause, is almost paramount.'

In the face of such arguments, based on the nature of the governing forces in society, progress towards professionalization was neither easy nor swift.

Lubbock and Herschel, for all their great talents, were themselves too much identified with the gentlemanly sections of contemporary society. Lubbock was a good mathematician and astronomer, but he was even more a gentleman. John Herschel had grown up in the environment of Slough, Windsor, and his father, the King's personal astronomer. Even he was a gentleman first, and a scientist afterwards.

A man of equal ability, but cast entirely in a professional mould, was required to complete the professionalization of the Society. This proved to be William Robert Grove who, before he became an eminent lawyer, had become an even more eminent scientist.

IV

Grove the Scientist

GROVE invented the nitric acid Voltaic cell known by his name, and the fuel cell. The latter produces electric current directly from chemical reactions. Though Faraday's electromagnetic induction, which was discovered eight years earlier, has won the race in electricity generation so far, it may in the future be overtaken by the fuel cell. If the same effort had been put into the development of the fuel cell, it is possible that the last hundred years would have seen developments in chemical engineering which would have rendered a large part of electrical engineering unnecessary. The age would have been far more chemical and far less electrical, than it has been.

In his own day, Grove was widely known scientifically for his exposition of the idea of the correlation of physical forces, and the convertibility of one kind of force into another. Among other things, it was a forerunner of the theory of the conservation of energy. His first lecture on this topic was printed in 1842, when he was thirty-one.

As a scientist and inventor, Grove was comparable with Babbage. In character and policy he was the very opposite. Where Babbage was dashing and optimistic, with large social and political views, Grove was cautious and pessimistic, with high but limited objectives. While Babbage was tactless, Grove was modest, unassuming, and shrewd. Babbage behaved with the confidence of the son of a wealthy banker, Grove like a city solicitor. Babbage sought to advance by direct assault, and was largely frustrated; Grove obtained limited but concrete advances by legal subtlety.

It was Grove who found the key to the final problem of how to restrict the Royal Society to practising scientists, and thus complete its professionalization.

Grove was born at Swansea on July 11th, 1811, the son of John Grove, a magistrate and deputy lieutenant of the county of Glamorgan. He received his early education at Swansea, and at Bath. He went to Brasenose College, Oxford, where he graduated with a pass degree in 1830. He appears not to have made great intellectual progress there, and his exceptional talent made no particular impression. During the rest of his long life, he never exhibited enthusiasm for Oxford. Brasenose never elected him a fellow.

He studied law with the intention of entering the legal profession, and in 1835 was called to the Bar at Lincoln's Inn. He joined the Chester and South Wales Circuits, but was prevented from practising much, owing to ill-health. He devoted himself to scientific study and research. While he read widely in many branches of physical science, he became particularly interested in the Voltaic battery. This was the basis of the new science of direct current electricity and its applications. It was to electricity what the steam engine was to heat: a new prime mover.

Grove had the first-class scientist's gift for recognizing, and choosing for research, a subject of major importance. His study of the properties of the cell, especially of the phenomenon of polarization, which reduces its efficiency, led him to a clearer understanding of the electro-chemical principles underlying its operation, and to his fundamental inventions.

He deduced from this theoretical clarification that it should be possible to construct cells in which the voltage produced was the result of the addition of the effects of two chemical affinities, instead of their difference, as in the existing types.

The primitive Voltaic cell produced an electric current which soon decreased and fluctuated in strength. Porrett, Becquerel and Daniell had shown that it was possible to construct a cell giving a constant current by using two compartments instead of one, as in the primitive cell. The two compartments were separated by a porous wall, through which an electric current could pass easily, but through which different liquids diffused slowly. Thus electrical conduction through the cell was preserved, while different solutions could be used for surrounding the respective electrodes, each in its separate compartment.

The aim of this development had been constancy of current. Grove pointed out, however, that it also presented the theoretical possibility of finding an arrangement, which enabled the addition, instead of the difference, of chemical affinities to be utilized in producing the current, thus giving a higher voltage.

Presently, Grove saw how this could be done. He gave the first description of his discovery at the Birmingham meeting of the British Association in 1839. He placed a zinc electrode and dilute sulphuric acid in one compartment, and a platinum electrode and strong nitric acid in the other, obtaining a much higher voltage than had previously been got from a cell, and also a low internal resistance, giving a strong current.

As he put it, he had 'lately been fortunate enough to hit upon a combination which I have no hesitation in pronouncing much more powerful than any previously known'.

The Grove cell was not invented as the result of accidental observations, or random experiments. It is a classical example of a practical invention conceived directly from theoretical reasoning.

His invention was immediately appreciated. He was asked to lecture at the Royal Institution in 1840 on polarization in the Voltaic cell. At the end of the lecture he demonstrated experiments with a battery of Grove cells 'which did not cover a space of sixteen inches square, and was only four inches high'.

The strong current from the battery was used to produce a powerful electric arc. Faraday assisted by holding an iron bar in various positions near the flame of the arc, showing how the flame was attracted or repelled through electromagnetic effects. 'Bars of different metals were instantly run into globules and dissipated in oxide.'

'Mr. Pattison, who navigated the Neva with Prof. Jacobi in October last' in a boat driven by electricity 'had observed that the batteries employed were on Mr. Grove's construction, which the professor without hesitation admitted'.

He followed his nitric acid cell with the far greater invention of the fuel cell, a modern development of which is to be used in spacecraft intended for navigating the moon in the later 1960's or 1970's.

V

The Fuel Cell

GROVE'S invention of what he called the 'gas battery', now known as the fuel cell, also arose out of his investigations of the action of the Voltaic cell.

The phenomenon of polarization, in which the hydrogen released at one of the electrodes in a Voltaic cell sets up a back-voltage, and thus reduces the effective voltage of the cell, attracted research on the electro-chemical reactions between gases and metals. This led Grove to the conception of a cell in which the electric current arises as the result of the chemical reactions between the constituents of gases, instead of between metals and liquids, as in an ordinary Voltaic cell. His first publication on the subject was also in 1839, under the title of the *Synthesis of Water by Voltaic Action.*

He fixed two vertical strips of platinum through the base of a glass vessel. Dilute sulphuric acid was poured into the vessel, so that the liquid came a considerable way up the platinum strips inside. The ends of the two platinum strips projecting through the bottom were connected to a delicate galvanometer.

Grove now placed an inverted glass tube containing hydrogen over the upper end of one of the platinum strips, and a similar tube containing oxygen over the upper end of the other platinum strip. The galvanometer immediately registered a distinct current; the platinum strip in the hydrogen tube behaving like 'the zinc element of the pile'.

Grove concluded his note of four hundred words with his 'hope, by repeating this experiment in series, to effect decomposition of water by means of its composition'.

The modern theory of its operation is that the platinum electrode in the oxygen gas catalyses a reaction between oxygen, water and electrons which produces hydroxyl ions. These hydroxyl ions then react with hydrogen ions in the electrolyte, to form water; the hydrogen ions being catalysed at the platinum electrode in hydrogen gas. In this reaction the molecular hydrogen is adsorbed on the platinum in the form of separate atoms of hydrogen. These atoms then split into hydrogen ions and free electrons. When the external circuit is completed, these free electrons flow through it, and produce the observed current.

Grove thoroughly explored his discovery, and published a long paper on it in the *Philosophical Transactions* for 1843. He succeeded in obtaining electric current from many other pairs of gases. The use of oxygen and carbon monoxide produced 'notable effects', while chlorine and hydrogen 'gave very powerful effects'. Only two chlorine-hydrogen cells in series were sufficient to decompose water. These two gases provided 'the most powerful gas battery'. He noted that a weak current could be obtained from oxygen and ethylene.

Grove's gas battery produces electrical energy directly from the chemical combination of atoms from pairs of gases, which under other conditions will burn together and produce heat. It is equivalent to a dynamo driven by a steam engine which derives its energy from the combustion of fuel gases in the boiler furnace. For this reason it is commonly described as a fuel cell.

The steam-driven electric generator is a fundamentally more complicated system than the fuel cell. Both ultimately derive their electrical energy from chemical combination, equivalent to the burning of fuel, but the steam engine or turbine is theoretically far less efficient. It wastes from 60 to 85 per cent of the energy in the fuel, whereas the loss in a fuel cell is only 20 to 30 per cent.

Grove was quite aware of its potentialities. He subsequently wrote: 'If, instead of employing manufactured products or educts, such as zinc or acids, we could realize as electricity the whole of the chemical force which is active in the combustion of cheap and abundant raw materials, such as coal, wood, fat, &c., with air or water, we should obtain one of the greatest practical desiderata, and have at our command a mechanical power in every respect superior in its applicability to the steam-engine.'

Efforts to develop the fuel cell industrially have long been made, so that the hydrocarbon gases from coal or oil could be combined with oxygen from the atmosphere, to produce electric current directly on a large scale. The difficulties are formidable, and have not yet been overcome.

The prospects of the fuel cell for special uses have, however, been transformed by the requirements of craft for exploring space. Consequently, since the development of modern rockets during the Second World War, which made space exploration possible, there has been an intense renewal of interest in the fuel cell, for it promises to be the most suitable source for producing the power in a spacecraft, which is needed for operating its machinery and equipment. It produces about three times as much power from the same amount of fuel as a steam engine, without emitting smoke or products of combustion. In addition, it works silently. The last two qualities are very important advantages in a spacecraft containing a human crew.

Grove's discovery led the way in the nineteenth century to the development of the secondary battery, in the form of the common lead accumulator. This is a device for making use of hydrogen and oxygen, produced from the electrolysis of water in the charging process.

Grove's splendid electrical inventions led to his election to the Royal Society in 1840, when he was twenty-nine years old. In the same year he was appointed professor of experimental philosophy in the London Institution.

VI

The London Institution

THE LONDON INSTITUTION, like the Royal Institution, was one of the many founded at the beginning of the nineteenth century 'for the advancement of literature and the diffusion of useful knowledge'. It was started in 1805, with £80,000 collected by public subscription. An imposing stone-columned building, costing £31,124, was erected for it in Finsbury Circus. It had an income of £3,000 a year, and collected a fine library of 70,000 volumes, on which £16,533 was spent between 1806–12. The great Greek, but also bibulous, scholar Richard Porson was appointed Librarian at £200 a year with rooms. Porson was no administrator, and the place was soon in a muddle.

The Institution had one or two professors, who were expected to give popular lectures in the manner then in vogue; for this they received a small stipend. The Institution gradually declined. Its building was adopted in 1917 for housing the Institute of Oriental Studies.

In 1874 the science professor was paid fifty guineas a year, and a similar sum for laboratory expenses. This was the professorship upon which Grove embarked in 1840. He held it with great distinction for seven years. His duty was to give expository lectures on science to an intelligent but untrained audience, illustrated by experiments. These were based on the subjects in which he was personally interested, and in which he was pursuing experimental researches. He tried to explain in the simplest language the theoretical ideas which his experiments raised in his mind, and prepared striking experiments, often original, to illustrate them. For instance, he demonstrated electric light from platinum filament lamps, fed with current from his nitric acid batteries.

The most important physical researches of the period had arisen out of the electrical discoveries of Volta, Ørsted and Faraday. Grove followed and extended them, contributing his own notable inventions, the Grove cell and the gas-battery or fuel cell.

Long preoccupation with the electrical effects of chemical reactions, and of the chemical effects produced by electric currents, directed his attention to the relations between the different kinds of forces, chemical, electrical, mechanical, etc. Following this line of thought, he extended it to cover the whole of physical phenomena. He reflected on the universe as a single great complex of acting and reacting forces: chemical phenomena resulted in electrical effects; electrical effects produced mechanical effects; these in turn produced electrical effects, which in turn produced chemical effects, and so on. These led him to his conception of the *Correlation of Physical Forces*, on which he lectured at the London Institution in January 1842.

He subsequently wrote that 'the word itself had not been previously used' as a scientific term. It meant 'a necessary or reciprocal dependence of two ideas, inseparable even in mental conception', and there were 'a vast variety of physical relations which cannot certainly be so well expressed by any other term'.

In his 1842 lecture he discussed the correlation of Heat, Motion, Electricity, Magnetism and Chemical Affinity, and concluded that they 'are all convertible material affections; assuming either as the cause, one of the others will be the effect: thus heat may be said to produce electricity, electricity to produce heat; magnetism to produce electricity, electricity-magnetism; and so of the rest. . . .'

Grove started by discussing the nature of scientific ideas, and the psychology of ideas: how a discovery requires a break from a system of established ideas, while such a system is also necessary as a basis for science. The discovery involves 'a laborious remodelling of ideas, a task which the public as a body will and can rarely undertake, the frequent occurrence of which is indeed inconsistent with the very existence of man in a social state, as it would induce an anarchy of thought—a perpetuity of mental revolutions'.

Philosophers had previously noted certain correlations of physical forces. For example, Bacon, 'the great remodeller of science', Rumford and Davy had noted and experimented on that of heat and motion.

But in Grove's opinion, the precision and multiplicity of correlations did not become evident until after the discovery of current electricity, with the development of electro-magnetism, thermo-electricity, photography, and many other examples of the conversion of one kind of physical phenomenon into another. For his part, he said, the convertibility of forces had been 'strongly impressed upon my mind at a period when I was much engaged in experimental research'. It had been stimulated especially by his researches on the conversion of chemical into electrical action, and vice versa.

He considered such a correlation in terms of cause and effect, and in the light of Hume's theory of cause, he noted the reciprocal or dialectical nature of physical phenomena.

Grove's ideas broadly comprehended the notion of the conservation of energy, and were published several months before J. R. Mayer's first paper. They were wider in philosophic scope, but qualitative only, whereas Mayer's were quantitative as well as qualitative, deducing a numerical figure for the mechanical equivalent of heat. In the following year, 1843, Joule gave an experimentally established figure.

Grove expanded his lecture into an essay on the *Correlation of Forces*, which he published in 1846. Helmholtz's essay on the *Conservation of Force*, which contained highly original and profound extensions of the ideas of his predecessors, appeared in 1847.

Grove was not exactly the first promulgator of the theory of the conservation of energy, but he was an immediate forerunner, and was in fact concerned with a wider range of ideas than merely the conservation of energy. However, in this connection, he did not like to have his contribution overlooked. 'It would be affecting an indifference which I do not feel if I did not state that I believe myself to have been the first who introduced this subject as a generalized system of philosophy, and continued to enforce it in my lectures and writings for many years, during which it met with the opposition usual and proper to novel ideas.'

In the succeeding editions of his *Correlation of Physical Forces*, he extended the idea to the correlations between chemistry and biology, in the growth of plants and human physiology. Deeper knowledge of the chemical and physical structure of living organisms would help to explain their characteristics. 'It seems to me no extravagant thought that, if alcohol and hereditary disease do not destroy the human race, a time may come when, from what will be known of the characteristics of some of the planets, a reasonable hypothesis of the characters of their inhabitants may be framed.'

Grove quoted, as supporting evidence for his views on the convertibility of forces, Newton's famous Query, in which he asked 'Are not gross bodies and light convertible into one another. . . . The changing of bodies into light and light into bodies is very conformable to the course of Nature, which seems delighted with transmutations. . . .'

He went on to discuss the problem which had often occurred to him, as to others, whether light merely becomes weaker as it progresses through interstellar space, or presently actually disappears. In connection with this he discussed the implications of Olbers's paradox, which has such a prominent place in cosmology. He does not refer to Olbers, so he may have rediscovered the idea for himself, as he did in other cases. He says: 'Every increase of space-penetrating power in the telescope gives us a new field of visible stars. If this expansion of the stellar universe go on indefinitely and no light be lost, then, assuming the fixed stars to be of an average equal brightness with our sun, and to fill up every point of space, and that no light be lost other than by divergence, the night ought to be equal with the day . . . it is difficult to understand why we get so little light at night from the stellar universe, without assuming that some light is lost in its progress through space—not lost absolutely, for that would be an annihilation of force—but converted into some other mode of motion.'

This hypothesis assumes that the stellar universe is illimitable, which 'seems a far more rational assumption to make than that the stellar universe is limited'. Each increase in telescopic power had revealed new realms of stars and nebulae. Grove forecast from his study of the correlation of known forces that other forces would be discovered in nature. This was 'as far certain as certain can be of any future event'.

'The probability is that, if not all, the greater number of physical phenomena are, in one sense correlative, and that, without a duality of conception, the mind cannot form an idea of them: thus, motion cannot be perceived or probably imagined without parallax or relative change of position . . . in all physical phenomena, the effects produced by motion are all in proportion to the relative motion. . . . The question of whether there can be absolute motion, or indeed, any absolute isolated force, is purely the metaphysical question of idealism or realism. . . .'

Such were the ideas which were shaping in Grove's mind while he reflected on his experimental researches in electrochemistry.

In 1847, at the age of thirty-six, he resigned from the ill-paid professorship at the London Institution, to devote himself primarily to the law. 'Avocations necessary to the well-being of others have prevented my following' the theory of the correlation of forces 'up experimentally, to the extent that I once hoped'. He had instead to earn more to support a growing family; ultimately, he had six children: two sons and four daughters.

VII

The Royal Society

As Lyons has observed, a marked change in the policy of the Society occurred in 1821, when Humphry Davy succeeded Banks as President. For the first time a majority of the members of the Council were practising scientists. More attention was paid to the improvement of the administration. 'All this was the outcome of the steady growth of interest in scientific knowledge and in its application to technical industry.' In fact, the Industrial Revolution in this country had made many realize how much larger and more important a part science, and the application of it to industry, was to play everywhere in the immediate future. Ultimately, it was from this source that the inspiration came for the reorganization of the Society.

The Council appointed a committee in 1823 to review the Society's statutes, but did not deal with the urgent question of the regulation of the number and qualifications of fellows. In 1827, on the motion of Babbage's friend, the astronomer James South, a committee was formed under the chairmanship of W. H. Wollaston, and consisting of Gilbert, John Herschel, Young, Babbage, Beaufort, Kater and South himself, to 'consider the best means of limiting the members admitted to the Royal Society, as well as to make such Suggestions on that subject as may seem to them conducive to the Welfare of the Society'. The report was received in June 1827, but action on it was postponed, ostensibly on account of its importance, but actually owing to opposition.

Davy resigned the presidency in the following month. His friend and former patron Davies Gilbert considered that his successor should be an influential social figure; Sir Robert Peel was sounded. As Home Secretary in 1825, he had been the medium through which the King had founded the Society's two Royal Medals.

When the fellows in favour of a scientific president heard of the proposal, they attacked it. Adam Sedgwick said that 'the republic of science will indeed be degraded if the Council of the Royal Society is to become a political junta and we are to sit under a man who *condescends* to be our patron. . . . Why don't some of you propose Herschel? He is by far the first man in London, and would do the work admirably. . . .'

As Peel would have been opposed, his name was dropped, and Gilbert was elected President for the remainder of the Society's year. He was a member of Parliament, and active in the House of Commons on matters of scientific interest.

Gilbert prevented further action on the Wollaston Report, and sought for a successor to himself in the presidency, looking for a person of social influence. He approached and persuaded the Duke of Sussex to stand, with the results that have already been described.

During the presidency of the Duke, all of the members of the Council of the Society were practising scientists, apart from himself, so considerable progress had been made towards their acquiring control. His successor, the Marquis of Northampton, who tried to steer a middle course, agreed that proposals for further reorganization should be adopted, on the assurance that they would not infringe the Society's Royal Charters, by which fellows possessed the right of electing to membership anyone, without restrictions.

Grove had been elected a fellow of the Society in 1840, at the age of twenty-nine. He immediately joined the reformers, and in 1846 became a member of the Council. He continued in this position in 1847, the year in which he resigned from the London Institution, and in 1848–9 he became one of the Secretaries.

Shortly after Grove joined the Council, it adopted a resolution in favour of the revision of the Charters of the Society, 'with a view to obtaining a supplementary Charter from the Crown'. In addition to this, the chief officers of the Society were instructed to form themselves into a Charters Committee, to consider and report on what should be introduced into the Supplementary Charter.

This Committee was then given more specific instructions on their enquiries as to what alterations were required, 'and whether such alterations would be most advantageously made by Charter or Statute; and that the Committee have power to add to their membership'. Grove was thereupon coopted onto the Committee.

They were specifically instructed to enquire whether, in the event of the Society obtaining a New Charter, it would be possible to insert clauses limiting the number of fellows elected in any one year; and the mode of election.

The revision of the Charters raised a number of legal complexities. Grove steered the Committee through these difficulties in the direction it wished to go. After much detailed discussion, the Committee formulated a number of recommendations.

Election of ordinary fellows, excluding the privileged classes of peers and privy councillors, were to be held on one day only in the year. Formerly, there had been four elections annually, which hindered adequate discussion of candidacies.

The number of fellows elected annually, excluding the privileged classes, was not to exceed fifteen in a year.

Rules for election were proposed, which would ensure that fellows were adequately informed of the qualifications of candidates, and had ample time to study them.

The Charters Committee then obtained the opinions of the Attorney and Solicitor-Generals whether it would be legal for the Society to pass a statute restricting the number of ordinary fellows in one year to fifteen. The Law Officers of the Crown gave their opinion that it would not. The Society was accordingly halted in its object.

Grove found the way round this difficulty. He suggested that the Council could obtain its aim by adopting the statutes:

(1) That the election should take place on one day.

(2) That the Council should recommend to the Society the most eligible candidates; such selected candidates not to exceed fifteen in any one year.

In practice, no one cared to dispute the names recommended by the Council, so the election was in effect restricted, without being so legally.

The effect of the new statutes, piloted through by Grove, was to give the Society the character it now has. It acquired this gradually, as the restriction on the election of ordinary fellows took effect. The old amateur fellows, who would never have been elected under the new statutes, died, and the Society became essentially a closed body of professional experts.

Moreover, it had become a body of professionals with an inherently autocratic and self-perpetuating organization, for the Council recommended candidates for election, which in practice amounted to choosing the new fellows.

These changes were warmly welcomed by many fellows, but there was also substantial opposition, not only by the amateurs of science who saw that people like themselves would be excluded from the Society, but also by some fellows who foresaw that the new statutes might, in the long run, weaken the Society's connections with the world of politics and affairs, and convert it into a body of highly qualified professionals, the large majority of whom would be, however eminent, some kind of scientific employee.

Grove formed a dining club, called the 'Philosophical Club', to hold together those who supported the aims of the new statutes. It was limited to forty-seven, in memory of what had been accomplished in 1847. Many ideas canvassed at their dinners were subsequently adopted by the Council of the Society. One of the earliest was that the Society should ask the Government to be given accommodation in Burlington House in Piccadilly, where in 1964 it still was. Grove was a sociable person. After he had become a successful lawyer, he liked to rent large houses in the country, for shooting parties to which he invited scientific and other friends.

The new statutes gave the practising scientists the majority by 1860. The number of amateurs had fallen by 146 since 1830, and the number of practising scientists had increased by 117. The average total membership fell to about 500 by the 1870's, and remained at around that figure for the next hundred years.

The Society had taken a form that reflected the ideas of Grove. It became less suited to participate in affairs, and did not begin to modify itself once more until the needs of British society in the second quarter of the twentieth century impelled changes. These included increases in the number of fellows elected annually, and more attention to applied science and technology. However, the changes made still left the Society with a character, policy and organization inadequate to the needs of the second half of the twentieth century. In 1964, reform was taken further by raising the number of annual elections to thirty-two, and allotting more places to psychology and technology.

VIII

The Law

WHEN Grove resumed the profession of law he made a considerable practice in patent cases, where his scientific knowledge was helpful. He became a Queen's Counsel in 1853. The most famous criminal case in which he was involved was as counsel for the defence of the notorious poisoner, William Palmer of Rugeley, in 1856. The trial aroused interest not only throughout England, but in Europe.

It was thought that his expert knowledge of chemistry would

be of special value for dealing with the difficult problems raised by the nature of strychnine poisoning. He carefully coached the leading counsel for Palmer, Sergeant Shee, in the scientific points, so that he could undermine the evidence of the expert for the prosecution, Dr. Taylor. Shee did not succeed, nor were the expert witnesses for the defence, who also had been coached by Grove, able to withstand cross-examination by Cockburn, the future Lord Chief Justice.

Grove was a member of the Royal Commission on the Patent Laws, and the Metropolitan Commission on Sewers, in both of which his technical knowledge was specially valuable. In 1871, he was appointed a judge, and in the following year was knighted.

Among his important decisions were that which affirmed the unrestrained power of the Crown to dismiss a military officer, and that a railway was liable for injury caused at the station of another line over which it had running powers.

Grove had the reputation of being a painstaking, accurate and competent judge; independent and courageous in opinion. It had been thought that he would have been particularly valuable in hearing patent cases, but in this he was not as much appreciated as had been expected. He was apt to become interested in the technical aspects of the patent. Instead of attending entirely to the question of infringement, he began to think about the device, and sometimes suggested technical improvements. He asked why this or that had not been done, and seemed to become concerned more with the advance of technology than with the administration of the law.

The opinion of his legal colleagues was that he was greater as a scientist than a lawyer. Scientific colleagues repeatedly expressed the opinion that it was unfortunate that he had withdrawn from a scientific career. Francis Galton, an experienced and acute critic, recorded that the most striking intellectual conversation he ever heard was between Grove and Thomas Henry Huxley.

Grove preserved his scientific interests, and continued to publish original research. He gave the Bakerian Lecture of the Royal Society in 1852 on 'The Electro-Chemical Polarity of Gases', in connection with which he announced the discovery of the striae in the electrical discharge in gases at low pressures. He was President of the British Association in 1866, and devoted his address to the subject of 'Continuity'. It was in the style of his *Correlation of Physical Forces*. He reviewed the growth of the main branches of physical and biological science, tracing how one small advance followed another, until the extraordinary achievements of modern science had been reached.

'To my mind a far more exquisite sense of the beautiful is conveyed by the orderly development, by the necessary inter-relation and inter-action of each element of the cosmos, and by the conviction that a bullet falling to the ground changes the dynamical conditions of the universe, than can be conveyed by mysteries, by convulsions, or by cataclysms.

'We, this evening assembled, Ephemera as we are, have learned by transmitted labour, to weigh, as in a balance, other worlds larger and heavier than our own, to know the length of their days and years, to measure their enormous distance from us and from each other . . . and to discover the substances of which they are composed; may we not fairly hope that similar methods of research to those which have taught us so much may give our race further information, until problems relating not only to remote worlds, but possibly to organic and sentient beings which may inhabit them—problems which it might now seem wildly visionary to enunciate—may be solved by progressive improvements in the modes of applying observation and experiment, induction and deduction?'

IX

Retrospect

GROVE was present, in his eightieth year, at the Jubilee of the Chemical Society in 1891. He was one of the three founder-members to be there, another being Lyon Playfair. He said that Graham was the leading spirit in founding the Society. Grove also was very active. He sounded Faraday on becoming their first president, but Faraday indicated that he considered he could do more by research than in joining in the construction of such a body, and declined the honour. Grove recalled that he had heard Dalton deliver his famous lecture at the Royal Institution on the atomic theory. Dalton was then aged, of great simplicity of character, and 'thoroughly devoted to his subject'. He made drawings of atoms, and depicted six spheres around one, which when pressed together, formed a hexagon, like the honeycomb. Grove commented:

'I think the name atomic theory was an unfortunate one. . . . To my mind the infinitely small is as incomprehensible as the infinitely great. I use the word incomprehensible advisedly. I do not say that you may not believe in the infinity of the universe; but we cannot comprehend it, we cannot take it in. And so with the atom. Therefore I think that it would have been better to have taken a different word—say minim—which would have been a safer term than atom.'

Thus Grove foresaw the need for the idea of a 'quantum'. He said that 'There are two ways of regarding science: first, as seeking natural revelations; secondly, practically, as applied to the arts and industries.' For his own part, science to him 'generally ceases to be interesting as it becomes useful. Englishmen have a great liking for the practical power of science. I like it as a means of extending our knowledge beyond its ordinary grasp. . . .' He remarked that he ought to have discovered spectroscopy. 'I had observed that there were different lines exhibited in the spectra of different metals when ignited in the voltaic arc; and if I had had any reasonable amount of wit I ought to have seen the converse, viz., that by ignition different bodies show in their spectral lines the materials of which they are formed. If that thought had occurred to my mind, I should have discovered the spectroscope before Kirchhoff; but it didn't.'

Grove said he agreed with Alphonse of Castile, that if he had had the making of the universe, he would have done it much better. He would have made man improve with age, and 'then be translated from this world to a superior planet, where he should begin life with the knowledge gained here, and so on'. He would indeed have been pleased to know that his fuel cell may help in doing just that.

He said he had sometimes been reproached for having to a great extent given up science for his profession. He need not emphasize that he would have preferred the former; 'But the necessities of a then large family gradually forced me to follow a more lucrative pursuit.' He preferred contemplative to applied science. 'We are overdone with artificial wants, and life becomes in consequence a constant embarrassment.' There was, however, one practical problem he recommended to his fellow members, that was to find out how 'to prevent the existence of London fogs even under a constitutional and representative Government'.

Grove died in his home in Harley Street, London, after a slow decline, on August 1st, 1896, in his eighty-sixth year. He was one of the most gifted men of the nineteenth century. Unfortunately, his profound mind was associated with an introspective temperament, which made him too modest, or too pessimistic. He believed that scientists should be organized and their influence extended, but his own retreat from a scientific profession acted against those beliefs.

His great and particular abilities gave him more influence than any other individual in forming the Royal Society's present corporate characteristics. The increased efficiency with narrower scope, the more middle-class quality, and the withdrawal from the governing classes, which were the outcome of the reforms he piloted, reflected to some extent his own temperament, his middle-class social conceptions, and his own retreat from the scientific life. He helped to professionalize the occupation from which he himself withdrew. He imported into science the neat and limited professional spirit of the legal profession, to which he had given his final allegiance.

Lyon Playfair

1818–1898

I

Underrated

LYON PLAYFAIR was the first to succeed in securing for science and technology sustained consideration within the system of British government. The nature and magnitude of his achievement were not fully grasped by his contemporaries, and have become more conspicuous only through the light of twentieth-century experience. Even his admirable biographer, Sir Thomas Wemyss Reid, said that 'he never rose to that dazzling eminence which justifies the world in describing a human being as supremely "great". He did not pretend to the genius which lifts a few men high above their fellows. It cannot be affirmed that he was one of the great figures of his generation. Yet his life, though it was lived without ostentation and without parade, was undoubtedly one of the fullest and most useful lives of his time.'

Reid was a Liberal political journalist and publisher, who regarded Gladstone as the measure of greatness, an opinion shared by Playfair himself. Reid wrote biographies of W. E. Forster, Monckton Milnes and Charlotte Brontë. With such a background, it was scarcely possible for him to perceive Playfair's full importance. To Reid, Playfair 'was always more of a philosopher among politicians than a politician among philosophers. Yet he achieved one or two rare successes even as a politician....'

Against a background of science and technology, such a man as Gladstone, physically, energetically, eloquently, dominant appears like a Greek hero or a tribal chieftain. He was a master leader of politicians as a tribe; he had little feeling for the factors which were causing the most fundamental changes in the age, and there was little understanding between him and the man who understood them so well.

Sympathetic scientific admirers, like H. E. Roscoe, emphasized the modest character of Playfair's original contributions to science, and felt it necessary to dwell on this, as if anyone who was not a Faraday or a Joule could not be a person of first importance in connection with science. Roscoe said that his peerage was 'given him more for his political than his scientific eminence'.

This attitude, both from the political and scientific sides, that Playfair and his work were not quite of major importance, was a reflection of the backwardness of nineteenth-century capitalism in understanding the need for the organization of science and technology.

Playfair had the personality which enabled him to work in an uncomprehending environment for more than fifty years for a better organization of science and technology. He was short in stature, only five feet four inches high. One of his relatives reported that he never said a cross word in his life. He was both intellectually lively and diplomatic. Liebig said he had 'a natural gift of eloquence'. With his liveliness and eloquence he aroused people's interest, and with his diplomacy secured their support. He was proud of his diplomatic skill, yet he had the firmness of principle to face unpopularity; in particular, in Parliament in the interests of his party.

Playfair's various qualities enabled him to have an important part in the stimulation of the study of organic chemistry in England. This led to the discovery of synthetic dyestuffs and the modern chemical industry.

He persuaded Bunsen to come to England to apply his recently perfected system of gas analysis to blast-furnace gases, and thereby helped to place the production of iron and steel on a scientific basis.

The modern petroleum industry arose directly out of his suggestion to James Young to investigate the natural oil exuded in the Derbyshire hills.

His reports on the sanitary conditions of the British cities were a major contribution to the development of modern sanitation.

His realistic reports to Sir Robert Peel on the potato disease in Ireland emphasized the danger of imminent and widespread famine, and contributed to Peel's decision to repeal the Corn Laws.

This might have seemed in itself sufficient to raise considerable respect for Playfair's achievement, yet his part in connection with that very important event has been severely criticized. E. C. Large in his book on *The Advance of the Fungi* has given a very interesting account of the unravelling of the scientific problem of the potato disease, describing how it was due to the spread of fungi which occurred when climatic conditions happened to be very favourable to them. The solution of the scientific problem of the disease required a biological approach. Playfair, as a pupil of Liebig, followed his teacher in trying to explain the biological phenomena in terms of existing chemical knowledge. Liebig had had a number of brilliant successes in this direction, but for most branches of biology his approach was over-simple. He and his pupils proceeded to explain various biological phenomena, which required a vastly more developed chemistry than was at their command. As Liebig's great rival Pasteur conclusively proved, many of the biological phenomena were at that time only susceptible of a biological explanation. For example, living things could only be obtained from living things.

Playfair went to Ireland hoping to find that the potato disease was chemical in nature, and capable of being effectively treated by chemical means. The chemistry of his day was quite inadequate for such a purpose, so his specific chemical approach proved of little technical value. The London *Medical Times* dismissed the chemists as 'the Giessen-bitten boys of the present day', who were mesmerized by the 'tasmalic name of Liebig'.

Large, as a protagonist of the biological approach, and a critic of Government ineptitude in scientific affairs, scornfully relates that 'when the potatoes were rotting in Ireland in 1846, the incomparable Dr. Lyon Playfair had announced with confidence that the rotting was due to some purely chemical action, analogous to that which caused the familiar and well-known souring of milk. Now the souring of milk was shown to be due to a living organism, and there were many besides Dr. Playfair who would have to eat their words.'

Large described Playfair as 'a minor chemist' and 'a great sitter-upon-commissions', who 'subsequently insinuated himself into the household of the Prince Consort, became a Baron and endeared himself for ever to connoisseurs of fatuity by announcing when exhibiting the synthesis of water to Queen Victoria, that oxygen and hydrogen would *have the honour* of combining in her royal presence!'

Large also referred with contempt to Playfair's suggestion 'that the English gentlefolk should make a practice of having the eyes cut away from all potatoes used in their kitchens, and placed on one side, as they would do for sets which could be distributed judiciously, and at little cost, amongst the deserving poor'. The practical part of this proposal is similar to one of Lysenko's recommendations for combating potato shortages in Russia during the Second World War.

In the short run, the Liebig-Playfair chemical approach to biological problems fails when contemporary chemistry is not sufficiently advanced. In these circumstances, the biological approach, associated with Pasteur, produces quicker results. In the long run, however, the chemical and biological approaches converge.

As the prime minister's scientific adviser, Playfair was representing the authority of science. His objective and courageous assessment showed that a scientist could exercise good general judgment in a very serious situation, and did not necessarily look at it merely as an opportunity for the application of technique. A scientist could be worth listening to as a man of sense as well as a technical expert.

As a commissioner for the Great Exhibition of 1851, and personal adviser to the Prince Consort, Playfair had a large part in making the Exhibition a practical success. His subsequent services in ensuring that the profits of the Exhibition were well used and not frittered away, were even more important. He helped to steer the permanent organization set up to achieve this purpose, and realize at least in part the Prince Consort's grand idea of a national science centre. The group of scientific institutions which have arisen at South Kensington owe their existence mainly to the initiative and persistence of the Prince Consort and Playfair.

The success of the Great Exhibition led to the foundation of the Government's Science and Art Department, for promoting science, and scientific and technical education. Playfair became joint secretary of the Department, and subsequently Inspector-General of Government Museums and Schools of Science. In these positions, and later as a member of Parliament and minister, Playfair had the leading part in continuously prodding the groping and fitful development of British technical and scientific education.

His intelligent, varied and long-sustained efforts were a tribute to his own qualities, but their slow effect provided striking evidence of the unsuitability of the British social and political order, in the middle of the nineteenth century, for the creation of a modern scientific and technical organization. He sat in Parliament for twenty-four years, slowly but steadily forwarding measures for the improvement of science, education and sanitation. He had the chief part in reorganizing the Civil Service, and introducing the grades of executive and administrative civil servant.

Playfair first sat in Parliament on behalf of the Universities of Edinburgh and St. Andrews. He represented this Tory constituency for seventeen years, in spite of being a progressive Liberal. By 1885, the gap between the views of his constituents and his own had become too wide to be covered even by his diplomatic skill; in 1885 he felt it necessary to withdraw his university candidature. He was offered the choice of thirteen industrial constituencies, and chose that of South Leeds, latterly held by Hugh Gaitskell. He sat for South Leeds for seven years until 1892, when Mr. Gladstone offered him a peerage instead of a place in his last administration. Playfair was then seventy-four, though Gladstone himself was eighty-three.

One of the last and most fruitful of Playfair's ideas was the foundation of a substantial number of scholarships for scientific research. He reformed the finances of the Standing Commission of the Great Exhibition of 1851, and secured agreement that the income so obtained could be drawn upon and devoted to this purpose.

It was through one of these scholarships that Rutherford was enabled to come from New Zealand to England, and help to create the modern age.

II

Background and Education

LYON PLAYFAIR belonged to a Scottish family of clergymen, educationists and administrators which had already made some mark in the eighteenth century. His grandfather, James Playfair, became Principal of St. Andrew's University in 1799. He married Margaret Lyon, a kinswoman of the Earls of Strathmore, whose seat is the Castle of Glamis, where Macbeth murdered Duncan. The present Queen-Mother, the widow of King George VI, and Chancellor of the University of London, is a kinswoman of Lyon Playfair.

The most intellectually distinguished of Playfair's kinsmen was the mathematician and scholar John Playfair, 'so celebrated for his clear and eloquent power of exposition that he rarely trusted himself to make a speech, lest he should injure his fame as a writer'.

Playfair used to spend his school holidays in the manse at the gate of Glamis, in the shadow of the castle's obscure and romantic history.

His grandfather had four sons, three of whom served in India, while the fourth and youngest entered commercial life in Glasgow. The eldest son George, who became Lyon Playfair's father, was a surgeon in the East India Company, and rose to be the head of its medical service.

Lyon Playfair was George Playfair's second child. He was born at Chunar, Bengal, on May 21st, 1818. At the age of about two he was sent to St. Andrews, where he was reared by an aunt, Mrs. Macdonald, and became a favourite of his grandmother, the wife of the Principal. Mrs. Macdonald used to write to Playfair's mother in India on the progress of her children. When Lyon was six, she made some interesting observations on his character. She described how 'Lyon is too ready with his admonitions'. He was 'still *auld-farrant* (old-fashioned) in his remarks, more correct in his conduct than George (his brother), and too apt to tell on George when he has got into a scrape'.

He did not see a subject in reading or relating nearly so quick or accurately as George, but when it came to action, George was behind Lyon. She thought that 'Lyon must have the bumps of veneration and observation', and George 'the bump of clear understanding'. Lyon had been head of his class for ten days in reading and spelling, and was in great fear whether he should lose his position. The more she studied the two boys, the more she observed 'the moral principles deep in Lyon's mind and carried instantly into action. . . '.

Playfair did not see his father again until he was grown up. His father encouraged him from afar, being 'full of kindness and consideration in his correspondence,' encouraging him in his scientific studies, and supplying him freely with money to prosecute them. His mother returned to St. Andrews when he was about eight, but later on rejoined her husband in India, and Playfair did not see her again during his youth.

She had, however, been with him at the beginning of his education. He said that to her and her surroundings he owed all his early knowledge, and 'precious little' to the grammar school which he subsequently attended. His mother had a friend, the Reverend Dr. Macvicar, who gave popular lectures on science, and was an independent thinker. He had bold and original views on the atomic constitution of matter, and believed in the theory of the complex molecular structure of substances. He taught Lyon the use of the microscope, and his earliest ideas on science, opening his eyes to surrounding subjects.

Playfair left a touching description of his going to meet his parents at the ship bringing them home from India. He saw on it 'a stout elderly gentleman' looking like Colonel Newcome, and 'a sweet motherly-looking lady' writing at a desk. On enquiring he learned that they were indeed his father and mother.

Playfair was sent at the age of six to the parish school at St. Andrews. At that time, the children of all classes attended, and the effect of the admixture was excellent. He said that in later life no congratulations were more appreciated than those from his old working-class schoolmates, who used to stop him in the street and remind him of old times. Playfair recollected the parish school with as much pleasure as he had contempt for the grammar school, where he was taught Latin only, and wasted years of his life at a most impressionable age.

Playfair entered the university at the age of fourteen, but found the course hard, as he had been so badly prepared. He struggled with Latin, Greek and mathematics, but was not entered for the classes of chemistry and natural philosophy, though he went to them when he could.

The departure of his mother to India caused him to be sent, at the age of fifteen, to his commercial uncle in Glasgow, to become a merchant. His uncle, who was often away in Canada, had another clerk, named Ramsay. Playfair and Ramsay were often left to their own devices, and had not half-an-hour's work a day. They passed the time inventing instruments for telling the true time from the lengths of lamp-post shadows in the streets.

Playfair became disgusted with what he thought was the universal idleness of the mercantile life. He asked that his engagement should be cancelled, so that he could begin to study medicine. He moved into lodgings in the home of Ramsay, whose mother was the widow of a chemical manufacturer, the first to manufacture bichromate of potash. He had more scientific than commercial aptitude; he did not make a fortune, but his scientific aptitude passed to his descendants. One of his sons, Andrew, was a keen geologist, and Playfair and Andrew Ramsay pursued geology together. Andrew became his most intimate friend, and ultimately head of the Geological Survey. One of Mr. and Mrs. Ramsay's grandchildren became Sir William Ramsay, the great chemist and co-discoverer of the inert gases.

Playfair decided to start his medical studies by taking chemistry, his favourite subject, first. Instead of entering Glasgow University, with its famous medical school and one of the best-known and most senior chemical teachers of the age, Professor Thomas Thomson, Playfair, who was seventeen, chose to go to the more working-class and technical Andersonian College, which had a younger professor. This was Thomas Graham, the son of a Glasgow manufacturer, whose lectures lacked broad appeal, and who could not preserve discipline, but was a profound investigator. Graham's researches on water of crystallization, the diffusion of gases, and phosphoric acid had already secured for him a high reputation among the chemists of Europe. He subsequently founded colloid chemistry, besides making other original contributions. Graham received public as well as scientific recognition, for he was appointed Master of the Mint in 1855, and was consulted by the Government on many matters. Yet apart from his personal achievement, his influence on the development of science in Britain was not in proportion to his abilities.

In 1836, Playfair gained the first prize in his chemistry class. It was a copy of Lyell's *Geology*. He took it on a trip to Arran, and expounded its contents to a charming lady, beside whom he sat on the steamer. She was amused, and presently told him that she was glad her husband had such an enthusiastic admirer. She beckoned to Lyell, who was on the other side of the ship, and introduced Playfair to him. They continued to be friends for life.

Playfair made many excellent exercises of judgment in his life, but his decision to go to Graham was probably the most important of them all. Glasgow University would almost certainly have given him more help to a medical career, but Playfair probably knew that in his heart he was more interested in science than in medicine, and that the talented Graham could give him more inspiration in the way he really wanted to go. Later on, like many other eminent men, Playfair relinquished medicine and turned to science.

Among Playfair's fellow-students were David Livingstone and James Young, who, with Playfair, were Graham's favourite pupils. Livingstone was about six years older than Playfair, and so poor that he could not pay laboratory fees. When, twenty years later, Playfair received enquiries on scientific matters from the explorer in the course of his journeys, he did not realize that they were from his old fellow-student. When Livingstone visited him in 1857, to follow up his scientific enquiries, Playfair realized with astonishment that he had been the shy friend of his youth. One of Livingtsone's observations of scientific interest was his description of the familiarity of African tribesmen with the electrical sparks produced by the handling of fur objects.

James Young was a carpenter, employed to repair instruments in Graham's laboratory. Like James Watt in an analogous situation, he became interested in science, and ultimately was engaged as a laboratory assistant. Playfair suggested to Young in 1847 that he should manufacture useful oils from petroleum exuded in Derbyshire. This led to the development of the modern oil industry.

After Playfair had been attending the Andersonian College for two years, Graham was invited to become professor of chemistry in University College, London. He took Young with him as assistant, and as the chief attraction of Glasgow was now gone, Playfair moved to Edinburgh to continue his medical studies. Among the friends he made there was Professor Syme, the celebrated surgeon.

Playfair found that the anatomical dissection rooms gave him violent eczema. He was advised, to his grief, that he should abandon medicine. On his father's advice, and that of his physician, he sailed for India on the Cape of Good Hope route, hoping that the long sea voyage would improve his constitution, and with the intention of looking for a career in India.

When Playfair reached Calcutta he found that his father had again arranged for him to take up a mercantile career. However, his heart was in science, and he soon became acquainted with the British scientists in Calcutta. Several of them, noting his talent and enthusiasm, privately advised his father that he should be sent back to Europe to continue his chemical studies. Accordingly, Playfair returned to England, without seeing his parents, who were in an inaccessible place in the Upper Provinces.

Playfair went to work under Graham at University College, London. His old professor, who still had James Young with him as assistant, was delighted to have him back, declined to treat him as a pupil, and appointed him his personal assistant. Graham was as unsuccessful a lecturer in London as he had been in Glasgow.

Playfair resumed attending medical lectures with the intention of taking his medical degree. Then, in 1839, Graham strongly advised Playfair to go to study under Liebig. Playfair's generous father had provided means for such travel, so Playfair set off to Giessen, where he was able to learn the virtually new science of organic chemistry, which had arisen out of Liebig's revolutionary development of the chemical analysis of organic substances. Liebig increased the speed of organic chemical analysis by a factor of about sixty, and simplified it so that it could be performed effectively by persons of moderate ability. This quantitative advance was so large that it effected a qualitative change in the nature of the subject. Like the introduction of the computer, it made possible researches which had hitherto been impracticable. In this way, it led to the creation of a new branch of chemistry, with new perspectives. He combined this enormous technical advance with a theoretical imagination of appropriate power. Consequently, he could see what should be done, and had the technical means to do it.

Playfair, twenty-one years old, intelligent, and sufficiently trained by Graham to appreciate that he was participating in one of the most inspired moments of science, found Liebig as striking and handsome a personality as his work. When he arrived and introduced himself as a pupil of Graham's, the great chemist laughingly said: 'You might have added that you are the discoverer of iodo-sulphuric acid,' which Playfair says he had recently described in short papers. What these short papers were seems a little obscure, for Roscoe remarked that their titles 'are not, however, to be found in the Royal Society's Catalogue'.

Liebig had virtually invented systematic organic chemical research. His laboratory was unique, and had attracted many young men of high ability. They were engaged at the time in working over and systematically extending the researches of

Chevreul on fatty substances. Liebig asked Playfair to join in, and Playfair, like many of the others, was soon adding to knowledge, discovering a new fatty acid in the butter of nutmegs, and a new crystalline substance in cloves.

Liebig had accepted an invitation to attend the meeting of the British Association in 1837 at Liverpool, where he had spoken with inspiring power on the new chemistry. 'In the country in which I now am,' he had said, 'whose hospitality I shall never cease to remember, organic chemistry is only commencing to take root. We live in a time when the slightest exertion leads to valuable results, and, if we consider the immense influence which organic chemistry exercises over medicine, manufactures, and over common life, we must be sensible that there is at present no problem more important to mankind than the prosecution of the objects which organic chemistry contemplates.'

He was asked by the Association to write a report on organic chemistry in its application to agriculture and physiology. This was published in 1840, and made a profound impression. Liebig envisaged nutrition, growth and decay as different stages in one chemical process. He conceived life as based on a continuous series of chemical changes. When these had been identified, it became possible to suggest chemical means for promoting the aims of medicine, agriculture and industry, which are all concerned with the treatment of organic materials. Disease due to chemical abnormality, could be cured by the appropriate chemical treatment. Better crops and livestock could be obtained by the provision of those chemical elements discovered to be essential for growth and health.

Liebig saw life, medicine, agriculture and industry as one grand symphony on a fundamental chemical theme. He revealed the connections between them, and their basic unity. Liebig's conception of chemical substances which persist through the changes of plant life led him to conceive clearly that coal, which consisted of fossilized plants, ought to contain substances related to the useful products of plants. Hence it should be possible to obtain from coal substances hitherto obtained only from plants. He provided the scientific vision required for the foundation of the synthetic chemical industry.

When Playfair arrived in Giessen, Liebig was writing his great book. He invited Playfair to translate his manuscript into English. Playfair arranged for the translation to be published by an English firm, who paid him one hundred pounds; it was the first money he earned.

The landed magnates and improving landlords still had a great deal of power in England. Their leaders, following the tradition of Coke and the agricultural lectures of Davy, were keenly interested to learn more of Liebig's revolutionary work and ideas. He was again invited to attend the meeting of the British Association, at Glasgow in 1840, but could not go. He appointed Playfair his representative, who set off to Glasgow accompanied by several of Liebig's most talented German students. When he arrived at Glasgow, he found that he had been appointed Secretary of the Chemistry Section.

Playfair was twenty-two. He had revolutionary scientific information to expound. He deeply impressed some of the senior scientists there, especially the eminent geologist Dr. Buckland and Sir Henry de la Beche, the head of the Geological Survey; both of whom had important social and political as well as scientific connections.

Soon after the meeting Playfair returned to Giessen, to take his degree as a Doctor of Philosophy, and then, in 1841, he had to look for a suitable post.

Playfair regarded his career as an example of what could be achieved by one starting in life without money or influence. He had no private fortune, and his relatives did not possess political influence, but in fact he was fortunate in the kind of connections which could help a man with his particular capacities. Liebig himself at first had had less advantages, for he was the son of a tanner. The aid he subsequently received was attracted by his own extraordinary abilities.

III

The Prime Minister Intervenes

After securing his doctorate, Playfair had to look for a way of earning a living. He had met chemical manufacturers at the Glasgow meeting of the British Association who had noted his ability. Shortly afterwards, he received an offer from Mr.

Thomson, a famous calico printer, to become chemical manager of his Primrose works at Clitheroe in Lancashire. Mr. Thomson asked him to call at a particular date and time at his London office for an interview. Playfair arrived exactly on time, finding himself before a stately old gentleman, seated, and holding a watch in his hand.

'You are very punctual,' said Mr. Thomson. He outlined the nature of the work, and said he had intended to offer him £300 rising to £400 a year, but in view of his punctuality, he proposed to raise his offer from £400 to £600.

Playfair accepted, and presently learned that Thomson had previously written to Liebig and Graham for advice, and both had recommended him.

Playfair returned to Germany to wind up his affairs, and found himself accepted by the leading scientists in Berlin, as well as by Liebig, as a colleague. Liebig treated him with an affection which was striking in the perspective of their difference in position. He gave him magnificent advice on his prospective work at Clitheroe.

'In all that you do, do not forget science, and keep fresh and vigorous your taste for mental work, for unless a man is making progress in that which gives nourishment and life to industry, he is scarcely in a position to fulfill the demands of his times.' He should not trade on his experience and chemical knowledge, but give advice and help where they could be useful without caring about receiving any reward. He would find that this would bear rich fruit in the future. He should never neglect to do some research every year. All that he asked of him was to be true to himself and to science.

Finally, he had heard that he was engaged to be married. He would like to know whether this was true, for his wife and he were deeply interested. . . . 'Farewell, my dear friend. Write to me again soon.

Your most affectionate friend

J. v. Liebig.'

So Liebig wrote to Playfair in August 1841. The enthusiastic regard of the world-famous chemist for the young man of twenty-three is engaging. Liebig was himself, however, still only thirty-eight years old. The greatness of his reputation seemed to imply that he was much older than Playfair. In fact, both were young men; Playfair very young, and Liebig not yet middle-aged.

In November 1841, Liebig addressed Playfair as his 'valued

friend', and wrote that he was 'exceedingly pleased and satisfied' with the first sheets of the English translation of his book. 'You make me greatly wish to come to England next spring, in order to help with your experiments. . . . Accept my best thanks for the gooseberries and for the excellent Cheshire cheese. English cheese is the only kind which my weak stomach can digest. . . .'

In the spring of 1842 Playfair sent an invitation to Liebig to attend the forthcoming British Association meeting at Manchester. Liebig was very anxious to accept, in order to have an opportunity of visiting British agricultural districts, but the date had been fixed in June, which was before the end of his course of university lectures. He said he could not desert his students, and suggested that the British Association meeting should be held later, for the early date precluded continental professors from attending. It was his opinion that the general interest should take precedence of that of the geologists, who naturally liked to have fine weather for their excursions. If the scientists intended to try to make discoveries during the meeting, then according to German experience it was the wrong time of the year. '. . . we have always found bad, especially rainy, weather more favourable to our object than fine clear weather. There is more temptation in fine weather to wander off in different directions, but bad weather keeps the party together. This is no joke, dear Playfair, but the simple truth. . . .'

Liebig's desire for the meeting to be delayed until the time at which it is now usually held, the end of August and the beginning of September, could not be met, so he arranged to come to Britain after it.

Playfair had in the meantime settled down to his work at Clitheroe. He found that the Thomson works made only products of the finest quality, which were prized by customers of wealth and taste throughout Europe. The market was small; expensive prints and *mousseline de laine* were going out of fashion. But Mr. Thomson 'manufactured for the upper hundreds, and not for the millions'. He absolutely refused to countenance the production of low-quality products to supply the mass market. He would listen to Playfair's advice on all other subjects, but not on this.

Mr. Thomson shared the cultural interests of such earlier leaders of the Industrial Revolution as Wedgwood and Boulton, though he combined them with a less acute business sense. This early manufacturing capitalist assumed that an employer should be a gentleman, and was being superseded by the more purely profit-seekers of the nineteenth-century. His family was highly cultivated, and without having aptitude for business, could see that his works was doomed, unless he undertook 'to produce for the million instead of for the few'. They were surprised when they found that the new chemist agreed with them, and not with their father.

One of Thomson's daughters, who was about ten years older then Playfair, was an accomplished Greek scholar. She subsequently married Braun, a well-known antiquarian in Rome, and helped him with his researches. Playfair said that she was perhaps the most cultured woman he ever met. He had hitherto read mainly scientific authors, and through her influence, he acquired 'wider habits of reading'. He was not treated as an employee, but as a friend of the family, with whom he dined several times a week.

While at the Thomson works, Playfair met and became friendly with John Mercer, the famous inventor of mercerized cotton. Mercer was then about fifty-one; nearly thirty years older than Playfair. He had been a bobbin-winder at nine, and then a handloom weaver. After being fascinated by the orange colour of a dress of his infant half-brother, he became passionately interested in dyeing. This caused him to teach himself chemistry. He made considerable chemical discoveries, besides many inventions in textile chemistry. He was the first to propose a rational theory of catalysis. He believed that there was a fundamental relationship between the chemical elements, and he had anticipations of Pasteur's germ-theory of disease.

Mercer's works was in the neighbourhood. Playfair used to visit him at his house, or at a little scientific society that they formed for philosophical talk. At one of these meetings, Mercer reported an observation which led Playfair to his most important scientific discovery: that of the nitro-prussides. Playfair said that Mercer's natural abilities would have made him 'a Dalton or a Faraday had he been differently placed.'

Mercer did not patent many of his textile discoveries, and from some of these others made fortunes. He was an earnest Wesleyan, and a supporter of Cobden in politics. Cobden had been the London agent of a Lancashire textile firm for which he had worked.

Playfair confided to Mercer his doubts about the future of the Thomson works in making high-class goods for a declining demand. Mercer expressed strong disapproval of Thomson's manufacturing principle.

In the great labour demonstrations against bad conditions in 1842, Playfair had a leading part in saving Mercer's works from being sacked. Thousands of workers marched on it. Playfair offered to parley with them, so that Mercer, as the employer, whose presence might have been regarded as provocative, could be kept in the background. Playfair told the demonstrators that they knew their numbers were irresistible, and suggested that they should send a deputation to remove the plugs from the boilers, so that the works could be put out of action without doing any damage. He offered himself as a hostage, so that this could be done without suspicion of any treachery to the deputation.

While Playfair was with the demonstrators, their leaders explained their demands, many of which he found reasonable, and were subsequently conceded. The demonstrators announced they would march on Thomson's works, but, instead, they went to Blackburn; there they were met and dispersed by troops.

Seeing that the Thomson business must go down, Playfair presently gave notice, parting from the family with regret and goodwill. He found the manufacturing experience he had gained at Clitheroe of value during the rest of his life.

While at Clitheroe, Playfair gave several scientific lectures in Manchester. This led to an invitation to be Honorary Professor of Chemistry in the Royal Institution of that city. This was one of the institutions, of which the Royal Institution in London was the most distinguished, founded at the beginning of the nineteenth century for the promotion of scientific and literary interests.

Playfair set up a teaching laboratory in the cellars, which was soon crowded with pupils learning practical organic chemistry. The ventilation was bad, and he nearly poisoned himself and some of his pupils with fumes from charcoal burners used for heating the tubes. On one occasion he fell ill, and went home to rest. After a time, a cab came to take him back to the laboratory. When he arrived he found two of his pupils lying outside unconscious. He instantly poured pails of cold water over them, and they fortunately revived. Playfair said he never forgot this lesson on ventilation.

He secured as one of his assistants Robert Angus Smith, a

noted chemist, a fellow-pupil of Liebig, and one of the founders of the chemistry of sanitation. Playfair's lectures were popular and successful, Dalton, 'supported on the arm of Dr. Joule', came daily to hear about the 'new organic chemistry'.

In October 1842 he received a letter from Faraday, whom he had never yet seen, saying that he had been asked to advise on the choice of a professor of chemistry for Toronto University. 'Will you allow me to hope I shall not give you offence if I ask whether the following offer would be worth your consideration?' wrote Faraday, then fifty years old and at the summit of fame, to the twenty-four-year-old unpaid professor at Manchester. Faraday said that the salary would be about £450 a year with house and garden, the usual professorial position, and an allowance for laboratory work.

Playfair went up to London, saw Faraday, and accepted the offer. But, said Playfair, 'On describing my appointment to my various scientific friends in London I found that, instead of congratulating me, they censured me for want of faith in an English career. A few days after, to my great surprise, I received an invitation from the great Sir Robert Peel, then Prime Minister, to visit him at Drayton Manor. As I had not then the honour of his acquaintance. I was inclined to believe that some one was playing a practical joke upon my vanity. The letter had undoubtedly the post office stamp of "Tamworth," and the seal was that of Sir Robert Peel. So I took the letter for identification to Dr. Buckland, and found not only that it was genuine, but that he also was invited for the same date. Why the great statesman should care to see a young man like myself was to me an insoluble mystery, but I accepted the invitation with much pleasure.'

Playfair was apparently unaware that even before the offer of the Toronto chair, he had been brought to the notice of Peel. His friend the geologist Sir Henry de la Beche, who had recently been knighted, asked Buckland early in 1842 to write to Peel on the urgency of introducing the new organic chemistry into England, in order to improve agriculture. Playfair, as the translator of Liebig, wrote Buckland, was the 'one man only in this country' fully conversant with the new subject. It was very desirable that he should be provided with the means for pursuing a series of systematic experiments on the application of organic chemistry to agriculture.

Peel did not respond to this first proposal, for he did not believe that Parliament would be prepared to subsidize agricultural research, except on condition that similar subsidies were provided for research in connection with other industries. The idea of general government support for research in all branches of industrial science was politically inconceivable in the atmosphere in the contemporary House of Commons.

The offer of what de la Beche called 'an American professorship' to Playfair later in the year enabled de la Beche and Buckland to force Peel's hand. As de la Beche put it, 'if Playfair is to be saved for England, there is no time to lose'. To see him 'snatched from us in England' was deplorable. He proposed that a member of the staff of the Museum of Economic Geology, of which he was the head, should be moved to another post to make way for Playfair. It was essential to counter 'this offer from the other side of the Atlantic, sweeping him away'. There were but a few days left for action, so nothing could be done through official channels. Only an appeal to the Prime Minister could help. That Playfair 'would prefer England to America' was known full well. De la Beche had not corresponded with Peel on this subject, so could Buckland write to him at once?

As Playfair's biographer puts it: 'Evidently de la Beche was desperately afraid that Playfair's departure for Canada—or, as he vaguely describes it, America—would mean a great loss to the intellectual capital of Great Britain.'

While Peel did not respond to the suggestion of state support for agricultural research, he did respond to the appeal to the national interest. He was inclined to the suggestion of making a vacancy for Playfair at the Museum of Economic Geology, if this could be accomplished by mutual agreement. However, before sanctioning any action to this end, he wanted to see Playfair to assess his personality, and it was for this reason that he invited the young chemist to visit him.

At Drayton Manor, Playfair found Buckland; Smith of Deanston, the authority on farm drainage; Pusey the agriculturist, and others.

Peel told Playfair, who was then twenty-four, that he had had letters from several scientists regretting his acceptance of 'a colonial professorship', and now that he had seen him, he also regretted it. Playfair bowed, and thanked him for taking an interest in his personal affairs. Peel pointed out that it was his interest in public affairs, not in Playfair's personal affairs, which had prompted him to take action. Playfair remained silent after this reproof, and waited for Peel's next remark.

Peel then suggested that when the Prime Minister and other influential persons desired him to stay in England, he could be confident of his future in this country. Playfair said that Peel handed him a memorandum indicating that if he 'would abandon the idea of going to the colonies, he would make it his duty to obtain' employment for him suitable to his abilities.

Playfair refused to accept the memorandum, saying that the prime minister's remarks were quite sufficient for him. Peel was pleased with this attitude, and gave the document to Buckland, which was found among Buckland's papers after his death. It ran:

'Drayton Manor,
'October 18th, 1842

'We, that is Lord Lincoln and Sir Robert Peel, understanding that unusual decision is required, are ready to consent to this: If Mr. Phillips can be induced voluntarily to relinquish the appointment he holds, and shall signify by a letter to Lord Lincoln his willingness to resign it, Dr. Lyon Playfair shall be appointed to a corresponding office at the annual salary of £400. We cannot take any step for the purpose of inducing Mr. Phillips's retirement. It must be voluntary on his part.'

Peel was sixty years old when he made this written statement on behalf of Playfair. It was an almost unparalleled action by a prime minister on behalf of any man; and for a scientist, still to this day remains unique.

The effort to make a post for Playfair did not immediately succeed, but he was saved from America. Phillips refused to surrender his post, and everyone had to search for an alternative. The prime minister wrote: 'We are all, that is, all official men—inclined to do whatever we can, consistent with our duty, and therefore with the true interests of Dr. Playfair, to procure his services for the public.'

Peel never forgot the young chemist, who found him not 'stately, reserved and unbending', according to the common opinion, but 'dignified, frank, courteous, and full of kindness'. Playfair visited him frequently, in country and town, and was with him for nearly an hour on the morning of the day in 1850, when Peel was thrown from his horse, and fatally injured.

Playfair's daughter Jessie subsequently married one of Peel's cousins.

Peel had remarkable gifts of listening and comprehension. He understood and objectively assessed the general lines of the ideas which scientists, economists, and other experts put to him, even when they conflicted with his own opinions. He showed bold initiative in trying to use scientists. The results were less fruitful than he had hoped, for the reason that there was no scientific organization to support them, and work out and apply their suggestions. Peel commented on the importance of statistics in assessing the effects of the Corn Laws on food prices, and then remarked that there was no adequate statistical organization to conduct the necessary research.

His intelligence on scientific matters was to a large extent sterilized by the absence of a scientific organization to pursue the things which he saw should be done. He realized that such organizations were required, such as institutions for research in agriculture, but he believed that the political conditions for their foundation were not yet ripe.

A prime minister of high intelligence and judgment, together with individual scientists of original ability and administrative capacity were not sufficient to create an adequate state scientific organization. This required also a demand for such an organization from the productive sections of society, and the people as a whole. Unless they call for it, the efforts of the most gifted politicians and scientists to create one are sterile.

IV

Finding his Feet

As Peel's interest in Playfair and the significance of organic chemistry for British agriculture and industry did not immediately lead to a government post, Playfair's headquarters continued to be in Lancashire. His honorary professorship gave him standing, and he secured a living from fees for special pieces of scientific work, or consulting.

In the late autumn of 1842 he organized a tour of Great

Britain for Liebig. He arranged visits for him to Peel's country house at Drayton Manor, and to the other great agriculturists, Spencer, Ducie, Fitzwilliam, Pusey and others. At every place meetings were held, at which Liebig spoke and Playfair interpreted for him.

Liebig, accompanied by Buckland, visited towns as well as great houses, and spoke to industrialists as enthusiastically as to agriculturists on the importance to them of the new chemistry. He convinced the agriculturists that it would make their estates prosperous, and the industrialists that it would cheapen food and reduce manufacturing costs, produce new processes and increase profits.

Playfair said that 'the tour was a personally conducted one, like Cook's tours in the present day'. Playfair was the conductor, guide and public relations officer, 'who took care that the effects of the tour should be felt in all the chief centres of Great Britain'. The immediate effect of the tour was 'to make chemistry a popular science, and to induce colleges to open laboratories for teaching it'.

When Liebig visited Manchester he appeared not only as a distinguished visitor, but as Playfair's personal friend, which raised Playfair's standing in his place of work. In 1844, the British Association provided funds for Bunsen, with the collaboration of Playfair, to carry out their classical research on the chemistry of blast-furnace gases. Bunsen had already made important investigations on charcoal iron furnaces, but it was necessary to come to England at that time to extend the research to coal and coke furnaces, with hot and cold blasts. Playfair ascertained that the Derbyshire iron-master, Mr. Oakes, could provide them with the best facilities.

Bunsen and Playfair succeeded in elucidating the chemical changes by drawing specimens at every foot depth from the top of the furnace. They showed that 81·5 per cent of the fuel was being wasted in the form of combustible gases escaping from the furnace mouth. They suggested how these might be usefully utilized; they showed, too, that in the upper part of the furnace the contents were being distilled rather than burned. A valuable amount of ammonium chloride was being produced, at the rate of about 2 cwt. a day in this particular furnace. Playfair said that forty years passed before the iron-masters began to extract this valuable by-product.

Playfair's research in Mr. Oakes's works had other notable

results, besides his participation in the revolutionizing of the chemistry of iron smelting. He came to know Mr. Oakes's family and two years later, he married his youngest daughter. Then, through this family connection, he became aware of the exudation of natural oil on one of Mr. Oakes's Derbyshire estates. On December 3rd, 1847, Playfair wrote to James Young:

'You know that mineral naphtha is a rare natural product, no spring of it occurring in this country, all being imported from the Continent or Persia. Lately a spring of this valuable product has been discovered on an estate belonging to my brother-in-law (Mr. Oakes), near Alfreton, Derbyshire. It yields at present about 300 gallons daily. The naphtha is about the consistence of thin treacle, and with one distillation it gives a clear, colourless liquid of brilliant illuminating power. It dissolves caoutchouc easily. My brother intends to set up stills for it immediately; but, as they are iron masters, this would be a separate industry, so I have advised them, if possible, to sell the naphtha in the crude state to chemical manufacturers, and thus avoid carrying on an industry foreign to their occupation. Does this possibly come within the province of your works? If it do, I will send you a gallon for examination. Perhaps you could make a capital thing out of this new industry, and enable my friends to do the same. You are aware that naphtha is now largely used for adding to the illuminating power of gas, and that the tar residue is a valuable product.'

This led Young to the development of the shale oil industry, which provided the spur to the development of petroleum prospecting, and the sinking of Drake's famous oil-well in Pennsylvania in 1859. Young used some of the profits from his new industry to finance the African explorations of David Livingstone, the old fellow-student of Playfair and himself.

Playfair's letter to Young, written when he was twenty-nine, was at least as important for mankind as any written by Mr. Gladstone. Not once, but several times, Playfair exercised decisive judgment leading to scientific and technical developments of world significance. Yet recognition of his stature has had to wait until the second half of the twentieth century.

It is striking how, before he was thirty years of age, he was in close collaboration, on the one hand with the political, and on the other, with the scientific leaders of the age. He was a close and very understanding link between them.

The very fact of his success in this shows, however, that that is not enough for the proper development of science and its application. Even when prime minister, industrial leader and scientist are so close as to be in family relationship together, that is not sufficient. There must also be an adequate scientific profession and organization to follow up and work out the discoveries and ideas, and make use of the possibility for important social and national action, when virtually perfect contact and understanding exists between the leaders of politics, industry and science. Genius in each and all of these is not enough; there must be the appropriate social apparatus to use it efficiently.

In 1844 Liebig made another tour in Britain, again visiting Peel, who wrote of the occasion to the Prince Consort: 'I have some very distinguished men on a visit here. Dr. Buckland, Dr. Lyon Playfair (the translator of Liebig), Professor Wheatstone (the inventor of the electric telegraph), Professor Owen, of the College of Surgeons, Mr. George Stephenson, the engineer. . . . I invited yesterday my principal tenants to meet them at dinner and acquire information, which was most kindly and liberally given by all the philosophers on points connected with vegetation, manure, the feeding of animals, draining, etc.'

During the 1844 tour, Liebig learned from Buckland that coprolite stones were the fossilized excrement of ancient saurians. He at once pointed out that they should contain phosphate, and therefore provide the raw material for a phosphate fertilizer. Playfair sent specimens to his Manchester laboratory, and it was proved that they did indeed contain phosphate. Liebig did not, however, find a practical method of utilizing the discovery. Lawes and Gilbert, the founders of Rothamsted, followed it up, and with their combined knowledge of agriculture and chemistry, completed the invention of artificial phosphate fertilizer.

At last the interest of prime minister and geniuses resulted in action: the School of Mines was opened in Jermyn Street, with what was then regarded as an excellent laboratory. The product was minute in comparison with the political and scientific powers involved. A little later, however, in 1845, the Royal College of Chemistry was founded, with A. W. Hofmann as director. Hofmann was one of Liebig's most gifted pupils, who had married one of his nieces. His laboratory was to have a very influential history; but still, no kind of national organization of science was yet in sight.

In 1843 Playfair received a letter from Peel, offering him a place on the Royal Commission which was to be set up to investigate the health of large towns. This had been inspired by the revelations of Edwin Chadwick's famous report on *The Sanitary Condition of the People*. The President was to be the Duke of Buccleuch, and it was to include Lincoln (the future Duke of Newcastle), de la Beche, Richard Owen, George Stephenson, Cubitt, and Smith of Deanston.

Playfair's appointment was criticized on account of his youth, but he became the most active member. He succeeded in securing Chadwick's friendship, in spite of differing from him on administrative principles. He recognized him as the great sanitary reformer of the age. Chadwick, who lived to the age of ninety-one, belonged to the line of North Country reforming Dissenters among whom Joseph Priestley and Thomas Percival, the founder of the Manchester Literary and Philosophical Society, and an important writer on medical ethics, were eminent predecessors. His strong mind and personality were dedicated to sanitary reform, which he pursued with an unswerving devotion that politicians found stiff, but could not evade. Chadwick was convinced that the necessary reforms could be carried out only by a strong centralized administration.

This was contrary to the Liberal principles Playfair supported, of giving the administrative tasks to the local authorities, and exercising only supervisory functions from the central government. Chadwick replied to Playfair's arguments with the observation: 'Sir, the Devil was expelled from heaven because he objected to centralization, and all those who object to centralization oppose it on devilish grounds!'

Playfair asked that the Commission should assign the large Lancashire towns as the field for his part of the investigations. He secured the aid of Angus Smith as an assistant commissioner to carry them out. They found that one-tenth of the population of Manchester, and one-seventh of that of Liverpool, was living in cellars. They gave details of the effect of bad sewerage, defective water-supply, and use of opiates by the miserable poor. They gave examples of the frustration caused by conflicting local authorities, and the darkness and dirt caused by the window tax. They reported that in 1844 more than one-half of the children born in the large manufacturing towns died before they reached the age of five.

'I would remark,' wrote the twenty-seven years' old Commissioner in his Report of 1845, 'that all the facts elicited during the inquiry tend to show that excessive mortality is due to adventitious causes, in almost every instance removable by the combined action of physical improvements, and by the extension of education. Humanity calls loudly for the interference of a paternal legislature to remedy the evils widely spread and deeply rooted—but not irremovable. Sound political economy cannot be in any way opposed to true humanity; and I would say, that all the principles which conduce to the good order and prosperity of the State are involved in the improvement of the sanitary condition of the population. I have endeavoured to show that the present removable causes of evil produce, in addition to excessive disease and death, the physical and moral deterioration of the survivors; that while they occasion an immense infantile mortality, they do, at the same time, cause every year a destruction of adult life unparalleled in the annual loss sustained in the most cruel war of modern times; that, while they are productive of a mortality so great, they do not retard, but, on the contrary, rather favour the increase of population by inducing early marriages; and, lastly, that they entail immense pecuniary burdens on the community, for the support of the war of removable disease against an unprotected population. The great mistake in all the labours of charitable institutions and of individuals, has been in expending their efforts in amelioration, and not in the endeavour to prevent the necessity for that amelioration, by the removal of the causes of disease.'

There was 'not one single professional man appointed,—not one public endowment or provision made, to ensure attention to the means of prevention,—nothing devoted to ascertain the causes of death,—nothing done to remove those causes of disease, which are proved to be removable;—nothing done to warn against defective drainage and to promote external and internal cleansing,—no visits to ensure the due ventilation of schools or workshops, of mines or houses;—nothing done to point out the influence of various noxious agencies, to the public health,—cesspools, slaughter-houses, grave-yards, or offensive and injurious trades!'

The young Commissioner dealt with the disgraceful facts in splendid, trenchant style, but he was already in difficulties over the conflicts between the principles of humanity and political economy, and central and local organization. Nevertheless, by persistent effort, restricted by political conditions to piecemeal improvement, he contributed much during the next fifty years towards the gradual removal of some of the worst evils arising from the unplanned development of industrialism.

When the Health of Towns inquiry was nearly completed, Peel offered Playfair the post of Chemist to the Geological Survey, which had now become vacant. This gave him the opportunity of coming to London. There was no room for a proper laboratory, as the institution had not yet been moved to Jermyn Street, so Playfair fitted up a small laboratory in Duke Street. Here he completed his best-known scientific research: the classical work on the atomic volume of salts, on which he had started at Manchester, in collaboration with Joule. This explained the disappearance of the volume of the acid and the base of crystals in hydrated salts.

Playfair and Joule were born in the same year. They were young men together, and Playfair had the opportunity of seeing Joule's genius unfolding, with its modest, keen, unerring power, before it had been recognized elsewhere. Playfair persuaded Joule to stand for the chair of natural philosophy at St. Andrews, but he was not appointed, on account of a slight deformity due to curvature of the spine. It was thought that this would have interfered with his keeping discipline in lectures.

In the Duke Street laboratory Playfair also established the existence of his 'nitro-prussides'. These formed beautiful crystals and gave a splendid purple colour with alkaline sulphides, and became a favourite preparation for pupils in practical classes.

Playfair claimed that his greatest discoveries at this time were not of new scientific facts and laws, but of men. He had two assistants. One was a young German, Kolbe, whom he persuaded to persevere in original research. Kolbe became one of the great leaders of German chemistry. The other was Frankland, who achieved a comparable eminence in British chemistry. Later on, Playfair engaged an assistant named Dewar. He became the inventor of the famous vacuum flask, and low-temperature investigator. Roscoe wrote that 'as Davy's greatest discovery was Faraday, so it may be said that Playfair's was Dewar'.

After Playfair's death in 1898, Dewar referred to him in a letter of condolence to his widow as 'great and illustrious'. He spoke of his 'life-long love and veneration' for him. 'He was my Master in everything and I owe all to him.' If he had only been spared a little longer, he would have been able to tell him, which he wanted to so much, of his success in liquefying hydrogen, and of the new work he had in hand.

Before Playfair started on his new post in London, Peel invited him to Drayton Manor to meet the personalities under whom he would be working, Lincoln, now the Duke of Newcastle, who was head of the Board of Works, and de la Beche, the head of the Geological Survey. Among the other guests were George Stephenson, Buckland, and a distinguished lawyer named Follett. During a discussion after dinner, Stephenson expressed his belief, in his strong Northumbrian dialect, that the original source of power in steam-engines was the sun, which conserved its force in the plants of which coal is the residue. This was before the theory of the conservation of energy had been generally proved and published, and before the announcement of the theory of evolution.

Stephenson's views were regarded as ridiculous by the geologists present, and were laughed at. He became silent. Next day, Peel asked Playfair what he thought of Stephenson's ideas, for he had noticed that he had not taken part in the discussion. Playfair said they were by no means ridiculous, and could be supported by good arguments. Peel asked Playfair to explain these to Follett, and said he would invite Follett to advocate them after dinner. Accordingly, the question was raised again, and Follett demolished the objections of the geologists, while Stephenson looked on in amazement, and exclaimed: 'Of all the powers in Nature, the greatest is the gift of the gab!'

Playfair described Stephenson and Mercer as natural geniuses, and regretted that he had kept no notes of their daring scientific speculations, so that it could be seen how far they had foreseen modern discoveries.

De la Beche brought the organization of the Geological Museum and Geological Survey in their new building in Jermyn Street into an efficient state, and started to organize a School of Mines, to train men in the new knowledge, and enable better use of it to be made in mining and industrial practice.

Andrew Ramsay, Playfair's old Glasgow friend, became head of the Geological Survey, and his Edinburgh friend Edward Forbes, the naturalist, professor of paleontology. Other members of the professoriate included T. H. Huxley, E. Frankland, N. Lockyer and R. Willis.

The courses of day and evening lectures attracted a varied audience, ranging from the Duke of Marlborough to members of the working class.

Playfair said that 'unfortunately', his reputation as an inquirer into public questions continually interfered with his scientific career. Like his biographer, he took it for granted that this was a misfortune. The first demand on him by the Government after he settled in London was to report on the sanitary condition of Buckingham Palace and Eton College. 'The condition of the palace was then so bad that the Government never dared to publish' his findings. A great main sewer ran through the court-yard, and the palace was in open, untrapped connection with it. Over this, Queen Victoria and her young family were living. The cost of the necessary repairs and alterations was considerable, and members of Parliament wished to see the report which had occasioned the expenditure, but 'it was considered too frank and brutal for production'.

Then Playfair was asked to report on graveyards, the foul state of the Serpentine, and steam coal for the Navy. The latter led to extensive study of the calorific value of all the coals in Britain. The report of de la Beche and himself on this subject determined Admiralty policy on steam coal for the rest of the century. He was asked to report on coal-mine explosions, and used the experience gained in this work to aid him as an arbitrator in disputes between mine owners and miners.

In 1845, he was consulted by Peel on the potato famine in Ireland, as has already been mentioned. Peel invited him to Drayton Manor, discussed the problem in walks round the garden, and asked him whether he would go on a commission of inquiry to discover the true situation, and whether he could nominate two more scientific experts. Playfair suggested the botanist Lindley, and Sir Robert Kane, the head of Queen's College, Cork. He was the author of the *Industrial Resources of Ireland.*

Playfair said he told Peel that he had no hope of remedying the disease, but hoped to obtain a true estimate of its magnitude and consequences, and Peel had replied that he did not expect more. However, according to Peel's *Memoirs*, Peel himself wrote on October 18th, 1845:

'Dr. Lyon Playfair, Buckland, and Josiah Parkes are here.

'They are impressed with a belief that it may be possible to mitigate the evil of the potato disease by some chemical application, and by the issue of plain practical instructions for the treatment of those potatoes which are not at all, or only partially affected by the disorder. . . .' Lindley and Playfair were to report on 'the result of the chemical experiments which they will make upon the potato.'

By October 28th, Playfair had reported that the position was even worse than had been feared, and on November 1st Peel was saying: 'We have sent eminent men of science to Ireland, who are directing their inquiries into the cause of the disorder, the palliatives of it, and the probable effect of it upon the quality of the seed for a future year. . . . They are proceeding cautiously —are unwilling to suggest remedies which may be delusive—but will at the earliest period offer to the public the simplest and most practical remedies which observation and scientific knowledge may enable them to offer.'

Playfair and his scientific colleagues were unable to offer any quick solution, but they gave Peel the 'dispassionate judgment as to the real character and extent of the evil to be apprehended, and to give the most trustworthy information as to facts, and the best opinions as to the remedies which it might be possible to apply'. He thought they would be able to do this because they were 'men of the highest eminence in the department of science to which they belong', and had 'no connection with Ireland', and were 'free from the contagion of undue local apprehensions'.

Sir James Graham, the Home Secretary, said that Lindley and Playfair had 'stated that in their opinion one-half of the whole Irish potato crop of this year is already destroyed; that a large proportion of the remainder, unless unusual precaution be adopted, will not keep beyond the winter; and that in the spring, the supply of potatoes, whether for seed or food, will be very scanty'.

Playfair believed that their reports were 'the last straw to break the back of the protective duties on corn', and finally decided Peel to repeal the Corn Laws.

Such were Playfair's main achievements before he had reached thirty years of age.

V

Making Royal Power useful for Science

PLAYFAIR regarded his years from 1847 to 1849 as comparatively quiet. His main work was as professor at the School of Mines, but he was active on more commissions, including that of the cholera epidemic of 1848–9. He went to some of the worst-affected towns, and started operations against the disease by improving the sanitary conditions.

Playfair was naturally qualified for journalism, by the nature of his abilities and his wide interests. He began to write articles for the *Athenaeum*, the *Daily News*, and other papers, in the middle 1840's. Through this connection, the *Daily News* sent him to report on the revolution in France in June 1848. He was detained in Paris, but released when a letter from Palmerston to the British Ambassador was found in his pocket. He met and became friendly with Louis Blanc, who described to him how he had been duped by Louis Napoleon.

Playfair had previously taken part in the police precautions in London against the great Chartist demonstration in April of that year. Along with Louis Napoleon, de la Beche and thousands of others, he was enrolled as a special constable. He was instructed to join in the patrol of Whitehall.

Another slight ripple in his quiet year of 1848 was his election to the Royal Society which, as he said, 'is always appreciated by workers in science'.

The next major step in his life occurred in 1850, when he was brought in to assist the Prince Consort and Henry Cole in the preparations for the Great Exhibition of 1851. Playfair said that he had nothing to do with its inception and the original preparations. He regarded the Exhibition as the suggestion of 'the Prince Consort in consultation with Sir Henry Cole', who were President and Secretary of the Royal Society of Arts.

This institution had appointed an executive committee to organize the Exhibition, but it had not the resources for carrying out so great an undertaking. A Royal Commission was therefore appointed to provide the necessary support. Playfair was not originally a member either of the executive or the Commission.

It soon became clear that the success of the project was in doubt, owing to inadequate administrative arrangements, and lack of interest on the part of industry. The Government became anxious, because the Prince Consort had become deeply involved in it, and the Queen uneasy that it might fail.

The Prime Minister, Lord John Russell, and his colleagues considered the matter very carefully, and decided that Playfair should be invited to become a Special Commissioner, with the right of attendance at all committees. The aim was to provide a means of resolving differences between committees and between personalities, so that a general workable administration could be created.

Playfair did not at first accept the invitation. He feared that the appointment would take him away from his scientific work for two years, and turn him into a public man. His chief, and all his professorial colleagues at the School of Mines supported his refusal, for they considered that his absence would weaken and upset the balance of the school's scientific courses.

Ministers having failed to persuade him, Sir Robert Peel, not in office but a supporter of the Government, was then prompted to approach him. Peel was very anxious that the Exhibition should succeed, and urged that he had a claim on his services. This was an argument which Playfair could not resist. Peel then took him to the Prince Consort, said he had entire confidence in him, and that the Prince would find that he could do what was required.

This was not Playfair's first meeting with the Prince. Peel had previously advised him to consult Playfair on an invention he had made for filtering the fertile content from sewage, so that it was not wasted in the effluent. Playfair subsequently suspected that Peel had invented this consultation in order to enable the Prince to see what sort of man was being recommended to him, virtually to supervise the organization of the Exhibition.

At this second interview with the Prince, Playfair explained how difficult his position would be, for it would be different from that of other members of the Executive Committee. He accepted the invitation only on an understanding with Peel that he would be able to consult him on any serious problems.

In fact, it was on Exhibition business that Playfair had his long interview with Peel on June 27th, 1850, in the morning of the day on which Peel had his fatal accident. This was a profound loss for Playfair, who had long enjoyed his friendship and encouragement, and who regarded him as 'perhaps the greatest Parliamentarian that England ever had'.

Peel's unwonted death, arising from an accidental fall, gave the same kind of shock to the younger man that Rutherford's death, also due to an accidental fall, gave to the younger generation in 1937.

Cole, whom Playfair regarded as the mainspring of the Exhibition, from beginning to end, and its chief driving force, was much upset at finding a new member on the Executive, who was in a higher position of confidence. Shortly after his appointment, Playfair happened to meet Cole outside the door of the Home Office. Cole told him he was on his way to see the Home Secretary, with his resignation which he had in his pocket. Playfair took his arm, walked up and down Whitehall, and talked him out of it. He asked him whether he thought the Exhibition would fail. Cole said this was already certain, because of lack of support from industry. Playfair then told him he was 'the real pilot of the vessel', and it was wrong for him to desert what he thought was 'a sinking ship'. He said he would separate his own work from Cole's, and concentrate on raising support in the industrial districts. Cole destroyed his letter of resignation, and they thenceforth succeeded in carrying the Exhibition forward together.

Playfair drew upon Peel's support in dealing with deputations from the industrial districts, which in some cases wanted to impose conditions for cooperation that were contrary to the aims of the Exhibition. The Home Secretary, Granville, and Peel were present when Playfair and his colleagues received the deputations, and greatly helped them by their 'tact and sagacity'.

Playfair found that the Prince Consort tenaciously held to the view that the exhibits should be classified in three classes: The Raw Materials of Industry; the Manufactures made from them; and the Art employed to adorn them. This was far too general a classification to apply in a direct way to the vast variety of industrial products, and was one of the chief obstacles to the industrialists, who could not easily see how their particular products fitted into the scheme.

With great labour, Playfair prepared a new classification in twenty-nine classes. He submitted his scheme to leading manufacturers, and revised it according to their criticisms. Playfair remarked that this piece of planning revealed 'whether the Exhibition was deficient in certain industries', and hence whether action should be taken to remedy this.

This appears to have been a piece of unconscious Baconian planning. Playfair said it was 'the first attempted [classification] of industrial work'. It 'met with great success, and had the good fortune to be highly commended by Whewell and Babbage, both masters of classification'. They were both Baconians. 'Ultimately,' the new classification was adopted both by the Prince and the Commission.

It was sent to all the leading manufacturers in the United Kingdom, who 'now knew the nature and the objects of the undertaking, and began to prepare for taking part in it.'

Cobden came to his aid in rallying the laggard manufacturers of Lancashire. Playfair was 'much impressed with his singleness of purpose, and tact in overcoming difficulties'.

The Government contributed no funds towards the organization, and very little came in from subscriptions. Cole suggested a large guarantee fund, which was started by Mr. Morton Peto with £50,000; he subsequently became a baronet. The Prince Consort underwrote £20,000, and all the members of the Executive, including Playfair, guaranteed £1,000 each.

Playfair helped to solve the problem of adopting Paxton's iron-and-glass design for the Exhibition building. This was held up by the refusal of the Commissioners of Woods and Forests to allow three large trees to be cut down. Paxton suggested building a gigantic dome over them, but there were doubts whether the trees would survive in this situation, so Playfair drove out to Turnham Green to consult Lindley, his old collaborator in Ireland. Lindley's opinion was favourable to Paxton's proposal, so his design was finally accepted. The building was erected with a speed which astonished contemporary opinion.

Playfair's principal work after the opening of the Exhibition was the superintendence of the composition and functioning of the juries making awards for exhibits; these were international in character. Playfair attended all meetings at which disagreements had to be resolved. He consequently became known as 'the stormy petrel', for his appearance indicated the existence of trouble.

After the Great Exhibition closed, Playfair was offered the choice of a knighthood or a Companionship of the Bath; he selected the latter. Then, in 1851, the Prince Consort offered him the position of Gentleman Usher in his household. The Prince wrote that there were 'no duties attached to the office, except occasional attendance at the Queen's Levées and Drawing Rooms, and the salary is insignificant'. In this position, Playfair was able to promote the Prince's projects and interests in 'education, science and art'. They constituted a kind of little private forerunner of UNESCO.

Playfair was informed that 'the longer the Prince considers and weighs the subject of the disposal of the surplus (the financial result of the success of the Exhibition), the more convinced he becomes that no arrangement for its appropriation can be satisfactory that does not include the interests of all the world . . . the distinguishing feature of this Exhibition over all others was that *it was for all nations*; and both in maintenance of this principle, and for the ultimate benefit of this country, this great distinction ought to be scrupulously adhered to. . . .'

The Prince suggested that public 'Lectures on the Exhibition' should be given. In this connection, Playfair delivered a lecture on 'Industrial Instruction on the Continent'. In it he referred to the close connection between the sciences and technology in certain continental institutions. 'Mathematical science is not studied and kept apart as a separate branch of knowledge, as is too frequently done in some of our most important schools and colleges, but she is used as the handmaid and interpreter of all the other sciences, and it is with this view that so much time is devoted to her study. Perhaps Aristotle was too limited in his views when he said, 'Physics and mathematics make practice': but Bacon was certainly not in error when he wrote: 'For as physical knowledge daily grows up, and new actions of nature are disclosed, there will be a necessity for new mathematical inventions.' And what a commentary on this text is our present knowledge in astronomy, navigation, logarithms, surveying, the theory of the tides, the wave-theory of light, the attraction of spheroids, and the mass of the earth!'

He pointed out that 'comprehensive education' enables the student to become a manager, and design factories and processes. 'The interests of a nation extend much beyond the interests of the one generation which forms its present population, and the statesman will feel sure that the effects already in action will operate with a much increasing power in the future.'

Playfair enthusiastically pressed forward with proposals for a national system of technical education. Like Laplace in another connection, he left God out of it, with no place for religious instruction.

There was immediate opposition to his proposals from religious bodies, and like Laplace he received a Royal reproof for his temerity. He was informed by a letter from Windsor Castle in November 1851, that the Prince was as anxious as he was that the movement for 'the extension of science to productive industry should not be allowed to fall dead'. What had just happened to Playfair showed the great danger of raising 'any suspicion or alarm' in 'the mind of the *religious* world'. In spite of the success of the Exhibition, it was doubtful whether he would be able to resist the cry of '"*godless* instruction".... Already you have been brought upon your knees; and the question is whether your repentance, however deep and sincere, will avail you....'

Any proposal for 'National Education' raised the question as to who was to conduct it. Everyone had made up his mind and was wedded to one system or other, and all held to their differing opinions equally doggedly. The fate of all measures so far introduced in Parliament to such an end provided a warning, and it was necessary to avoid drawing the opposition which they provoked onto any system for extending 'the application of science and industry'. It was indicated that the Prince thought a more promising line of action was to extend practical instruction through the development of the activities in the existing Mechanics' Institutes. This was one of the lines of advance which was immediately adopted.

The draft of the first Report of the 1851 Commissioners was largely prepared by Playfair. It was rather sharply criticized by the Prince, who said that it was too long and detailed. In particular, Playfair was told that where he went into new matter, he went too quick; for example, with regard to his suggestion of scholarships. He entered into that with a detail which was 'quite premature'. Playfair's scholarship suggestion ultimately proved to be one of his most fruitful proposals.

The Report led to very considerable developments in science and technical education, but these were to prove far less than they should have been. From the beginning, the ideas in the Report had a cool reception. They were not in accord with the dominant social and political ideas of the time, and could be realized only piecemeal through many years.

The Prince aimed at the founding of a great central institution for the promotion of science and art and their application to productive industry. His centralism was in fundamental conflict with the numerous independent institutions which had come into existence at various times, and with different standards, aims and modes of organization, according to the impulses of individualism.

The first task of the Commission of 1851, after it had been made a perpetual institution, was to connect and mould, as far as was possible, existing institutions into a system which could be regarded as, to some extent, a realization of the Prince's idea. Besides the multitude of institutions differing in aim, type and history, each with a very lively sense of its own autonomy, there was confusion over such things as the word 'Art'. To the Royal Academy and the aristocracy it meant painting and sculpture; to the industrialists it meant technology, the way in which things were manufactured, as well as attractive design of products to increase their saleability.

The creation of a unified organization for dealing with science and its applications, together with art in both its senses, was indeed a formidable task. In 1853 the Science and Art Department was established to carry it out as far as was practicable. Playfair said that this was done largely on the Prince's advice. Schools of design, already operating in various cities; the Museum of Practical Geology and the School of Mines; and some other existing institutions were brought under the new department, and an advanced college of science and art was projected.

Cole was made Secretary of the Art Department, and Playfair of the Science Department. No single person was in charge, and the arrangement did not work, so Cole was made Inspector-General and Playfair Secretary of the united departments.

The new Science and Art Department was placed under the Education Department of the Privy Council; existing institutions which had formerly been under the Board of Trade were transferred to it.

The advanced college of science, projected as part of the scheme, was organized by Playfair, and became the Royal College of Science.

The art exhibits at the Exhibition were collected as the nucleus of a museum, which, through Cole's efforts, developed into the South Kensington Museum, and finally into the Victoria and Albert Museum.

Exhibits of raw materials, especially of food and grain, became the nucleus of a Food Collection, in which the exhibits were labelled with their food-values. This stimulated the foundation of schools of cookery.

Playfair went to Edinburgh to persuade the Scots to found a national Scottish Museum. This was started in 1855, with the learned chemist Dr. George Wilson, author of the admirable *Life of Henry Cavendish*, as director.

At first, the schools of art, extending from the basis of the existing schools of design, expanded more rapidly than the schools of science. Apart from the Andersonian College in Glasgow and Owens College in Manchester, there were no advanced schools of science. Playfair therefore embarked on a crusade for technical education. He said it was dreary and weary work, and his voice sounded to himself like that of one crying in the wilderness.

His aim was to reform British education so that the nation was better fitted to meet the increasing world-competition. 'The improved methods of locomotion both by sea and land had altered the whole conditions of manufacturing industry. The possession of raw materials, such as coal and iron, had long given to a country like Great Britain a supremacy in manufactures, because economy of production was the most important condition for success. When science offered new and economical production through improved machinery, and when the demands of an increasing civilization required the best forms of art to adorn the products, it became obvious that a nation which cultivated science and art must have a great advantage over a country which depended too exclusively on the more practical aptitudes of its people. Raw material had now become a decreasing factor in production, while intellect, trained in the application of science and art, became an ever-increasing factor.'

Besides beginning a series of expositions and analyses of the effect of science and technology on industry and civilization, which he sustained to the end of his life nearly half a century later, Playfair proposed technical innovations in other directions. During the Crimean War he proposed the use of incendiary shells containing phosphorus dissolved in carbon disulphide, in metal containers made brittle with antimony.

He suggested poison warfare with shells containing cyanide, and was infuriated when his proposal was rejected on humanitarian grounds. He found the argument incomprehensible. 'War is destruction, and the more destructive it can be made with the least suffering the sooner will be ended that barbarous method of protecting national rights. No doubt in time chemistry will be used to lessen the suffering of combatants, and even of criminals condemned to death. Hanging is a relic of barbarism, because criminals might be put to death without physical torture.'

Playfair had a similar impatience of anti-vivisectionism and opposition to slaughter in combating cattle disease. He was a most patient and skilful negotiator, but under his diplomacy there was no sentimentality.

The Department of Science and Art developed slowly, and with difficulty. The concept of such a department of state was in conflict with the ideology of current individualist industry and science. Playfair's attempts to promote it by appeals to self-interest and self-improvement, according to the classical principles of Liberal *laissez faire*, made tardy progress. The Prince's reaction over religious opposition illustrated the limitation of the support which could be expected from him. His public position was delicate, and he was chary of exciting opposition on points which could be represented as irrelevant to the main object of the promotion and application of science.

Playfair began to feel that the Department of Science and Art was not going to develop rapidly into a major department of state. It did not offer an adequate career, for which the sacrifice of his academic scientific interests would be worth while.

Sir John Herschel had spent five unhappy years as Master of the Mint, the official position which had been held by Isaac Newton, and for this reason in particular was attractive to many scientists. It became vacant in 1855. Playfair very much desired the appointment, but his old master, the eminent Thomas Graham, told him he would like to have the post, and asked Playfair's aid in securing it. Playfair loyally did his best for Graham, who was duly appointed. Graham, though a great chemist, was not suited to direct such an institution. Later on, his administration was criticized in Parliament, and Playfair defended it in the House of Commons.

In 1855, Playfair secured the first British official recognition for scientific effort in the 'colonies'. This was for geology in Canada, which was then of colonial status. The Canadian Geological Survey had done distinguished work under the direction of William Logan. He brought a splendid collection of minerals for the French Exhibition, and Playfair suggested to the Prince Consort that 'colonial science' should be recognized by the conferment of a knighthood on Logan, which was duly done.

In the same year, 1855, Playfair's first wife, Margaret Oakes, died. In the following year, his post was changed to that of Inspector-General of Museums and Schools of Science. A year later he married the well-to-do Miss Jean Ann Millington. The income that she brought enabled Playfair to have his government work reduced to a half-time appointment.

Then, in 1858, the chair of chemistry at Edinburgh fell vacant. Playfair was an old student of the department which had been made famous by Joseph Black. He had done his first research there, which had earned for him Liebig's regard. It provided the best opportunity for a return to academic science. Perhaps, too, his new wife preferred the social atmosphere of a senior university post to a minor official position in Whitehall.

Playfair was tough under his tact and diplomacy, but he was not insensitive to the view common in scientific circles, that his government work was inferior in status to academic science and pure research. Many scientists regarded him as a 'good man gone wrong'. He was not prepared to be looked down upon, for the sake of a government position which should have been potentially of major importance, but was developing slowly. He applied for the Edinburgh chair, which would at least have given him a major academic position, and was duly appointed.

He found his departure from London life a severe wrench. He had acquired a unique position in what was then the centre of the world. He was a member of the Prince Consort's household, a competent scientific personality, whose aid was continually sought by ministers of state, and whose company was welcomed by the leading hostesses.

Playfair excused his departure to the Prince Consort by indicating that he had found his 'scientific knowledge rapidly slipping away' owing to his 'public duties'. and he 'could not resist the only chair which was worth having' in order to devote himself 'more exclusively to science'.

He resigned from his position in the Royal household in 1859, in spite of the Prince's efforts to make it still less onerous.

VI

The Reforming and Propagandizing Professor

PLAYFAIR viewed his new task as 'a sort of missionary to bring chemistry into relation with the industries of the country, which had too long been carried on by the rule of thumb'.

He re-equipped the chemical laboratory, and reorganized the practical teaching of chemistry more in the spirit of his old teacher Liebig.

He introduced a tutorial system to give the large numbers of chemical students a better training. Instead of restricting medals to the first two or three, he awarded a bronze medal to each student who gained more than a certain percentage in the examinations. This comprehensive system of awards encouraged the average student. Playfair later found it was widespread in America, and he thought it might have been initiated from Edinburgh.

He participated in 'restoring the dignity of the University' by making the ceremony of graduation more stately. He had a leading part in the reform of the administration of the University, which revivified the academic life.

The Medical Faculty was at the height of its fame. It included Christison, Simpson and Syme. These eminent medical men, each accustomed to great authority in his own department, were fiercely jealous of any exertion of authority of one over the other. When the principalship of the University became vacant in 1868 through the death of Brewster, Simpson, the famous discoverer of chloroform anaesthetics, but no administrator, considered that his services had earned the post. Christison, who was a good administrator, and fearing the appointment of Simpson, intimated that he was willing to stand. His life-long friend Syme, the great surgeon and bitter rival of Simpson, wishing to save the University from Simpson, felt it necessary to stand. Christison and Syme tried to solve their dilemma by agreeing to withdraw, on condition that Playfair should stand; Playfair was unyielding, as he was friendly with Simpson, Finally, an outsider was appointed, who proved very successful.

Playfair was only forty years old when he became professor, but he did not resume any considerable pure research, even if he had hoped to do so.

The Government and Royalty continued to call on him for advice. He was appointed president of the Royal Commission on the herring fisheries, in which T. H. Huxley was the leading figure. The report of this commission provided the basis for modern fishery legislation for sea fish, as distinguished from river fish.

In his professorial period, Playfair served on the Cattle Plague Commission, which recommended the ruthless control and slaughtering of infected animals, which has ever since been found to be the most effective measure. It was received with indignation and fury, and for a time Playfair faced much unpopularity.

He was pressed into service as organizer of the juries for the Great Exhibition of 1862. While engaged in this work, he was compelled to take a house in London.

The Exhibition of 1862 demonstrated that other nations had made great progress since the Exhibition of 1851 in catching up and overtaking Great Britain in the technical and industrial field. This redoubled Playfair's concern for the development of technical education. He pointed out in 1867, in a letter to the chairman of the Public Schools Inquiry Commission, 'that as an inevitable result of the attention given to technical education abroad and of its neglect in England, other nations must advance in industry at a greater rate than our own country; . . . this result has already arrived for some of our staple industries.'

Playfair's concern for Edinburgh and the Scottish universities caused him to join in the request that they should be represented in Parliament. He, and his Conservative colleague Campbell Swinton, went to London to ask that this should be included in the Conservative Government's Representation of the People Act of 1868. Campbell Swinton lobbied the Conservative Government for this, while Playfair approached Gladstone, and persuaded him to agree.

In the following General Election of that year, Playfair was invited to stand as Liberal candidate for Edinburgh and St. Andrews. The University electorate was essentially Conservative, whereas he was an advanced Liberal. Nevertheless, he defeated the Conservative candidate, Campbell Swinton, by 250 votes. Playfair thought at first that this was because of his public work, and wider public reputation, but formed the opinion later that it was more probably due to the large size of the chemistry classes at the University. Chemical graduates felt that they must loyally vote for their old professor, whatever their own political opinions might be.

Playfair resigned his chair, and moved to London once more. He continued to sit for Edinburgh and St. Andrews for the next seventeen years. It was a remarkable exhibition of political tact and diplomacy.

VII

The Scientist in Parliament

PLAYFAIR said that as a Liberal representing a Tory constituency, through all his seventeen years as a University representative, he 'could not take an active part in party politics,' and was obliged to limit himself 'to neutral subjects connected with science, education, public health, and social welfare'.

Both inside and outside Parliament, he gave sustained attention to all these subjects. His situation tended to confine him to the valuable and original politico-scientific work which he was particularly qualified to pursue. While it kept him out of the forefront of the party political battle, his reputation, expert knowledge, and diplomatic skill gave him considerable influence within his party.

One of his first general proposals in Parliament was the introduction of the halfpenny postcard, which was adopted.

He gave W. E. Forster able support in carrying his Bill for the establishment of a national system of education. This was one of the more important English events of the nineteenth century. He enthusiastically supported a bill for opening Trinity College, Dublin, to Roman Catholics. This was opposed by Gladstone, who, unknown to Playfair, was preparing to introduce a bill of a wider character dealing with university education in the whole of Ireland. When Gladstone introduced his bill, Playfair attacked it, especially on the ground of the exclusion of philosophy and history from the university courses. Gladstone replied to Playfair's strictures with all his eloquence and power, but on the vote being taken, he was defeated by a majority of three.

The Government resigned, but Disraeli refused to form a government, so Gladstone's administration returned. Playfair said that his friends told him he had made an irreconcilable enemy of Gladstone; but shortly after, Gladstone offered him the Postmaster-generalship, though expressing doubts whether he would be a reliable colleague, because he was apt to have strong views of his own.

Only three months after his appointment as Postmaster-General, the Government was dissolved, and the Liberals were defeated in the ensuing election. This occurrence interfered with Playfair's career as a conventional politician.

Playfair ever afterwards had a curious hankering after the Postmaster-generalship. It seems that he revelled in the scope it provided for comprehensive organization, and in its technical aspects. Sir Charles Wheatstone, the inventor of the electric telegraph, was one of his close friends. The pair were small in stature and very similar in appearance. Lady Wheatstone once mistook Playfair, addressing him as her husband.

If Gladstone had continued in power, Playfair would probably in due course have become a Cabinet Minister, and a leading politician of the conventional type. Gladstone resigned the leadership of the Liberal Party in the course of this turmoil. Forster, by virtue of his great Education Act, should have been his successor, but he had antagonized the religious bodies. Playfair was asked by party chiefs to sound the feeling of the rank-and-file. He found that Forster was unacceptable, so he was deputed to ask him not to stand for the leadership. He called on Forster, who was a warm personal friend, and emerged with a statement containing his withdrawal. Hartington, the son of the Duke of Devonshire, became leader.

After Disraeli had formed the succeeding Conservative Government, he had a Commission appointed to reorganize the Civil Service. He asked Playfair, though a Liberal, to preside over it. It was considered that this was a fair exchange with the Conservatives, for a leading Conservative had aided the former

Liberal Government by going to the United States to help to settle the controversial Alabama claims, which had caused serious friction between the two countries.

The Commission reported in 1875, with recommendations for a completely new Civil Service system; it became known as 'The Playfair Scheme'. It gave the Civil Service the form it has retained ever since. The essence of it was to divide the Service into two branches; the administrative, for work requiring intellectual ability, entrance to which was to be governed by high competitive examination; and the executive, for carrying out routine work. Promotion in both branches was to be by merit, not seniority.

The new system was bitterly attacked by the members of the lower branch, but it recommended itself to governments because it led to a reduction in the cost of the Civil Service.

At this period, in 1874, Playfair attempted to obtain the appointment of a Minister of Education, instead of having educational matters conducted by a committee of the Privy Council, but he did not succeed. The raising of the political status of education was essential if education were to receive due attention.

Shortly after this, he introduced a bill to regulate experiments on living animals, so that no operation which caused pain could be performed without an anaesthetic. Playfair was keenly interested in this question, for his friend and colleague Sir James Simpson, the founder of the British school of anaesthetics, had been in the habit of taking excessive risks in experiments on himself. Playfair considered it ludicrous and almost anti-social that a creative genius of scientific medicine should lightly risk his life on experiments, many of which could be performed on animals with little or no pain, when conducted under properly controlled conditions. Playfair's proposals virtually became law, and he became the *bête noire* of anti-vivisectionists.

Throughout his period as a University member, Playfair was naturally active on behalf of the Scottish Universities. In 1876, a Royal Commission on the Scottish Universities recommended reforms. Playfair, T. H. Huxley and Froude the historian, were sent to promote their acceptance. They suggested that students should be allowed a free selection of subjects as alternative courses for degrees in arts and science. The universities were slow to accept this.

In the following year, Playfair had a leading part in the final rehabilitation of Lord Dundonald. He approved in principle of Dundonald's idea of applying science to the improvement of military weapons. This inspiring naval commander and inventor had been elected a Radical Member of Parliament during the Napoleonic Wars. He was falsely condemned by Ellenborough in 1814 as having participated in a Stock Exchange conspiracy. Dundonald had proposed the use of chemical warfare, and during the Crimean War, in his old age, revived his proposals as a quick method for taking the fortresses at Sebastopol and Cronstadt. His methods were referred by the government of the day to Graham and Playfair, who reported unfavourably on what he regarded as the major part of his invention, but favourably on the minor. Seventeen years later, in 1877, and after Dundonald's death, Playfair and others secured the completion of his rehabilitation, persuading the Government to give Dundonald's heirs his back-pay from 1814.

Playfair's knowledge of the science of nutrition led him to be a sustained opponent of the tax on salt in India. He pointed out that a minimum of ten pounds of salt a year was essential for health. It was as necessary for the poorest as for the richest man. To tax it so that the poor could not afford to buy the necessary amount was essentially unfair, and actually damaging to the people's health.

He retained his concern with questions of sanitation. He was called upon to be chairman of a commission on Manchester's application to take water from Lake Thirlmere. The commission approved the plan of making Thirlmere bigger, which was generally accepted. In 1883, by informed and incisive speeches in the House of Commons, he had the leading part in defeating attempts to repeal the compulsory vaccination laws.

Playfair, who had done so much as a Special Commissioner for the Exhibition of 1851, was appointed in 1869 a permanent member of the perpetual Commission of 1851. He was consulted on virtually all scientific aspects of exhibitions for the rest of his life. In 1878, he was appointed chairman of the Finance Committee of the Commission for British exhibits at the International Exhibition in Paris.

Playfair was offered the influential post of Chief Party Whip by Gladstone in 1880. With his gifts of tact and diplomacy he was very well qualified for the post, but he refused it. The post was lower in status, even if higher in influence, than the Post-master-generalship which he had formerly occupied. Playfair probably felt that he should have been offered a Cabinet post, and not one entirely identified with party affairs. As a Liberal representing a Tory university seat, he had concentrated on issues on which the parties did not generally have a strong bias.

He was, however, persuaded to accept the apparently neutral position of Chairman of Committees and Deputy-Speaker. Unfortunately for him, this position proved to be the very opposite of what he had expected. In 1880 the Irish members embarked on their policy of obstruction of the Parliamentary procedure, in order to force the grant of home rule to Ireland. As Chairman of Committees and Deputy Speaker, the brunt of the battle fell on Playfair. Until the systematic Irish obstruction arose, Parliament had dealt only with individual members who were wilfully obstructing the procedure.

Gladstone introduced group-suspension by moving that twenty-eight members be suspended in a single resolution for defying the chair. This was accepted by the House.

The Irish members protracted the proceedings of the committee dealing with Irish affairs, of which Playfair was chairman, for twenty-three days. They extended the debate on the seventeenth clause for nineteen hours. Playfair considered the chair was being treated with contempt, and decided to have the Irish members suspended.

His action was interpreted by opponents as an assault on political freedom in general, and Irish freedom in particular. He was bitterly attacked in the Press, and the Cabinet indicated that they no longer supported his interpretation. This was in spite of his having followed Gladstone's own precedent.

Playfair soon resigned from his untenable post. It made his advance as a conventional politician still less probable, but his action forced, as Gladstone recognized, the need for revision of the rules of parliamentary debate, to prevent systematic obstruction. Playfair found that after his resignation he became for a time one of the most popular men in the Commons. Whenever he rose to speak, he was cheered from all sides.

Shortly after his resignation as Chairman of Committees, Playfair was appointed, in 1883, Knight Commander of the Bath. He was asked to become Honorary Secretary of the Commission of 1851, the affairs of which had been mismanaged. He reorganized the Commission's finances, which enabled it to extend its operations into new and fertile directions, especially in developing the system of scholarships for scientific research, which he had suggested more than thirty years before, but which the Prince Consort had thought premature.

As Playfair grew older he moved further to the left of the Liberal Party. It became clear that he would no longer be returned as member for Edinburgh and St. Andrews. When it was known that he would be prepared to stand elsewhere, thirteen of the most radical constituencies in England invited him to become their candidate. He chose South Leeds, well-known in recent years as the constituency for which the late Mr. Gaitskell sat.

In the General Election of 1885, Playfair had a resounding victory in South Leeds. The constituency was socially at the opposite extreme from Edinburgh and St. Andrews. Its population was almost entirely working-class, with a high proportion of skilled workmen. To this audience, Playfair was able to speak his mind with a completeness which had been politically impossible in his Tory university constituency. His new audience listened closely to a stream of speeches on the future of British industry, the need for technical education, the effect of technological progress on employment, and on Liberal economic policy.

These were subjects which bored or annoyed the university audiences, and were not supposed to appeal to the passions of the working class; but, like Brougham before him, Playfair had a most enthusiastic reception from his Yorkshire supporters. No meetings in the county during the fierce campaign of 1885 were more densely crowded and appreciated than Playfair's in Mechanics' Institutes and other halls. His biographer Wemyss Reid was editor of the *Leeds Mercury* at the time, and saw the enthusiasm.

After the election, Gladstone astounded the country by adopting the policy of Home Rule for Ireland, and reversing, at the age of seventy-six, the views which he had formerly held through his long political life. His action split the Liberal Party. Joseph Chamberlain and others entered into negotiation with the Conservatives. As the leading representative of the Birmingham interests, closely connected with engineering and armaments manufacture, he was in sympathy with the protagonists of the preservation and extension of the Empire. Home Rule for Ireland appeared to be a reversal of this policy, so Chamberlain, who had been progressive, especially in municipal and home affairs, found himself, on the whole, more in agreement with the Conservatives than the new Gladstonian policy.

Playfair was one of the first to detect Chamberlain's manoeuvres, and he inspired the statement to the Press, known as the 'Hawarden kite', which contained the first public announcement of Gladstone's adoption of the Home Rule policy.

Playfair was one of those who supported Gladstone in his new policy. Nevertheless, he wrote at the time to a relative: 'I do not think he appreciates me, or perhaps he measures me better than the House generally does.' A few days after he wrote this, Gladstone offered him the Vice-Presidency of the Council. He refused it, but he was subsequently pressed by other leaders to accept. He went to see Gladstone, and was first met by Mrs. Gladstone, who told him her husband was very poorly, and his refusal was the cause of it. Then he saw Gladstone, who told him he knew he sympathized with him, but he could not put him into the Cabinet because he had taken little interest in party politics; but anyone who had stood by him in his emergency would have to go in soon. Playfair felt he was compelled to yield, and reversed his decision.

When Gladstone died in 1898, and Playfair himself was dying, and too ill to write, his wife wrote his condolences to Mrs. Gladstone, in which he referred to Gladstone as 'the greatest and most true-hearted Englishman of our age'.

He was appointed Vice-President of the Council, in charge of education. He thus had the position which should have been raised to the rank of a Ministry long ago.

Gladstone's new administration had a short and stormy career, owing to the intense opposition to the Home Rule policy. It was forced to resign after about six months. Nevertheless, in that short period, Playfair succeeded in carrying through a bill for the organization of the medical profession. Despite about thirty previous attempts, all such bills had been defeated, but Playfair was successful. His bill gave direct representation to the main body of medical practitioners on the General Medical Council, and made it obligatory in future for every medical man to pass examinations in medicine, surgery and midwifery. Thus Playfair's bill made the British medical profession properly qualified.

The defeat of Gladstone's Home Rule led to a General Election, and the return of a Conservative Government, at the end of 1886. Playfair therefore held no political office. However, he was active in the Queen's Jubilee Celebrations of 1887, especially as a former servant and friend of the Prince Consort, who had died twenty-six years before.

In the same year, the United States celebrated the centenary of the Declaration of Independence. The Americans had intimated that they would like Gladstone or Bright to represent Britain, but they were too old or occupied to go. Consequently, Playfair went. During the previous nine years he had become closely connected with the United States. After the death of his second wife in 1877, he had married Miss Edith Russell of Boston in 1878. He originally met the Russell family in Holland, during one of their continental tours.

This American connection gave Playfair a new field of interest and understanding as striking as any that he had had before. His Boston relations gave him an insight into America deeper than that obtained by a detached person. He was introduced to, and became friendly with, Longfellow, Emerson, Wendell Holmes, Lowell and others, not as a visitor, but one married to a Bostonian. As early as 1879, his new perspective had caused him to think about the future of the Anglo-Saxons. He wrote to his American relatives: 'Our colonies in South Africa have no natural boundaries, and it is cheaper to conquer border savage tribes than to make regular boundaries to keep them out. This is really the secret of Russia's great extensions and of England's annexations. I see in the future that England must fight every few years till she gets to the great Lake regions of Victoria Nyanza; and it is possible that we may meet Egypt stretching out her arms into the same region. Ultimately we may have to swallow Egypt also, and the English future will be to civilize Africa when perhaps we have lost our hold on India. Of course I shan't live to see this accomplished, but I daresay Edith will. The Anglo-Saxon has certainly a future greater than the Latin race, and will some day be dominant in three out of four quarters of the globe.'

In 1887 he returned to this subject. 'There should be an intimate union of heart and interests between the English-speaking people throughout the world, and more especially between England and the United States.'

His speech at the Centennial banquet contained accents not heard in his English orations. He said he spoke with mingled feelings of pride, humiliation and confidence. 'With pride, because this celebration is the triumph of principles of political liberty, and of constitutional government of a people by the people, in entire accord with the great traditions which have made England, in the reaction which followed the Cromwellian revolution, and which lasted until the close of the reign of George III. . . . Cromwell was the political father of Washington. . . .' The former Gentleman Usher of the Prince Consort found a less fettered form of political utterance.

Playfair said he regretted that Gladstone or Bright was not speaking rather than himself; he was 'only a humble Englishman, half scientist, half politician', with no claim to speak other than this ardent love of his own country, and his warm love of the United States.

He expressed intense admiration for the constitution of the United States. Whenever he thought of it, and the men who composed it, he was inclined to exclaim, in the words of Shakespeare: 'How beauteous mankind is! Oh, brave new world that has such people in't.'

He pointed out that the British Isles contained 36 million people, whereas the United States already had a population of 60 million. 'We know that you must become our big brother. . . .' He asked that the Americans should 'take pride in our common ancestry'. If so, 'the great Anglo-Saxon race throughout the world will become a security for peace'.

In the General Election of 1892, the Liberals, with the support of the Irish members, were returned with a majority of forty. As a result, Gladstone, at the age of eighty-three, was called to form the administration which was to be his last. He wrote to Playfair, saying that the nation would recognize his fitness to be in the Cabinet, but there was a public opinion against the age of some of the members of the last Liberal Government. He ought himself to be proscribed, and indeed at his age, it 'would be simply a favour'. If Playfair was agreeable, however, he would submit his name for a peerage. In this connection, Gladstone did not mention his services to science.

So, in 1892, Playfair was given a peerage, and took the title of 'Baron Playfair of St. Andrews'.

VIII

The Publicist of Science

PLAYFAIR exerted as much influence through his speeches outside Parliament as in. Throughout his career, he spoke and wrote on the subjects on which he was working. His public utterances and articles ran parallel, and were not restricted by official or parliamentary considerations.

He saw far into his subjects at the beginning of his career. In 1851, he chose for his Introductory Lecture at the Government School of Mines: *The Study of Abstract Science essential to the Progress of Industry.* He started by pointing out that if local industrial advantages were levelled, through any innovation which made raw material confined to one country readily attainable by others at a slight difference in cost, then 'competition in industry must become a competition in intellect'. In this situation, the nation which most quickly promotes the intellectual development of its artisans will advance, while that which neglects its industrial training will recede.

We were rapidly approaching, if we had not yet arrived at, 'that period of wonderful transition, when nations must speedily acquire the levels due to their different amounts of intellectual development'.

It was true that a nation with superabundant capital could for a time support its position even if it neglected intellectual training, but this would be only temporary, 'for though the purchase of foreign talent may infuse the necessary knowledge into home manufactures, this must have the ultimate effect of raising the intellectual element in the foreign country, and thus finally accelerate its success as a competing nation'.

At former periods in history, national prosperity depended on local or accidental advantages. The progress of science had, however, both 'created resources unthought of before,' and removed local barriers. For example, a land which doubles its agricultural production has in effect doubled its size.

'If England still continue in advance, it will not be from the abundance of her coal and iron, but because, uniting science with practice, she enables her discoveries in philosophy [that is, in science] to keep pace with her aptitude in applying them.'

English electrical discoveries promised a revolution in communication. For instance, 'it would not be difficult to have all the clocks in a town worked with perfect uniformity by the aid of electricity'.

It was a mistake to suppose that chemistry is merely the result of practical knowledge derived from industry. Such a view did little justice to the progress of the human mind, and the infinite development it has given to human resources and enjoyment. Who could have foreseen that the new substance, chloroform, discovered by Dumas in the distillation of alcohol and bleaching powder, was destined to remove many of the woes which man is heir to?

Playfair described how his master Liebig, in his research into the chemistry of plant nutrition, had been led to recognize the importance of guano as a manure, and 'by his intellect wafted fleets to the Ichaboes and to the Incas.'

Two years later, in England, he saw the fossil excrement of saurians, which he at once suggested must contain phosphates, and be the raw material of an artificial fertilizer. 'What a curious and interesting subject for contemplation!' said Liebig. 'In the remains of an extinct *animal* world England is to find the means of increasing her wealth in agricultural produce, as she has already found the great support of her manufacturing industry in fossil fuel—the preserved matter of primaeval forests—the remains of a vegetable world! May this expectation be realized! and may her excellent population be thus redeemed from poverty and misery!'

Liebig had pointed out that in the light of such developments 'The greatest desideratum of the present age is practically manifested in the establishment of schools in which the natural sciences occupy the most prominent places in the course of instruction. From these schools a more vigorous generation will come forth, powerful in understanding, qualified to appreciate and to accomplish all that is truly great, and to bring forth fruits of universal usefulness. Through them the resources, the wealth, and the strength of empires will be incalculably increased.'

Thus, concluded Playfair, the extension of scientific and technical education was a want of the age. The technical man was, perhaps, 'of more use to himself and to his time and generation than he who discovers the abstract laws applied to the purposes of industry'. though it was the abstract scientist who benefits all time, and confers universal and eternal benefit on society. It was of infinite importance to a nation, not only to study science as the foundation on which industry rests, but also 'to promote abstract science, the soul and life of industry'. Thus the importance of institutions for infusing this life into special departments of technology will be readily recognized.

'England has too long rested on the position she has acquired as a manufacturing nation. This position was gained when local advantages gave an impulse to our practical national mind. But now that the progress of human events has converted *the competition of industry into a competition of intellect*, it will no longer do to plume ourselves on our power of mere practical adaptations.'

It was indispensable that England should have a scientific education in connection with manufactures 'if we wish to outstrip the intellectual competition which now, happily for the world, prevails in all departments of industry. As surely as darkness follows the setting of the sun, so surely will England recede as a manufacturing nation, unless her industrial population become much more conversant with science than they now are...'

Playfair said all this one hundred and thirteen years ago. He delivered the lesson with variations and extensions for more than forty years, yet, even today, in 1964, it has been but indifferently learned.

In 1870 he developed his ideas in a striking presidential address to the Midland Institute at Birmingham on *The Inosculation of the Arts and Sciences*. This term, derived from a kiss, is used to describe the unification of two vessels by pipes or tubes in the animal body. He applied it to the mutual interaction of science and labour. The topic was a very suitable one, in the perspective of Birmingham's part in the industrial revolution, and the interaction between brain and hand in the ideas of Watt and the skill of Boulton's craftsmen.

He said that their interdependence was far from simple. 'It is not science which creates labour, or the industries flowing from it. On the contrary, science is the progeny of the industrial arts on the one side, and on the other, of the experiences and perceptions which gradually attach themselves to these arts. So that the evolution of science from the arts is the first circumstance of human progress, which, however, quickly receives development and impulse from the science thus evolved. Industrial labour, then, is one of the parents, and science is the child; but as often happens in the world, the son becomes richer than the father, and raises his position. . . .'

No science was developed in uncultured minds, or even in cultured ones, except as the result of very long experience and observation, arising in the first place from the need to meet the necessities of existence. The rich men of Greece were involved in manufacture and commerce. 'The learned class were the sons of those citizens, and were in possession of their accumulated experience derived through industry and foreign relations.' Thales was an oil merchant, Aristotle was a druggist before he was appointed tutor to Alexander, Plato's wealth was largely derived from commerce, Socrates, was a sculptor and Zeno a travelling merchant. It was from this social background that the Greeks developed their science.

Why, today, did eminent statesmen from the upper classes, exhibiting high intellectual talent, advance science so little? 'Precisely because, like the schoolmen of the middle ages, their education separates them from the fund of common knowledge accumulating among an industrious people.'

Just as Europe worshipped the philosophy of Plato and Aristotle, so China still worshipped that of Confucius and Mencius. 'So China chains herself to the past, allows the present to float past her.' The schoolmen would have done the same for Europe, if the industrial classes had not advanced beyond them in perceptions and experience. The journeyman craftsmen carried technical knowledge throughout the lands, and what they did for individuals, 'the great geographical discoveries did for nations'.

The new technical knowledge was expressed and published in the vernacular of the men who had discovered it. The learned class, with their intercommunications in Latin and Greek, became separated from this new knowledge, which was greater than that of the same kind in the best days of Greece and Rome.

The publishing of the new knowledge in the vernacular undermined the power of the pulpit and increased that of the Press. Then, at the close of the eighteenth century, teaching in English began to supersede that in Latin in grammar schools. This started to break down that great barrier to progress: the division between the learned and the industrial classes. These two classes started to unite, as they had done in the most creative period of Greece; but the upper classes still did not realize this. They continued to cut off one-third of the lives of their children by an exclusive devotion to classical literature. They rarely advanced modern science, though they made good statesmen, 'because they have had noble studies of human mind and human actions in the glorious records of antiquity; for these have the same springs now as when Greece had its greatest prosperity and intellectual vigour'.

Politics, ethics, sculpture, painting and architecture had advanced little since ancient times. But these, 'though they grace, do not now form the foundations of a nation's prosperity. That is formed from the applications of science to industry.'

When a nation can take from another raw material which the original possessor either does not use, or uses with less intelligence, then 'the first nation must be under the guidance of science. The science may be underdeveloped, dealing with qualities only and not with quantities, but science it must be....' It was this difference in science which had become 'the great element of industrial competition in the world at the present time'.

As the English evolved their 'initiatory science' from their industrial pursuits, they no longer sold their mineral wealth to distant nations, but manufactured valuable products from it. Intellect thus began to exceed the value of the raw material as a factor in production. It converted 'the brute labour of a man into an intellectual superintendence of labour performed'.

The British coal production represented a power almost exactly equal at that time to the manual labour power of the whole population of the globe. So the productive forces of 'our small insular kingdom' were vastly augmented.

But such substitution of physical powers for human force arose only in countries 'in which labour is free and unfettered by servile restrictions'. In slave societies progress was consequently stifled, and science choked. 'Both Greece and Rome perished as nations by accumulating slaves. These represented property, and the substitution of human labour by natural forces was a menace to that property. A citizen with slaves crushes invention, lest it should interfere with their value in the market; just as our workmen, two generations ago, destroyed machinery, as being likely to affect the selling price of their labour.' The great empire of Assyria was borne down by the number of its slaves, and 'slavery was the worm that gnawed to the root of Greece's prosperity'. So long as Greece continued in part to honour industry her intellectual development prospered. Rome depended far more on the spoliation of other countries. 'So when Rome, which had become a huge baracoon for slaves, exhausted the wealth that had been won by rapine and conquest, she had no elements for continued prosperity,' for 'slaves are mere machines, and cannot invent; for machines do not invent new ones'. Charlemagne's empire collapsed, in spite of his efforts to apprentice the slaves to crafts and trades, 'but he had not the courage to destroy utterly the accursed thing'. Slavery in the British colonies had likewise exerted a deleterious influence on Britain.

From his consideration of the rôle of liberty in technical and scientific development, Playfair concluded that 'if industries be hampered by selfish rules of unions, whether they be those of masters or men, by which production is retarded, and intelligence and skill discouraged, the industries must languish and die in those places deprived of a natural liberty'.

Following Bacon, he observed: 'You can neither create forces nor endow anything with properties. All that you can do is to convert and combine them into utilities. If you do this with knowledge, you are saved the dismal failures of ignorance; but if you try to use powers for your own purposes without understanding them, the invariable operation of law is shown in the punishment of your presumption. This is the cause of the heavy mortality and disease which follow in the wake of civilization.'

The English recoiled with horror from the site of Hindoos crushed to death under the wheels of their Juggernaut, but 'they think little of the far more terrible sacrifices of victims daily crushed to death by wheels and waggons in our overcrowded streets'. Playfair pointed out that the casualties from this and other kinds of violent death in peacetime exceeded those of the worst wars. Then he instanced the effect of ignoring medical and scientific knowledge. In consequence of this, Britain 'has 110,000 lives ruthlessly sacrificed every year, while 220,000 are needlessly sick all the year round'. Why? Because 'our systems of education are based on the refinement and embellishment of an existence which we are never taught how to preserve'.

Playfair expressed these views nearly a century ago.

LORD PLAYFAIR

IX

Science and the State

In 1885, Playfair made *Science and the State* the subject of his presidential address to the British Association for the Advancement of Science, which met in Aberdeen in that year. This was thirty-four years after his Introductory Lecture, at the School of Mines. He found that science was still lagging in Britain. He attributed this to the 'deficient interest taken in it by the middle and upper classes'. The working classes, on the other hand, were being roused from their indifference. He found the proof of this in contemporary political developments. Professors Stuart, Roscoe, Maskelyne and Rücker had been selected by the working class as candidates in the next general election. Even 'such a humble representative of science' as himself had been invited by more than a dozen working-class constituencies to be their candidate.

He did not doubt that before long a Ministry of Education 'would be created as a nucleus' around which the various necessary educational developments would crystallize. In view of the increasing importance of science to the national interests, its almost total exclusion from the education of the upper and middle classes was little less than a national misfortune. The working classes were in fact receiving better instruction in science than the middle classes. This was increasing the difficulty of the children of the latter in obtaining employment.

Playfair frankly regarded the public schools as the trainers of the ruling class. They were to produce administrators, whereas the schools of the middle class were to train executives. It was essential that the latter, at least, should have a knowledge of science. Playfair's reorganization of the Civil Service into administrative and executive closely reflected his view of the public and grammar schools respectively.

W. H. Perkin, the founder of the synthetic and modern chemical industry, had raised the question of why, when this new scientific industry had been invented in England, the lead in its later development had passed to Germany.

The answer is that 'Our systems of education are still too narrow for the increasing struggle of life'. One of the most serious difficulties was that there was widespread lack of perception of the situation. Faraday had remarked that 'our school-boys when they come out of school, are ignorant of their ignorance at the end of all that education'. This was in fact the condition of nearly all the nation with regard to science.

There was an absence of grasp of the magnitude of the financial provision required for an adequate system of education in science. The Treasury would be astounded if it were told to provide for London, with its population of four millions, as many scientific laboratories as Strassburg, with its population of 104,000.

Playfair said that if the Government were to provide laboratories purely for scientific research, they would not be successful, and they would injure science if they failed. It would be much better if the new laboratories were built in universities. At the time, even Oxford and Cambridge, which had done so much in adding laboratories and scientific staff, were still in quantity behind the standards of a second-rate German university.

He recommended the foundation by the Government of new science chairs in the universities. These new chairs should be 'for the sake of science and not merely for the teaching of the professions', and they would 'enable the poorer universities to take their part in the advancement of knowledge'.

For the elucidation of the relations between science and industry, Playfair appealed once more to the history of science. The slow progress of early science was due to experiments being made by trial and error to meet the needs of man. 'Then an experiment was less a questioning of Nature than an exercise on the mind of the experimentalist. Egypt, Greece, Rome and Arabia accumulated much real science, and the results of Greek science gradually filtered through the Romans and Arabians to fertilize the soil of Europe. Even in the dark ages, 'substantial though slow progress was made'.

The alchemists accumulated a knowledge of the properties of bodies. In the fifteenth century, Eck de Sulbach made a compound by heating mercury with air. Then he decomposed the compound further by heating. In the hands of Priestley and Lavoisier, this became one of the crucial experiments in science. By the end of the fifteenth century many important manufactures were based on empirical experiments. Around these, 'scientific conceptions were slowly concreting'.

The historical perspective prompted him to observe that 'the engines of Watt and Stephenson will yield in their turn to more economical motors; still they have already expanded the wealth, resources, and even the territories of England, more than all the battles fought by her soldiers, or all the treaties negotiated by her diplomatists.'

But 'our not very distant descendants will have to face the problem—What will be the condition of England without coal? The answer to that question depends upon the intellectual development of the nation at that time. . . .'

It may be that the situation will be saved by the importation of coal from Australia, or oil from Russia or America. But to be able to make effective use of fuel more expensive through the cost of transport, the technological efficiency of the nation must be higher than the average. Whether this has been brought about will depend on the intelligence of Government policy, and supposes 'that future Governments in England will have more enlightened views as to the value of science than past Governments have possessed'.

He pointed out that Solomon had said that 'They that hate instruction love death,' and Jules Simon had observed that 'That nation which most educates her people will become the greatest nation, if not to-day, certainly tomorrow.'

How was the necessary public opinion in support of science to be created? In ancient Greece, education was conducted in the vernacular, not in dead languages. It was necessary to create the corresponding interest in modern knowledge in living languages in the universities of our day. If the taste for science were created there, our scientists would be 'as numerous as our statesmen and orators'.

It was not possible to carry out important reforms without the support of the people. 'Statesmen, without a following of the people who share their views and back their work, would be feeble indeed. But while England has never lacked leaders in science, they have too few followers to risk a rapid march. We might create an army to support our generals in science, as Germany has done, and as France is now doing if education in this country would only mould itself to the needs of a scientific age.'

Playfair was speaking from the depth of a lifetime's experience.

He had learned that the future of science was not only a scientific question, it was even more a political one. It depended on making the correct political judgments, and acquiring the political power to carry them out.

'The public weal requires that a large number of scientific men should belong to the community. This is necessary because science has impressed its character upon the age in which we live, and as science is not stationary but progressive, men are required to advance its boundaries, acting as pioneers in the onward march of States. Human progress is so identified with scientific thought, both in its conception and realization, that it seems as if they were alternative terms in the history of civilization.

'Nevertheless, the divorce of culture and science, which the present state of education in this country tends to produce, is deeply to be deplored, because a cultural intelligence adds greatly to the development of the scientific faculty.'

How much more the world owed to Newton and Cavendish than to Erasmus! The intellectual result of Newton's work was vastly more important than the practical advantages it brought. The recent acceptance of evolution in biology had had a like effect in producing a far profounder intellectual change in human thought than any mere impulse of industrial development. Hence 'Abstract discovery in science is then the true foundation upon which the superstructure of modern civilization is built; and the man who would take part in it should study science and if he can, advance it for its own sake and not for its applications.'

Playfair's insight into pure science remained as fresh as into applied science, in spite of his long preoccupation with politics, administration and education. In 1891 he took part in the fiftieth anniversary of the founding of the Chemical Society, of which he had been one of the founders. His teacher, Graham, had been the first president, and other members were Liebig, then the pre-eminent chemist in the world; Dalton, 'who did as much for chemistry as Kepler did for astronomy'; Faraday, Grove and Joule.

These names showed that chemistry was actively cultivated in England. 'But it required association to bring the chemists together; it required association to encourage young men in research, and to give them that support which union among scientific men always adds to the promotion of investigation.'

Playfair then glanced back into the history of chemistry, and this inspired him to look forward into its future. 'There are periods of great activity in the progress of every science, and that has been manifested during the period terminating in our jubilee. When the Society meets to celebrate its centenary, what a different chemistry it is likely to be from the chemistry of to-day! Already analysis has led to synthesis, yet we know very little with regard to the processes that go on in organic bodies. With regard to the elements, we are beginning to doubt what they are, and even to hope for their resolution. When we find such an important law as the one that the properties of the elements are periodic functions of their atomic weights, what a field is thrown open for investigation! It is a field of discovery the borders of which we have scarcely yet crossed. The motions of atoms may ultimately be known to us, and even the ultimate elements themselves. We call them elements still, because they have a certain fixity, and we are at present unable to decompose them. But recollect that sometimes there comes a man who changes the whole features of a science. What did Newton do for astronomy? . . . we may hope that during the next fifty years there will arise a chemical Newton, who will enable us to know far more than we now know, who will bring under one general law the motions of atoms, and even the rupture of those which we now call elements simply because they have acquired a fixity in the order of things, and are able to resist changes in the struggle for existence. Let us have hope in the future. Veterans like myself and Grove will not live to see these great discoveries, but some of our younger men will participate in the chemistry of the future, and will look back with interest to the chemists of the fifty years we are now celebrating. There is no heart here so cold as to doubt the rapid and continued progress of our science.'

Thus not only had Playfair in his early years proposed, and in his later years established, the scholarship system by which Rutherford came to England, but also forecast in his old age the advent of the man himself, and the atomic physics which he created.

Playfair's splendid insight had comparatively little effect in his own day, and its profundity only began to infuse public understanding more than half a century later, through the effects of two world wars. What were the reasons for this? Some of them are to be found in his views on political economy.

X

Science Invention and Labour

In 1888, Playfair discoursed on 'The Displacement of Labour by Modern Inventions' and 'Industrial Competition'. He ascribed the universal depression which had existed during the previous fifteen years in all machine-using countries to two causes. The first was the improvements in machinery which had produced great changes in the speed and economy of distribution. He ascribed the change in speed particularly to the electrical discoveries and inventions of Oersted, Faraday and Wheatstone, which had made almost instantaneous communication of information possible. He mentioned incidentally that he had counted all of them among his personal friends.

Economy of transport had been particularly advanced by the development of the compound marine steam engine, at about the same time as his friend and collaborator, Joule had measured the mechanical equivalent of heat. This had provided the basis for a proper understanding of thermodynamics, and the economical use of energy.

The second cause was the effects of the improvement of productive machinery. He instanced the improvement in the production of iron and ammonia, following on the researches of Bunsen and himself on the blast furnace in 1845.

Bessemer's blast furnace for steel-making destroyed the capital invested in the puddling furnaces for making wrought iron, and threw 39,000 workmen out of that occupation. As many of them were skilled workers, they found other employment comparatively quickly.

These, and other illustrations, showed how largely modern inventions had increased production and displaced labour. Ultimately, however, educated working-men benefited by the changes, because increased production absorbed skilled labour and paid higher wages for it. Ignorant workers had a bad time, because the demand for unintelligent labour was constantly decreasing.

'Every invention produces social change and dislocation of

labour. The application of the invention demands higher intelligence in labour, so the labourers of low intelligence go to the wall.' It was the essence of invention to displace unskilled labour, and replace it by machinery, and all machinery tended to evolve from complexity to simplicity. Workmen required a superior intelligence to adapt themselves to the changes which continually arose through the economy of labour.

It was scarcely necessary to say that this cold-blooded discussion with regard to labour of quantity and labour of quality gave little sympathy to the unemployed. But 'Science is essentially colourless and impersonal'.

Some of the unemployed had actually invited Playfair to become the president of a European association for the destruction of machinery. 'They point out that the unemployed armies of Europe might be used for this purpose with economy and advantage to labour. Ah! gentlemen, do not laugh; these labourers of quantity are in this condition because they have no educated intelligence. . . .' People must remain in a low state of civilization until they acquire 'that labour of quality which is essential to give them entrance into the new forms of production'.

It was possible for labour to be displaced so rapidly that the industries of a nation may actually perish.

The effect of inventions was to raise the wages of those labourers who are able to carry on the industry under the new conditions.

The depression of the last fifteen years had nothing to do with Free Trade. It was the result of the failure of the world to accommodate itself 'to the wonderful changes which science has produced in the modes of production and in the exchanges of commerce'. This could not be done without a comprehensive development of scientific and technical education for all classes.

Playfair foresaw that industrial and technical development would occur throughout the world. 'An industrial revolution will take place when China breaks down her Chinese wall of exclusiveness; when Russia opens Central Asia and completes the Trans-Siberian Railway; when the Euphrates is paralleled by a railway; and when Africa fails to resist advancing civilization. None of these events are impossible, and some are in prospect of realization. . . .'

His understanding of the social relations of science and technology gave him insight into the future.

He expounded his views on the relations between science, technology, and economics in a still more pointed way in his speech 'On the Wages and Hours of Labour' delivered in 1891 to his working-class constituents in Leeds. The British working class was in a ferment, typified by the great dock strike of 1889. The ferment was alive in Playfair's constituents, and he had to address himself to the questions which it prompted.

He proposed to allude to what he thought were the fundamental causes which have produced the general agitation of labour questions throughout civilized communities, and led to 'the extreme views as to State interference with labour', as well as to the desire to make adjustments to the changed condition of labour.

He told his working-class audience that he would speak to them in the spirit of Burke's words to the Bristol electors: 'Your representative owes you not his industry only, but his judgment, and he betrays instead of serving you if he sacrifices it to your opinion.' He would not attempt to discuss 'the extreme views of Socialists, as they have no interest for a body of skilled working men', such as he had the honour to address.

'The chief fact is that machinery, applied to production and distribution, has largely encroached on the individualism of labour by making each man a small part of the general machine of industry, through the division of labour. In old times a workman knew the whole of his craft, and could work skilfully in any part of its details, so he loved and honoured his work, and was proud of his individual skill as a workman. When production became enlarged by machinery, the division of labour confined him to one small corner of the industry, while he was reduced to be a part of a great industrial machine, in which he largely lost his individuality, and might know little of the principles or practice of the industry in which he worked. Then industry was rapidly changing, in consequence of which labour experienced constant dislocations requiring new adjustments in its application.

'Hence arose the need of technical education to adapt a man to the constant changes in progress. Such an education was needed to restore the pride and dignity of the workman by giving him an intelligent knowledge of his calling, and restoring to him that individualism which he had lost. It is, fortunately, only in great factories that the great subdivision of labour acts so strongly against individualism, and they contain only one-tenth, or at most two-tenths, of the labourers. The other nine-tenths, less affected by subdivision of labour, still depend upon their individual capacity, skilled aptitudes, and manual dexterity. Not only technical education, but also the combination of workmen into Trades Unions, are necessary in order that they may understand and enforce the proper relations of capital and consumption to labour, and that they may aid in the direction of those forces which work together in social dynamics.'

Working men tended to underestimate the rôle of increased production, either by better methods, or still more from increased efficiency of working men in applying these methods, in raising wages. Capital was stored-up labour, which included high organization, good management, and great mercantile powers. It was one of the functions of trade unions to ensure that profits on capital were not too high.

When he was asked whether he was in favour of a limited working day, he replied, Yes, if the trade unions favoured it. But he would not vote for the establishment of an eight-hour day by law. 'I think that State interference with working men, in regard to the free use of their own time and the earning of their own wages, will result in much harm to them, and may even throw back the progress of the working classes for a generation.'

This was because the State is an assemblage of men and women who can take care of themselves. 'The State looks after the interests of all of us; Trades Unions look after the interests of some of us.' The two interests are not necessarily or usually the same.

It was in the interests of all that the weak should be protected against the strong. It was in the interests of all that health should be protected, because disease attacked everyone indiscriminately. It was in the interests of all that education should be 'universal, compulsory and efficient, because the competition of labour throughout the world has resolved itself into a competition of educated intelligence, and will do so increasingly in the future'.

On these subjects of 'general welfare the State has socialized itself'. But it had gone a long way further than some people liked, and it should be very cautious of overstepping the line. It was a very grave demand that the State should intervene between masters and men in their freedom of contract. It would be impossible for the State to intervene in the management of trade, because if it did so, it would become responsible for the success or failure of each particular undertaking.

'The true object of government is not to promote special industries or special interests, but simply to protect each individual, so that he shall use his powers for the benefit of himself and not for the benefit of another, leaving as much freedom as possible to the individual to secure his own happiness. It is a mark of loss of independence of character and self-reliance, when any class of men ask the State to make laws for the limitation of time or the equalization of wages, by which the idle and incapable shall obtain as much pay as workers of character and capacity. Each man should have freedom as to the use of his time and the earning of his own wages.'

He agreed with Burke that 'To provide for us in our necessities is not in the power of Government. It would be a vain presumption in statesmen to think they can do it. The people maintain them and not they the people. It is in the power of Government to prevent much evil; it can do very little good in this, or perhaps in anything else.'

He pointed out that during the previous half-century wages had risen by 20 to 50 per cent. There was a growing amelioration in the standard of living of skilled artisans. The luxuries of one generation became the comforts of the next, and the necessities of the third.

'I assert that industrialism is the chief factor in social dynamics, and that you should depend on yourselves to work out your own salvation.'

This speech did not go down perfectly with his working-class audience.

Playfair repeatedly expressed his awareness of the organizational nature of science. It proceeded through cooperation of men organized in societies, in nations and internationally. He was in unresolvable difficulties over his recognition, on the one hand that science is an organized social activity, while on the other he believed that individualism was the motive of all social development.

He had to accept individualist political economy, or he could have no place in the established politics of the day. He could not otherwise be a Liberal candidate for Parliament. But his ideology was incompatible with the planned development of science which could only be carried out by the State.

The political principles to which he had to adhere limited the possibility of doing what was required for the progress of science. Hence the effects of his scientific and technical insight inevitably failed to be in proportion to its profundity.

Playfair died on May 29th, 1898, at his home at Onslow Gardens in London, and was buried beside other members of the Playfair family at St. Andrews.

The Prince Consort

1819–1861

I

A Plan for Science

THE PRINCE CONSORT was one of the most influential statesmen of British science. As Chancellor of the University of Cambridge in the middle of the nineteenth century, he fostered the internal movement for the reform of its science teaching, which ultimately led to the foundation of the Cambridge school of physics, and its modern glories.

As President of the Royal College of Chemistry, he had the decisive part in bringing A. W. Hofmann to England, whose teaching of organic chemistry provided the environment in which W. H. Perkin discovered the first synthetic dye, and founded modern chemical industry.

As President of the Royal Society of Arts he conceived, in conjunction with Cole, the project for the Exhibition of 1851. Under the Prince's inspiration a large part of the profits of £186,436, and the further sum of £150,000 granted by Parliament, were devoted to the advancement of science. He envisaged an organized national system of scientific and technical teaching, research and application, with a central headquarters.

A century later, this is still far from being completely realized, but the complex of scientific institutions at South Kensington in London, including the Imperial College of Science and Technology, has arisen largely as a result of his original inspiration and persevering promotion. He was convinced that scientific and technical education were essential for the future prosperity of the country. He regarded the Great Exhibition itself as a sort of visual aid in technical education. He encouraged the establishment of technical education by the State, through the new Department of Science and Art, founded to carry forward the movements accelerated by the Exhibition.

How and why did the Prince have so much influence? It arose from many causes. One of these was that he really cared for science, and especially for its application. The Editor of his *Speeches* said that 'he loved knowledge on account of what it could do for mankind; and no man of our time sympathized more intimately with that splendid outburst of Bacon, where the great Chancellor exclaims—"knowledge is not a couch, whereupon to rest a searching and restless spirit; or a terrace for a wandering and variable mind to walk up and down with a fair prospect; or a tower of state for a proud mind to raise itself upon; or a fort or commanding ground for strife and contention; or a shop for profit or sale; but a rich storehouse for the glory of the Creator, and the relief of man's estate. But this is that which will indeed dignify and exalt knowledge, if contemplation and action may be more nearly and straitly conjoined and united together than they have been; or conjunction like unto that of the two highest planets—Saturn, the planet of rest and contemplation, and Jupiter, the planet of civil society and action."'

In his Presidential Address to the British Association in 1859, he referred to the Association as being devoted to the *inductive* sciences, that is, to 'all that are not approached by the deductive method of investigation'. In the inductive process we proceeded by 'taking nothing on trust, nothing for granted, but reasoning upwards from the meanest fact established, and making every step sure before going one beyond it, like the engineer in his approaches to a fortress. We thus gain ultimately a roadway, a ladder by which even a child may, almost without knowing it, ascend to the summit of truth and obtain that immensely wide and extensive view which is spread below the feet of the astonished beholder. This road has been shown us by the great Bacon; and who can contemplate the prospects which it opens without almost falling into a trance similar to that in which he allowed his imagination to wander over future ages of discovery!'

The Prince expounded his views on the rôle of science with particular force in his speeches on the occasion of the foundation of the Birmingham and Midland Institute in 1855. He expressed his gratification at hearing that the Exhibition of 1851 had stimulated a keener and more comprehensive study of the principles by which the exercise of man's productive powers is controlled. He regarded the founding of the Institute as one of the first public acknowledgements of an important principle which was destined to play a great part in the future development of

THE PRINCE CONSORT

the nation: 'the introduction of science and art as the unconscious regulators of productive industry'.

He wanted, as usual, to stimulate the idea of extending the scientific development of industry, without antagonizing the ideological principles of private individual enterprise. He used the thought of Bacon, that in any manufacturing operation 'it is not *we* who operate, but the laws of nature, which we set in operation'.

It was therefore of the highest importance that we should discover and know these laws: that is, that we should pursue science. Without such knowledge we are condemned either to do merely as our fathers did, or we try things at random, or we trust to ourselves alone to discover improvements.

One person can only try a limited number of experiments in a comparatively short period of time. The single mind, however ingenious, can work only with limited materials, and cannot therefore proceed very far. It is necessary for the laws of nature to be discovered by *science*, which is a cooperative effort of many minds, and then placed at the disposal of the producer for his aid. Hence no pursuit is too insignificant not to be capable of becoming the subject both of a science and an art.

'No human pursuits make any material progress until science is brought to bear upon them. We have seen accordingly many of them slumber for centuries upon centuries; but from the moment science has touched them with her magic wand, they have sprung forward, and taken strides which amaze, and almost awe, the beholder.

'Look at the transformation which has gone on around us since the laws of gravitation, electricity, magnetism, and the expansive power of heat have become known to us. It has altered our whole state of existence—one might say, the whole face of the globe. We owe this to science, and to science alone; and she had other treasures in store for us, if we will but call her to our assistance.

'Far be it from me to underrate the creative power of genius, or to treat shrewd common sense as worthless without knowledge. But nobody will tell me that the same genius would not take an incomparably higher flight, if supplied with all the means which knowledge can impart; or that common sense does not become, in fact, only truly powerful when in possession of the materials upon which judgment is to be exercised.'

The study of the laws which govern the Universe is therefore our bounden duty. Our academies and seats of learning had rather arbitrarily devoted themselves to mathematics and grammar. These are very important, but there are other branches of knowledge that we cannot do without. For example, there were the laws that govern the human mind, the subject of logic and metaphysics; the laws which govern the body and its connection with the soul (physiology and psychology); those which govern human society (politics, jurisprudence and political economy); and many others.

Birmingham was a manufacturing city, so the new Institute should devote itself mainly to mechanics, physics and chemistry; and the fine arts in painting, sculpture and architecture. This would soon have beneficial effects 'upon our national powers of production'. Other parts of the country would wish to emulate Birmingham, so that he lived 'in hope that all these institutions will some day find a central point of union, and thus complete their national organization'.

As ever, after paying every respect to private enterprise, he inculcated his message that the nation should organize its scientific activities, and their application, on a national basis.

The Prince had not a scintillating intellect, which was one of the reasons why he was so long underrated; but he had a rather profound understanding. He had the intelligence to grasp the general drift of scientific matters, the position to exert influence, the industry to master details, and the will to act. Of these qualities, the last has probably received the least attention, and is the most significant.

Why did this young man (he was born in 1819, married in 1840 and died in 1861), the consort of the Queen of the then most powerful country in the world, with infinite distractions, choose to devote so much laborious effort to the development of science? Light on this question is thrown by historical circumstances. The Prince belonged to the family of Saxe-Coburg-Gotha, one of the numerous German ducal families, which cultivated the extension of monarchy as a principle.

The Prince's uncle Leopold, who became the first King of the Belgians, was one of their ablest members. Leopold's son, the Prince's cousin, became the founder of the Belgian Congo. The young Prince Albert had been carefully educated under the supervision of Leopold's physician and adviser Stockmar. He was inculcated with the German notion of professional monarchy, and taught that sober hard work was essential for strengthening the monarchical principle.

He was a tall, handsome youth, only four months younger than Princess Victoria, the heiress to the British throne. He had a kind, earnest disposition, which had been strengthened by the thorough German Protestant tutoring. Leopold and Stockmar had thought it unwise to send him to the University of Berlin, the home of reckless political projects, so he went to Brussels, where he could be educated under the eye of the King, his uncle.

L. A. J. Quetelet was engaged as his tutor, and instructed him in 'the study of higher mathematics, and the application of the law of probabilities to social and natural phenomena'. The subject remained a favourite one with the Prince. Quetelet dedicated his *Du Système social, et les Lois qui le regissent*, published in 1848, to him.

In his last important public speech, made as President of the meeting of the International Statistical Congress in 1860, he referred to Quetelet as the Congress's first president, 'from whom I had the privilege, now twenty-four years ago, to receive my first instruction in the higher branches of mathematics—one who has so successfully directed his great abilities to the application of the science to those social phenomena, the discovery of the governing laws of which can only be approached by the accumulation and reduction of statistical facts'.

He discussed the distrust of the science of statistics; the bearing or lack of it, on the problem of free-will and determinism; its inspiration of 'that part of Mathematical Science called the calculation of probabilities'. and its establishment of 'the theory that in the natural world there exists no certainties at all, but only probabilities'.

The collection and comparison of 'the statistics of the increase of population, of marriages, births and deaths, of emigration, disease, crime, education and occupation, of the products of agriculture, mining, commerce, and finance' became 'an essential element in the investigation of our social condition'. It was necessary to compare these same classes of facts for different countries, and under varying political and religious conditions, occupation, race, and climate. Further, these should be compared at different times, for 'it is only the element of time, in the last instance, which enables us to test progress or regress—that is to say, life'.

He drew attention to the need for improvement in most branches of British statistics. 'An annual digest of the Statistics of the United Kingdom, of our widely scattered colonies, and of our vast Indian Empire,' could not fail to be a source from which most important results could be elicited.

He dealt with the need for definitions upon which statistics could be usefully founded. 'What is meant by a house, a family, an adult, an educated or an uneducated person; by murder, manslaughter, and so on?'

He hinted at the desirability of a decimal monetary system. 'We fancy here that our Pound, as the largest available unit, with its Florin, offers great advantages, particularly if further subdivided decimally.'

He would be happy indeed if their noble gathering should lay the solid foundation of an edifice, necessarily of slow construction, and requiring generations of 'laborious and persevering exertion', which promoted human happiness, 'by leading to the discovery of those eternal laws upon which that universal happiness is dependent!'

Expressed more than one hundred years ago, by the Consort of such a Queen, and such a woman, as Victoria, these were far from contemptible thoughts.

After leaving the instruction of Quetelet, the Prince was sent to Bonn, then a new university founded under the influence of the liberal Wilhelm von Humboldt. The Prince had learned an indelible lesson from Quetelet, but he had personal talents of other kinds; he had a gift for mimicking people. His official biographer says that at Bonn his 'talent for mimicry and the grotesque was often exercised for the amusement of his companions'. His 'excellent memory, and mastery of the various subjects dealt with, enabled him either to reproduce whole passages' from the professorial lectures, 'or to improvise excellent imitations of them. His powers in this direction, which appear to have been very freely exercised at the University, were never lost'.

The common picture of the Prince as a slow-witted Teutonic bore is misleading. He made jokes about bores in his Presidential Address to the British Association. To the King of Prussia, a fortnight before the Great Exhibition was opened, he wrote:

'Mathematicians have calculated that the Crystal Palace will blow down in the first strong gale; engineers that the galleries would crash in and destroy the visitors; political economists have prophesied a scarcity of food in London owing to the vast concourse of people; doctors that owing to so many races coming into contact with each other the Black Death of the Middle Ages would make its appearance, as it did after the Crusades; moralists that England would be infected by all the scourges of the civilized and uncivilized world; theologians that this second Tower of Babel would draw upon it the vengeance of an offended God.

'I can give no guarantee against all these perils, nor am I in a position to assume responsibility for the possibly menaced lives of your Royal relatives. But I can promise that the protection from which Victoria and I benefit will be extended to their persons—for I presume we also are on the list of victims.'

The Prince entered Bonn University about six months after Karl Marx left it to go to Berlin, for the very reasons that the Prince had not been allowed to go there. Marx desired to proceed to its more exciting intellectual atmosphere. The Prince and Marx lived almost at the same time in the Bonn cultural climate.

Soon after Queen Victoria's accession, Leopold and Stockmar were active in promoting the marriage between the young Queen and the still younger Prince. When Albert was sounded, he dwelt on the disadvantages as well as the advantages of the position he would have as consort. With his sense and good education he saw his position very clearly, and acted with cool but determined judgment. He agreed to the proposal, accepted Victoria's hand, and cautiously started to increase his power.

Albert found his position even more difficult than he had foreseen. The German theory of professional monarchy was unknown among the British governing class, who regarded the king not as a member of a special ruling caste but the first aristocrat among themselves.

Albert was never at ease with the British aristocracy. He found it impossible to regard himself as the first of English gentlemen. He could not share their avocations and pleasures. The attitude of the more bucolic peers was represented by the reference of the contemporary Lord Lonsdale to the Prince's friends as 'these damn'd scientific blackguards'. He grew into a big, heavy, active man, profoundly imbued with German ideas, who in spite of his position and influence always felt alien. In this he was not unlike Cherwell.

A good deal of the Prince's apparent dullness was due to his perpetual repression, in order to adapt himself to his very delicate personal, social and political position. The least error of judgment or action with regard to this brought instant reaction from the Queen, his wife, on the one hand, and the British ruling aristocracy, jealous of its power, on the other. His flat sleepy appearance was in part a mask, under which he started to secure some real political power.

He regarded the acquisition of *de facto* monarchical authority as his first duty, but was unable to do this by becoming, as it were, English. As he could not immediately participate in politics, he undertook useful tasks which the aristocracy regarded as politically harmless, such as fostering art and science.

In 1841 Sir Robert Peel became Prime Minister. He was the very able and intelligent son of a textile magnate, and did not belong to the aristocracy. The Prince found social relations with him far easier. Peel gave him his first opening in public life by offering him the Presidency of the Royal Commission on the Fine Arts in 1841.

In the autumn of 1850, when the Prince was striving to make the preparations for the Great Exhibition in the following year a success, he addressed a meeting at York of the mayors of the chief cities and towns of the United Kingdom, to secure their support and stimulate their enthusiasm. He referred with heartfelt regard to Peel, who had died through an accident some months earlier, the last act of whose life had been to attend the Royal Commission which was making the arrangements for the Exhibition.

'The constitution of Sir Robert Peel's mind was peculiarly that of a statesman, and of an English statesman: he was liberal from feeling, but conservative on principle. Whilst his impulse drove him to foster progress, his sagacious mind and great experience showed him how easily the whole machinery of a state and of society is deranged, and how important, but how difficult also, it is to direct its further development in accordance with its fundamental principles, like organic growth in nature. It was peculiar to him, that in great things, as in small, all the difficulties and objections occurred to him first; and he would anxiously consider them, pause, and warn against rash resolutions; but having convinced himself, after a long and careful investigation, that a step was not only right to be taken, but of the practical mode also of safely taking it, it became to him a necessity and a duty to take it: all his caution and apparent timidity changed into courage and power of action, and at the same time readiness cheerfully to make any personal sacrifice which its execution might demand.'

As the 'hungry forties' wore on, social conditions in Britain and Europe became more and more menacing to monarchy. Prince Albert became deeply perturbed, and almost desperate with frustration, as he lacked the power to intervene in support of harassed relatives.

He turned with redoubled energy to those channels in which he could work, anxious to do everything possible to demonstrate that monarchy could have a useful purpose. Together with action for bettering the condition of the poor, he concentrated on art, science and education. Peel advised him in 1847 to accept an invitation to stand for the Chancellorship of the University of Cambridge. He was elected in a hard-fought contest by a majority of only 116 out of a poll of 1,790.

He entered into his duties with great energy. Babbage, John Herschel, Peacock, Adam Sedgwick and others had been campaigning for a reform of Cambridge science teaching, which was essentially that of an earlier age, and based on geometry and astronomy. These had been the most important sciences in the mercantilist period, and had been raised to the apex of their greatness by Newton. Cambridge science was out of touch with the needs of the new industrial age.

The Prince started by asking for complete details of current teaching. Among many papers, he received one from Whewell, who, in 1841, when the Mastership of Trinity College, Cambridge, had become vacant on the death of Dr. Christopher Wordsworth, had written to Peel, asking for that position. Peel had replied: 'It will always be satisfactory both to you and to me to reflect that I named you to the Queen for the Mastership of Trinity College without solicitation, and previously to an expression of a wish on your part. . . .'

The internal Cambridge movement for reform was animated by Liberals but was under Tory control. In the disturbed political conditions of England and of Europe at this period, the

British ruling class could not allow the Tories and the instruments of the Monarchy to be left in charge of the reforming of the ancient university, so in 1850 the Whig Prime Minister Lord John Russell brusquely appointed a Royal Commission for this purpose. The Prince was rather hurt, but there is little doubt that if the reforming had not been taken over by the Commission, the right wing of the Tories would have frustrated the Prince's policy.

The Prince studied Whewell's paper and the others, and then sent them all to Peel for his opinion. Again, the masterful Master was put in his place. In his reply, Peel remarked: 'I think Dr. Whewell is quite wrong in his position—that mathematical knowledge is entitled to *paramount* consideration, because it is conversant with undisputable truths—that such departments of science as Chemistry are not proper subjects of academical instruction. . . .'

For Peel's family of textile manufacturers, chemistry was naturally the most important science. Peel argued that chemistry should not be ignored, 'because there is controversy respecting important facts and principles, and constant accession of information from new discoveries—and danger that students may lose their reverence for Professors, when they discover that the Professors cannot maintain doctrines as indisputable as mathematical or arithmetical truths.

'The Doctor's assumption, that *a century should pass* before new discoveries in science are admitted into the course of academical instruction, exceeds in absurdity anything which the bitterest enemy of University Education would have imputed to its advocates. Are the students at Cambridge to hear nothing of electricity? . . .'

Peel gave sage encouragement, and the Prince doggedly stood his ground. In words recalling those of Sir William Hamilton, the Scottish philosopher so enraged by Whewell, he said that 'the road to profit, honour and distinction being open only through the study of mathematics and classics, the offer of any lectures on other sciences will lead to no result, unless the system of examination be altered'.

One of the ultimate results of the reform movement was the introduction by Clerk Maxwell, as an examiner at Cambridge, of questions on heat and electricity into the mathematics papers, and the gradual orientation of scientific ability towards physics, a paramount science of the new industrial age.

The strength of the tradition supported by Whewell is illustrated by Clerk Maxwell's experience with the mathematician Todhunter, the editor of Whewell. Maxwell asked him whether he would like to see an experimental demonstration of conical refraction. 'No,' he replied, 'I have been teaching it all my life, and I do not want to have my ideas upset.'

The Prince worked in the main by finding out what should be done, securing able assistants, and helping them to carry it out. Peel recommended Lyon Playfair to him in 1849, to assist in developing the ideas and carrying out the preparations for the Exhibition of 1851. The Prince was thirty, and Playfair thirty-one. The two young men were of an age, which helped them to understand one another.

The Prince later added to Playfair's other posts a place at Court, which drew from an old courtier the complaint that he was 'A man of low birth, ordinary appearance and uncouth manners.' Playfair's kinswoman, Queen Elizabeth, the wife of George VI, subsequently became the Chancellor of the University of London, which the Prince Consort and Playfair between them did so much to develop.

One source of the Prince's peculiar influence was his detachment from English ideology. His distinctively different German education and ideas gave him an independent standard of comparison, which enabled him to see many things about the English scene to which Englishmen themselves, even when much more intellectually gifted, were generally blind.

His German sense of order, organization and thoroughness made him sharply aware of the deficiencies of English society and civilization in these qualities, and his position gave him the power of drawing attention to them with some effect.

Whenever he drew attention to the need of these qualities in the development of British science, and other aspects of British life, he was almost desperately careful to do homage first to the features upon which the English society of the day prided itself. For instance, in laying the foundation stone for the Great Grimsby Docks in 1849, he said with emphasis: 'This work has been undertaken, like almost all the national enterprises of this great country, by *private* exertion, with *private* capital, and at *private* risk. . . .'

In his speech at the Mayor of London's Banquet in March 1850, in support of the preparations for the Great Exhibition, he said that they were living in 'a period of most wonderful transition', towards an end to which all history pointed: '*the realization of the unity of mankind*'. This unity was '*the result and product*' of the conflict between nations with different characteristics and 'antagonistic qualities'.

He followed this Hegelian thought with a paean to the social influences of science. 'The distances which separated the different nations and parts of the globe are rapidly vanishing before the achievements of modern invention, and we can traverse them with incredible ease; the languages of all nations are known, and their acquirement placed within the reach of everybody; thought is communicated with the rapidity, and even by the power, of lightning. On the other hand, the *great principle of division of labour*, which may be called the moving power of civilization, is being extended to all branches of science, industry, and art.'

Knowledge which was formerly kept secret was now made at once the property of the community at large by 'the publicity of the present day'. The products of all the world were put at our disposal, for us to choose the cheapest and the best, and the powers of production were 'intrusted to the stimulus of *competition and capital*'.

After this, and other remarks which might have been almost a reply on behalf of contemporary capitalism to the threatening ideas of the *Communist Manifesto* published three years before, he went on:

'Gentlemen—my original plan had been to carry out this undertaking with the help of the Society of Arts of London which had long and usefully laboured in this direction, and by the means of private capital and enterprise. You have wished it otherwise, and declared that it was a work which the British people as a whole ought to undertake. I at once yielded to your wishes, feeling that it proceeded from a patriotic, noble, and generous spirit. On *your* courage, perseverance, and liberality the undertaking now entirely depends. I feel the strongest confidence in these qualities of the British people, and I am sure that they will repose confidence in themselves—confidence that they will honourably sustain the contest of emulation, and that they will nobly carry out their proffered hospitality to their foreign competitors.'

Her Majesty's Commissioners for the Exhibition were alive to the innumerable difficulties to be overcome, but all that they required to view the task without any apprehension was '*your confidence in us*', that is, in the State's appointees and apparatus.

After the utmost obeisance to the principles of private enterprise, the Prince diplomatically introduced the idea of state organization and action.

II

Reforming Cambridge

THE rise of industrial society and the Napoleonic Wars exposed the unsuitability of the education provided by Cambridge and Oxford for the new generation of students. At the beginning of the nineteenth century Cambridge was still governed substantially by the statutes laid down for it by Queen Elizabeth in 1570. These had made the heads of colleges officers of the University, and given them great influence in the control of the University. As most of the colleges had been founded by religious bodies in the Middle Ages, primarily to educate men for the Church, they were identified with religion, and with the Church of England, when it became dominant. Even as late as 1830, one-third of the undergraduates at Trinity College, which at that time was relatively so big that it constituted about one-quarter of the University, were qualifying for the Church.

For more than three centuries college and church interests had dominated the university. Students felt their loyalty was to their college, and when, in after life, they inherited estates or became rich, they made bequests to their college rather than the university.

Thus the situation arose that while the colleges became rich enough to provide their fellows who tutored their undergraduates with a satisfactory income, the university was too poor to pay its professors adequately. The income of the Lucasian professor, whose chair had the prestige of having been occupied by Newton, was about £100 a year.

In this situation, professors regarded their position as one of intellectual prestige, and did not take their teaching responsibilities seriously. The colleges reserved teaching for their tutors, and jealously kept as much of it as possible away from the professors. The occupants of some of the university chairs had not given professorial lectures for about a hundred years. Even great creative professors, such as Babbage and Peacock, delivered few or no professorial lectures.

When professors did lecture, the substance of their lectures was generally too advanced or specialized to be of use to undergraduates preparing themselves for examinations. They stayed away from professorial lectures, and they were encouraged by their college tutors to do so.

In the Middle Ages degrees were awarded on disputations, to which examinations were subordinate. According to Queen Elizabeth's statutes, undergraduates had to devote the first year to Rhetoric, the second and third to Dialectics, and the fourth to Philosophy. Mathematics had a subordinate place. In the course of centuries, the priority of the disputation gradually gave place to the examination, which became more and more important, and more and more mathematical.

By the beginning of the nineteenth century the examination had become completely dominant, and its content restricted almost exclusively to mathematics, with a little philosophy. Among the causes of this concentration on mathematics as the core of education was the interest of the college tutors in having a subject of instruction which lent itself to examination purposes. Mathematical knowledge is definite and concise, and of all knowledge is perhaps the most easily tested.

At the same time, it was remarkable that mathematics had become the chief subject of study of undergraduates, the largest section of whom were to become clergymen. It had ousted the classics, and even theology. No doubt the Church felt that it would be safer to superintend the indoctrination of the clergy after they had left the universities.

At the beginning of the century, the advocates of Latin and Greek learning were fighting savagely for equality with mathematics; as for the natural sciences, they were scarcely discussed as a possible medium for degree studies.

The main cause of the prestige of mathematics was its rôle in physical astronomy, which since the great explorations, the Reformation, and the development of mercantilism had become the premier science in England. The seal on its pre-eminence had been set by Isaac Newton, its incomparable professor.

Thus, since the time of Newton, Cambridge had, in response to the movement of social and national interest, and loyalty to her greatest son, concentrated more and more on Newtonian mathematics. A student body consisting largely of intending clergymen was an unsuitable instrument for developing the creative mathematic tradition so powerfully advanced by Newton. This was one of the reasons why, in spite of the idolatrous attention to the subject, its advance languished. The lead in mathematical research passed to the continent of Europe.

The French Revolution and the Anglo-French wars connected with it confirmed the isolation of English mathematics and its Cambridge citadel. Towards the end of the Napoleonic period the condition of mathematics at Cambridge had become grotesque. The students of the time, headed by Babbage, Herschel and Peacock, led the revolt.

The situation was educationally and socially so complex, and so much change was necessary that reform was slow. The antagonistic interests were expressed through political conflict. There were educational reformers who were political radicals and Liberals, and others, generally less radical educationally, who were political Tories.

Whewell and Airy, though moderate reformers, belonged to the Newtonian tradition. Airy applied modern mathematical methods to mechanics and astronomy, the typical Newtonian sciences. Whewell wrote on mechanics, and tried to combine Baconian and Newtonian philosophy. Airy was liberal in politics, but, wrote his eldest son, 'the great secret of his long and successful official career was that he was a good servant and thoroughly understood his position. He never set himself in opposition to his masters, the Admiralty.'

Men like Whewell and Airy, though technically in advance of most of their immediate predecessors, could not carry reform very far. Whewell tried to promote a strictly controlled moderate reform. He was very energetic in working for his objectives. Just as he had not scrupled to ask for the Mastership of Trinity College, which he regarded not only as a personal prize, but a vantage point for promoting his policies, he did not scruple, on the death of the reigning Chancellor of the University in 1847, indirectly to invite the Prince Consort, then twenty-seven years old, to stand for the vacancy.

Whewell wanted to secure his own nominee as Chancellor, and

also to keep out any Whig or Liberal nominee. It was ambiguously represented to the Prince that his election would be virtually uncontested. He was anxious to accept, because of the place it gave him in English educational life, so he gave his consent.

However, the Master and fellows of St. John's College, feeling a march had been stolen on them by their rivals at Trinity, insisted on putting up a rival candidate, a former member of the college, Lord Powis. It soon became obvious that a strong opposition to the Prince's candidature was growing. The prospect of having a German to tell the University what to do was uninviting. Anti-Germans, Anti-Royalists, and Tory reactionaries rallied around Lord Powis.

Opinion in influential circles in this period was reflected by the remark made three years later by the Chancellor of the University of Oxford, the Duke of Wellington, that though the University of Oxford intended to effect every desirable improvement, it did not intend to introduce German methods of education.

All Whig and liberal, and moderate Tory opinion was shocked at the possibility of the University falling into opposition to the Crown which in effect also meant the Government and established authority. The Whig Prime Minister, Lord John Russell, conscious of the strong popular criticism of the Crown and the ruling classes in the intense social unrest of the 'forties', was anxious that no serious conflict should arise between the Crown and the University, and was anxious that the Prince should stand and be elected.

The Prince in his embarrassment consulted, as usual, Sir Robert Peel, who strongly advised him to retain his candidature, contest the election, and accept the Chancellorship. This was in the interests of the Prince himself, and the Tory party.

A large part of the University electorate consisted of country clergymen, who were inclined to reactionary Toryism. The newly constructed railways enabled them to come in large numbers to the University to vote, with the result that the Prince won narrowly by 954 votes to 837.

Immediately after his election, the Prince entered with his customary industry into the duties of his new position. He did not, however, depend on Whewell as his chief source of information; the domineering master found himself snubbed for the second time. The Prince sought his information on the University through the mildly progressive and far more diplomatic Dr. Henry Philpott, Master of St. Catherine's College.

The Prince had himself been educated in a recently established modern university organized on a rational plan. He naïvely supposed that professors as such must have an important place in university teaching, and would determine university policy, intellectually and organizationally. He was astonished by the descriptions of the Cambridge organization and teaching system which were supplied to him. To an educated foreigner like himself, they needed a great deal of expounding and explaining. One of the merits of the Prince was that he was not a Cambridge or Oxford man, and belonged to an equally distinguished but different university tradition.

Unlike most of the members of the English ruling classes, he did not belong to the ancient universities. When he tried to understand and form opinions on the Cambridge system, he was not affected by unspoken arguments arising from old loyalties. Consequently, he had the effect of forcing men like Whewell, who were deeply involved in the old loyalties, to put their cards on the table. Viewed at Cambridge in the Cambridge atmosphere and historical and social situation, these seemed not altogether unreasonable; viewed at Windsor in the perspective of Wilhelm von Humboldt's Bonn, they appeared half-crazy.

With the Prince's encouragement as Chancellor, the Cambridge reformers made a number of progressive proposals. A university committee proposed two new honour examinations; in natural sciences and the moral sciences. The natural sciences honours examination was to include anatomy, physiology, chemistry, botany and geology as subjects, with the science professors as examiners. The professors of mathematics, together with mathematical examiners, were to constitute a board of mathematical studies, with the intention of bringing the subjects of the professors' lectures in closer relation to the material in the examination questions.

The Prince was delighted with these and other substantial proposals, which were passed by the Senate. He noted in his diary in 1848 that his plan for the reform of Cambridge studies had been carried by a large majority.

Superficially, the University seemed to be reforming itself from inside. Lord John Russell and other Whigs doubted whether the proposals would be implemented. They suspected that many in the University regarded them as a blind for delaying tactics. Parliamentary opinion, in the disturbed political situation, remained unconvinced; so he decided to appoint a Royal Commission, which would have the power of effecting the changes from outside, if necessary.

This Commission, to inquire into the State, Discipline, Studies, and Revenues of the University and Colleges of Cambridge, consisted of John Graham, Bishop of Chester; G. Peacock; J. F. W. Herschel; John Romilly and Adam Sedgwick; with W. H. Bateson (the father of the geneticist) as Secretary.

In its Report of 1852, the Commission confirmed what the Prince regarded as his reforms of 1848. The Commissioners included in their Report expressions of opinion that they clearly recognized the nature of the causes of the University's condition. The progress of that 'great innovator', Time, and 'the operation of social causes little within her control'. had made the University to be 'left out of her true position, and become imperfectly adapted to the present wants of the country, so as to stand in need of external help to bring about some useful reforms'.

They described themselves as 'following rather than originating' the 'opening source of amelioration', represented by the internal movement for reform headed by the Prince.

'The long-continued influence of literary and philosophical examples upon the sentiments and conduct of societies is perhaps in no place better illustrated than in Cambridge. The works of Bacon and Newton are, at this moment, influencing its studies for good. The prevalence of the Newtonian philosophy may have given a severity to a prominent part of its course which made it well-fitted for the benefit of the few, but in some respects ill fitted for the benefits of the many. Our recommendations, if acted on, would, we think, remove this objection, yet keep entire that high and honourable distinction given in Cambridge to the sciences which are of all others most exact and severe.'

The Commission paid more deference than the Prince and Peel to Whewell's views on mathematics, which illustrated the damping of criticism by Cambridge loyalties, but their report made the demand for reform more authoritative. The history and functions of the Cambridge mathematical and scientific chairs were analysed, illustrating the anomalies, and changes in conception of university science teaching. On the political side, the

Report stressed the need for the removal of barriers to the admittance of Dissenters to the University's degrees.

The Commissioners laid particular stress on 'the want of a course of instruction in Civil Engineering'. Such a course was easily allied to mathematics, and gave mathematics a practical application. They did not doubt that such an 'extension of the academical system would commend itself by its manifest utility of public approbation. They said that the need for the study of modern languages was still more obvious.

They proposed that a second professorship of chemistry should be appointed, and that the salaries of the mathematical and scientific professors should be improved. None of these exceeded £525 a year, while the professor of chemistry received only £241, and the Lucasian professor only £157. These compared with £1,854 for Lady Margaret's Professor of Divinity. All professors should receive from £400 to £800 a year at an early stage of their careers.

In their analysis of the history of the mathematical and scientific chairs, they showed how their conditions had affected the teaching of science. The Lucasian professor had a very small salary, and was excluded from holding any other appointment. This had made it difficult to secure good candidates.

On the other hand, one of the conditions was that the professor must deposit copies of his lectures in the University archives. This caused Barrow's lectures on geometry, and Newton's on optics, algebra and universal arithmetic to be preserved.

The professor of chemistry, whose chair was founded in 1702, was not supplied with any apparatus. Consequently, such as there was consisted of his private property.

Dr. Plume's chair of mathematics and astronomy had been founded in 1704, on a deed drawn up with the advice of Newton, Flamsteed and Ellis. It reflected Newton's opinion of what was to be expected of the professor. He had to provide a residence, an observatory, and an assistant, as well as the necessary instruments. He should make observations bearing on solar, lunar and planetary theories. He should give courses at his residence on astronomy, optics, trigonometry, statics, hydrostatics, magnetics and pneumatics. Students should pay for the experiments, and provide the professor with an adequate reward. It is evident that Newton lived long before the Robbins Report.

The appointments to the chairs were made in most various

ways. The Lucasian professors were appointed by the heads of colleges. The Lowndian professorship of astronomy and geometry was appointed by the Lord Chancellor and high officers of State. The Jacksonian professor of natural and experimental philosophy and chemistry was elected by Regent Masters of Art.

It was observed that since the days of Barrow, Newton and Cotes, the University had been looked to as more eminently the seat of abstract science in England, and the chief centre from which it had been diffused. 'It is impossible not to feel that the glory of the country itself is intimately bound up with our national progress in this direction.' In 1801, 43 had taken honours in mathematics; by 1851 the number had risen to 116.

The Commission recommended, however, 'that certain Mathematico-physical theories, which had obtained a temporary and questionable footing in the Examination, and which were felt to be in a state of considerable obscurity, involving great mathematical difficulties, and rather marking the frontier of science, than coming as yet fully within its ascertained range (those, namely, of Electricity, Magnetism and Heat), should not be admitted as subjects of examination'.

However, Mr. Ellis had said that Abel's Theorem on Elliptic Integrals, and Thomson's Theory of 'Electrical Images' were sufficiently clear to be suitable for examination questions.

The great private teacher William Hopkins, who within twenty years coached 175 Wranglers, including Clerk Maxwell, and 17 first Wranglers, said that the existing mathematics examination system had contributed to the distinctness of the student's knowledge in detail, but had rendered more difficult 'the perception of the logical connection of one part of a subject with another'. It promoted dexterity with symbols, and neglected fundamental ideas. 'In Electricity and Magnetism, there can hardly be said to have yet arisen any axiomatic principles whatsoever.' Clerk Maxwell's teacher cannot have left him in any doubt about one of the great lacunae in contemporary physics.

Hopkins recommended that prizes should be awarded not on examinations, but on essays. He was perhaps the greatest of that peculiar Cambridge personality of the nineteenth century—the private tutor. This class was brought into existence by the widening range of mathematical and scientific studies. The colleges had not enough tutors to cover the increasing number of subjects, and the professors were not interested in giving the kind of instruction required. Students therefore paid able private tutors to coach them for the honours examinations. The difficulty of making reforms, and the college obstruction, prevented the University from increasing its instructional staff, so the gap was filled by private enterprise. Great teachers, like Hopkins and E. J. Routh, made large incomes from the system.

The Commissioners stressed the need for experimental and illustrative science lectures, and for instruments for carrying out experiments of the kind 'which are in daily use in the hands of working men of science'. Stokes said that 'the want of such a collection is strangely inconsistent with the high character which Cambridge maintains for the study of the Exact Sciences, and astonishes foreigners who visit the University'.

The Commission said there should be a 'complete and thoroughly equipped laboratory' for chemistry, in which not only the professor but any other member of the University who wished to study this science should be able to work. The lack of such facilities was in startling contrast with the Royal College of Chemistry, the University and King's Colleges, and the Royal Institution in London.

The University should even find scientific occupations for the 'essentially' dangerous 'class in the social system of the place'. These were the gentlemen-students who were exposed to the temptation (like our moneyed youth of today) of finding 'mean and frivolous ways in which wealth may be squandered, and leisure abused'. The Commission's solution to this problem was to 'teach them handling of meteorological and magnetic instruments, and cameras'. If this were done, 'they may become Humboldts'.

When these various improvements had been carried out, it would not be possible to assign any reason 'why Cambridge should not become as great a School of physical and experimental as it is already of mathematical and classical instruction. . . .'

Whewell fought hard through his influence on the Royal Commission to regain the dominance which had been curbed by the Prince and his advisers. He left many visible marks on the report, but on the whole, the points for which the Prince had stood were unimpaired, and through the Commission now had not only the authority of himself and those in the University who agreed with him, but also that of the State.

III

The Exhibition of 1851

THE PRINCE became concerned with exhibitions in his capacity as President of the Royal Society of Arts. This institution had annual exhibitions of the work of British art and industry, and through concern with these, the idea of 'an Enlarged Exhibition of the Works of Industry of all Nations, to be holden in London in the year 1851' was conceived.

It became evident that the project was too large to be carried out by the Royal Society of Arts, and that Government support would be necessary. A Royal Commission was therefore appointed, which included scientists such as Rosse and Lyell, and politicians such as Peel, Gladstone and Cobden. One of the Secretaries was the noted engineer John Scott Russell, and among the Executive Committee were Henry Cole and Robert Stephenson. Lyon Playfair and Lloyd were appointed Special Commissioners to assist with the preparations and organization.

The area of the proposed exhibition was three to four times as large as any previous exhibition abroad. The covered area extended to nearly twenty acres.

Objection to the destruction of trees in Hyde Park for the erection of the exhibition building inspired Paxton to design the gigantic greenhouse in which the trees could continue to flourish unharmed. It was erected at extraordinary speed by 'the adaptation of mechanical contrivances to diminish and expedite labour.' Two thousand men and four steam-engines were used; 3,300 iron columns were erected; nearly one million square feet of glass were used to glaze it; 700 tons of wrought iron and 3,800 tons of cast iron were used in the construction. The cost was £107,780 7s. 6d., and an extra £35,000 was paid for quick work.

The Exhibition was opened on May 1st, 1851, before 25,000 spectators, and an adjacent crowd of 650,000. It lasted for nearly six months. Up to 90,000 people were admitted at a time, and the total number of visitors was 6,039,195.

In the later months of the Exhibition, Thomas Cook ran third-class return, three-week excursion tickets from Leeds to London, at 5s. each. His prices were somewhat lower than those of Dr. Beeching a hundred years later, but his Exhibition services nevertheless contributed notably to the growth of his famous travel business.

The larger results of the Exhibition were described in the Second Report published in 1852. The Commissioners explained that the Commission should be made perpetual, so that its aims could be continuously realized.

They said that no measure could be more in accordance with the aims of the Exhibition than the increase of the means of industrial education, and the extension of the influence of science and art upon the productive processes. The Permanent Commission should maintain and direct 'any Establishment or Institution to be founded in pursuance of any such plan'.

They were of opinion that the surplus should be applied 'in furtherance of one large Institution, adequate for the extended wants of industry, and in connection with similar institutions in the provinces it would be productive of important results'.

The greatest amount of benefit would be conferred on the community if 'the Institution were established in the Metropolis, and rendered capable, by means of scholarships and by other means, of affiliating local establishments over this country, in India [in Madras a Museum of Economic Geology had been recently founded, to which a School of Industrial Arts was attached], and Her Majesty's colonial possessions, whereby the results of its labours might be disseminated as widely as possible, and great advantage derived from a constant interchange of information between the parent institution and the bodies associated with it'.

The Prince had originally laid great stress on the international aspects of the Exhibition. Left to himself, he would probably have conceived it as primarily an international project, aimed at the utilization of science for the benefit of mankind in general, and in particular, the promotion of the unity of mankind and world peace, but practical political considerations caused him to acquiesce more and more in its national aspects, and a demonstration of British greatness.

In the Second Report, published in 1852, stress was still being laid on the international aspects. The metropolitan institution which was to be founded was to act in concert with foreign institutions of a similar character. Its advantages should be shared equally by the citizens of all countries. This would continue the friendly relations the Exhibition had inaugurated. It should give facilities to those who wished to visit Britain to inform themselves on science, arts, manufactures and commerce.

The central institution could be connected with provincial technical institutions, and the association of 222 Mechanics' Institutes, with a membership of 90,000, which had been formed in 1851.

The Report noted that a marked increase in continental production had been partly ascribed to the knowledge of natural forces communicated to those engaged in industry by technical institutions. 'In countries in which fuel and the materials of machinery either did not exist, or were not abundant, it was natural to depend more on the intellectual element of production than in this country, where their abundance gave an impulse to labour, and created much practical experience. It has long been a principle of Foreign States that the application of science and art to production would more than balance a greater cheapness in raw material; and that the increased facilities of locomotion rendered the latter of less value as an element of manufacture, while it enabled the experience of other nations to be more readily acquired, and consequently would, in process of time, convert industrial competition into one involving the most economical application of natural forces.'

The Germans had founded Industrial Universities, in which 'they rather teach a pupil how to be an intelligent manufacturer than profess to make him one at the institution'.

The Prince suggested that there should be Lectures on the Exhibition. Among these were the discourse of Professor Willis, on 'Machines and Tools for Working in Metal, Wood, and other Materials'. Their aim was 'to effect a more intimate union and greater confidence between scientific and practical men, by teaching them reciprocally their wants and requirements, their methods and power, so that the peculiar properties and advantages of each may be made to assist in the perfection of the other'. It was 'to promote a more universal knowledge amongst mechanics and artisans of the methods and tools employed in other branches than their own, as well as those employed in other countries in their own and other trades'.

The Commissioners were of the opinion that 'the active co-operation of the State, as well as of the public at large' would be necessary to achieve what was required. 'They consider that in no manner could this be ensured so well as by carefully preparing the basis and framework of a large and comprehensive plan and securing facilities for its execution, leaving it to the various interests concerned to give substance to it, whilst the perfect development of the system must be left to the progressive action of time.'

The English backwardness in large institutions for the extension of industrial instruction was due to 'the want of that harmony of system which would admit of an economic and combined action of the forces already in existence to a common end'.

One of the hindrances was the want of space for scientific institutions, especially in the metropolis. This was 'peculiarly great in this country, in consequence of the nature of the tenure on which ground is in many cases held'.

The Royal Society lacked space. The School of Mines had a chemistry laboratory which would accommodate only twenty students, and 'the size of the laboratory is the measure of the usefulness of such an institution'. The College of Chemistry had no ground on which to build a lecture room. The School of Design, the National Gallery, the Royal Society of Arts, the Collection of Medieval Art, the Royal Academy, the Map Office, the Geological Society, were also in the same position. The British Museum was in the worst position of all. The lack of space for printed books was very serious, and also that for antiquities, prints and drawings, and Natural History. Since 1836, the Zoological collection had increased tenfold, but space only threefold.

Two things were to be aimed at: 'the adoption of a *system*, and the securing of a *locality* where that system may be developed'.

With regard to Raw Materials, there was the Government Museum of Practical Geology, and its associated School of Mines, opened by the Prince in 1851, just after the Exhibition had opened.

In connection with the Royal Botanical Gardens at Kew, and the Zoological Society, 'there exists no institution combining the natural study of Vegetable and Animal Products with the study of chemistry'.

The College of Chemistry, founded in 1845 under the presidency of the Prince, lacked connection with other institutions, which 'prevented it from having that amount of influence on Manufacturing Industry which its projectors anticipated'.

'These means of education, which in this country are fragmentary, dissevered, and far from complete, are in other parts of Europe associated into one common system, and produce those striking applications to industry which were presented to us in the recent Exhibition.'

With regard to Machinery, the metropolis did not yet possess any special institution for instruction in its principles. Railway engineering had stimulated some temporary engineering colleges, and the need for standardizing railway equipment had led to the foundation of the Institution of Mechanical Engineers of Birmingham.

The great public interest in the machinery exhibits showed how eagerly opportunities for acquiring knowledge of machinery were used.

The Patent Laws required attention, and a place was required where models of inventions could be deposited. 'If means were offered for exhibiting and testing new machines under scientific superintendence [it] would soon give a new impetus to Invention.'

With regard to manufactures, institutions for teaching manufacturing processes 'should be systematized and be made of an importance adequate to the acknowledged wants of industry'.

As Professor Solly had pointed out, if the Royal Society of Arts had carried out its original objects, the nation would now have a most valuable record of the progress of human industry during the last hundred years, instead of a mere magazine or storehouse in which natural production and ingenious contrivances are piled up in endless confusion, and where they may remain buried for ages.

A Trade collection would be useful for 'the instruction of those who are to instil into industry that knowledge of Science which is so important to keep it in advance of the intellectual competition among nations'.

After reviewing the situation regarding Art Collections, the Report dealt with its action with regard to sites for institutions. They said that 'It has been usual, in purchasing property for public purposes, to obtain only the exact space needed at the time of the purchase, and even to re-sell any amount of ground that might remain over and above that called for by the exigencies of the case. The invariable consequence of this mode of proceeding is, that adjacent land, which might have been procured on reasonable terms in the first instance, immediately rises in value, passes into the hands of other persons who invest large sums in erecting houses and buildings upon it, and when at length it becomes absolutely necessary to obtain it, in order to satisfy the public wants—which will not remain stationary, and cannot be disregarded—the most exorbitant sums have to be paid for it!'

For instance, land for a railway terminus had cost four times its price ten years previously. The Commission had therefore bought extensive areas in South Kensington, with its own funds, and additional funds provided by the Government. The Commission's policy of investing its money in metropolitan land, instead of the more usual one of Government Funds, was largely due to the shrewd advice of their member Thomas Cubitt, the noted builder.

The complex should contain 'a building in which different societies might procure that juxtaposition, the means of affecting which . . . they have been for several years considering'.

Britain was 'the only country which has neither supplied (in any practical or systematic shape) scientific nor artistic instruction to its industrial population; nor provided for men of Science and Art, a centre of action, and of exchange of the results of their labours'. As the centre of the commerce and industry of the world, it needed 'such an organization more than any other'. The Exhibition had shown that unless it is speedily supplied, the country would 'run serious risk of losing that position which is now its strength and pride. Want of space and want of system have hitherto been the main impediments to their being satisfied.'

Having found the room and system, it was now for the voluntary effort of individuals, corporations, etc., to carry out what was necessary. 'We intend to pursue these objects by the same means, namely, by affording instruction and recreation to the greatest number of human beings, and by acting on the conviction that all sciences and all arts have only one end—the promotion of the happiness of mankind, and that they cannot perfectly obtain that end without combination and unity.

'We propose that in the advantages which the institution thus shadowed out may offer, the natives of foreign countries shall be received on a footing of equality which the inhabitants of our own land, and of Her Majesty's colonial possessions, and we anticipate the greatest benefit from the permanent interchange of the thoughts and acquirements of the different nations.

'We believe that we are able to point out and establish a system by which the Metropolitan Institution will be rendered only the centre of a system of local institutions, aided by local exertion and association, thus securing to our manufacturing population sound industrial knowledge; while, by confining our attention to technical instruction, and not extending it to general education in science and art, we shall be adding to, without interfering with, the means of instruction already existing in schools and colleges. As a preliminary knowledge of the principles of science and of art would be required by the students entering the institution proposed by us, the effect would be to give an impetus to general education, which could not fail to be of material advantage to those bodies.'

How much such an impetus was needed was shown five years later, in the Prince's speech to the Conference on National Education in 1857. Of the total population of 4,908,696 children in England and Wales between the ages of three and fifteen, only 2,046,848 attended any school at all, while 2,861,000 received no instruction whatever. Further, of the 2,000,000 attending school, only about 600,000 were above the age of nine. The nation might be the centre of the world's commerce and industry, but it was not educating future generations of either managers or workers.

The Commissioners for the Exhibition of 1851, under the Prince's presidency, had virtually conceived a national plan for the development of science and technology. The Special Commissioner, Lyon Playfair, devoted the main effort of the rest of his life in trying to secure the realization of part of it. His efforts have been described in the chapter devoted to him.

The most spectacular results were the complex of scientific institutions created at South Kensington, of which the Imperial College of Science and Technology is the most prominent.

IV

The South Kensington Complex

The Prince's part in the foundation of the complex of scientific institutions at South Kensington, and in particular of the Imperial College of Science and Technology, of which he is regarded as the Founder, has been recounted by Sir Patrick Linstead, in his Special Lecture on the centenary in 1961 of the Prince's death. The quotations in this section are from his lecture.

The movement which ultimately led to the creation of the Imperial College, and the other scientific institutions at South Kensington, was an aspect of the general social development of which the Reform Bill of 1832 was the most striking political manifestation. The founding of University and King's Colleges, and the University of Durham, were cultural manifestations of the same movement.

'English science was very largely unorganized and unsupported,' and the most famous English scientists of the day, 'Dalton, Davy, Faraday, Joule—had no formal education in science'. Broadly speaking, the young Englishman of 1832 who wished to be educated in science could only go to Cambridge to read mathematics, or to Scotland, or abroad. Of the eleven professors who had the greatest influence in the early period of South Kensington, only two had received any formal university education in England.

Education in the advanced application of science in industry was in an even worse condition. The Mechanics' Institutes, which had been founded with so much enthusiasm, provided only for part-time students. It was impossible for the bulk of part-time students, especially after working all day at the very long and hard hours then obtaining in industry, to carry their studies very far. After its enthusiastic start, this movement inevitably lost its early optimism.

The question arises, how did England succeed in producing men like Dalton, Davy, Faraday and Joule, when university scientific education was so scarce and limited? How, under these conditions, did England retain the industrial leadership of the world for so long?

The Industrial Revolution had been associated with 'the long swing from craft to science.' Craftsmen, of whom James Watt was the classical example, had necessarily taken a leading part in it, because they were the productive workers in the preceding form of society.

The early scientists of the Industrial Revolution, of which Dalton, Davy, Faraday and Joule were the classical examples, had essentially the craftsman's attitude to science. They made everything themselves with their own hands; they were heavily experimentalist. In the case of the last three, theory was very much the waiter on experiment.

Formal scientific education at the ancient universities, and especially Cambridge, was based on the scientific needs of society before the Industrial Revolution, which were mainly in astronomy and mathematics. No system of scientific education suitable for leaders of industry had yet been worked out in the ancient universities. In these circumstances, the beginning of various forms of higher scientific instruction started from outside.

The industrial development had greatly stimulated mining and geology. Sir Henry de la Beche started the first geological surveys of the country on his own initiative. He persuaded the Board of Ordnance in 1832 to start marking geological colours on their maps. This led to a Treasury Grant of £300 a year, the beginning of the Government's regular support for scientific and industrial research, which is today provided on a scale at least 100,000 times greater. From this beginning de la Beche succeeded, by 1841, in persuading the Government to support a Museum of Economic Geology, a Mining Records Office, and the Geological Survey and Museum.

At this time, the final triumph of industrialism over the society it had superseded was being consummated by the repeal of the Corn Laws. This meant that the industrial interest was being given precedence over the landed interest which had dominated the country for centuries.

The more far-sighted landlords looked to science to help them, after the abolition of protection. They welcomed Liebig's work on the application of chemistry to agriculture. Liebig's chemistry was as interesting to the industrialists as to the agriculturists. He had as enthusiastic a reception from the Lancashire textile magnates as from the landed aristocrats. Men like Sir Robert Peel, whose wealth had come from the Lancashire textile industry, and who had become a progressive landlord, were doubly interested in Liebig.

The new scientific interest in agriculture led to the founding of Rothamsted in 1843. John Gardner, one of the translators of Liebig, de la Beche and the geologist Murchison tried to start a college of practical chemistry in conjunction with the Royal Institution, but though Brande and Faraday were sympathetic, there was no room for it on the site at Albemarle Street.

The promoters therefore made a public appeal for the foundation of a College of Chemistry. Sir James Clark, the Queen's physician, was an ardent supporter of the project, and he interested the Prince in it. The College was founded in 1845, with the Prince as President.

Liebig was asked to recommend a director. He suggested Will, Hofmann and Fresenius. Hofmann was the son of the architect who built Liebig's laboratory at Giessen, and had married one of Liebig's nieces. He had studied philology and law, and then mathematics and physics, before becoming an organic chemist. He had great imagination as well as intellectual power, and became the exponent of Liebig's conception of science as the imaginative guide to spiritual and material betterment.

Will refused the appointment, and Hofmann, who was then at the University of Bonn, hesitated; it was, in the first place, for only two years. If it should prove a failure, his career would be imperilled. It happened that a Beethoven festival was to be held in Bonn a fortnight later. The Prince took Queen Victoria with him to attend it, and to visit his birthplace and university.

According to one account, the Prince went to visit the rooms he had occupied while at the university, and was astonished to find them full of chemical apparatus, around which an enthusiastic young man darted. This was Hofmann. According to another account, the Prince was introduced to Hofmann by Sir James Clark.

Hofmann's hesitation was overcome by the Prince and Sir James undertaking to ask the Prussian Government to promise him the rank of Extraordinary Professor (the rank which he believed he would have reached if he had stayed in Bonn), if he should have to return to Germany after the two years. The Prince personally asked the King of Prussia to agree to this request, which was immediately granted. In fact, Hofmann was at once made an Extraordinary Professor, and given two years' leave of absence.

The College had no state support, so in spite of Hofmann's wonderful achievement as teacher and leader of research, it was soon in financial difficulty, and kept going only by his surrendering his house and part of his salary. Besides the major figures of W. H. Perkin and Henry Bessemer in scientific industry, the College trained Warren de la Rue, F. A. Abel, E. C. Nicholson, C. B. Manfield, G. Merch, P. Griess and Martins, and scientists such as William Crookes and Edward Frankland.

Hofmann remained in England until 1863. Besides his outstanding professional position, he was a welcome guest in the Prince's circle, and after the Prince's death in 1861, England did not offer the same social attraction to him. The pressure of the Prussian Government on him to return home could no longer be resisted. He went to Berlin, and became the father of the German dye industry, continuing his great career with as much inspiration and distinction as he had started it.

Linstead has pointed out that 'Hofmann did more than carry out classical scientific work. The thing which he did and which had never been done before in Britain was to found a *school of research*. He laid the pattern for the future which was to be followed many decades later by the Cavendish and other famous laboratories. He collected round him a large group of ardent young men who heard his lectures, learnt his experimental techniques and promptly plunged into the almost unknown world of research in organic chemistry. This band of men were of unique quality. There had been nothing like them since Liebig's heyday in Giessen. . . .'

While the College of Chemistry had been launched on its brilliant but precarious career, de la Beche, with the support of Peel, succeeded in obtaining a fine new site for the Museum of Practical Geology in Piccadilly. He incorporated in it a school, which was called 'The Government School of Mines and Science applied to the Arts'.

The Prince opened the new building and school in the same month as the opening of the Great Exhibition. Its professors included Lyon Playfair for chemistry, J. Percy in metallurgy, Andrew Ramsay in geology and W. Smyth in mining. E. Forbes was professor of natural history, being succeeded in 1854 by

Thomas Henry Huxley, who continued his distinguished services for forty-one years.

The Royal School of Mines was the first educational scientific institution of university rank to be supported by the British State. In 1853, the Royal College of Chemistry was saved by combining it with the Royal School of Mines. Playfair vacated his chair, which was taken over by Hofmann, and started on his career of public service.

The Prince, Playfair and Huxley wished the combined institution to develop into a great scientific and technological university. Murchison, who had become director after the death of de la Beche, and Percy wished it to retain the characteristics of a school for the professional training of geologists, in which all the science teaching was subordinate to that end. At first, their view prevailed, in spite of the Prince pointing out that the institution should be not simply for training geologists, but 'a Government establishment for the diffusion of science generally as applied to productive industry'. He clearly conceived an institution like the Imperial College of Science and Technology, which gradually came into being during the next half-century.

The success of the Great Exhibition had enabled its Commissioners to purchase altogether 86 acres at South Kensington. The Prince had suggested that there should be four institutions devoted to the application of science and art to industry. He drew up a plan for four large 'Museums or Schools of Science and Industry', and reserved a large area for the scientific societies, and the Society of Civil Engineers.

He described it as a 'very crude scheme', but Disraeli wrote to him that: 'when realized, the creation of your Royal Highness will form an epoch in the aesthetic and scientific education of the people of England. . . .' From it has arisen the present Imperial College of Science and Technology, the Royal College of Art, and the South Kensington Museums. In the existing complex the Museums have been separated administratively from the educational side.

The scientific societies have not come to South Kensington, and the comprehensive Science Centre conceived by the Prince has still not been created anywhere in England.

The Prince's idea that the institution should be international gave way to the pressure that it should be imperial. It is now changing in character in order to meet the situation created by the dissolution of the British Empire and the change in the English social organization.

V

The Conflict and Unity of Opposites

THE PRINCE CONSORT had a comprehensive conception for the development of science far in advance of his English contemporaries, and he succeeded in launching a substantial part of it in his short life of forty-two years, only half of which were spent in England.

Contemporary men of judgment spoke highly of him. De Tocqueville said: 'I have rarely met so distinguished a man.' Hofmann referred to him as 'the high-minded Prince'. Murchison (who differed from him on scientific policy) described him as 'this sensible and gifted man', and Playfair said 'he was singularly affable and lovable'.

Babbage was impressed by his technological information. When the Prince and the Duke of Wellington called to inspect his calculating machine, Babbage asked them to look at a portrait of Jacquard on his walls. The Duke thought it was an engraving. 'No,' said Albert, 'it is not an engraving.' He had seen it before, and knew it was Jacquard's portrait of himself finely-woven in silk on his punched-card loom.

Babbage esteemed the Prince for having conceived the Exhibition of 1851: 'to have seen from afar its effects on the improvement, the wealth, the happiness of the people—to have seized the fit moment, when, by the right use of the influence of an exalted station, it was possible to overcome the deeply-rooted prejudices of the upper classes—to remove the still more formidable, because latent, impediments of party—generously to have undertaken great responsibility and with indefatigable labour to have endeavoured to make the best out of the only materials at hand—these are endowments of no ordinary kind.'

The accomplishment of his project was retarded because the planning of science which he advocated was incompatible with the capitalist individualism of the day. The majority of industrialists had little interest in science, and engineers were trained in the workshop and drawing office, through the apprenticeship system. They were more interested in profits than technical progress, and so long as they were prospering, few bothered about any long-range improvement in technique.

The Prince's idea of an *international* centre of science as a contribution to the strengthening of peace was still further beyond the conceptions of contemporary nationalism and imperialism.

The slow evolution of the odd conglomeration of South Kensington institutions into an organically unified scientific centre was the result of capitalism trying to carry out the Prince's plan in spite of its own principles.

While the industrialists gave tardy support to the new scientific institutions, the men they trained gave enormous aid to industry. This was particularly exemplified by W. H. Perkin's invention of synthetic dyes, and his foundation of modern chemical industry; and Henry Bessemer's revolution in steel-smelting.

Beside the long list of eminent scientists and technologists who have benefited from instruction in these institutions, there is one name of peculiar significance. Karl Marx, also an old Bonn student, had like the Prince emigrated to England, but for other reasons. While writing his chapter on 'The Development of Machinery' for *Capital*, he attended Professor Robert Willis's classes at the Government School of Mines and of Science applied to the Arts; one of the scientific institutions fostered by the Prince, and subsequently moved to South Kensington. He attended the 'practical course (experimental only) for workers', in order to clear up some points which he had ignored in the first draft of his chapter.

One of the Prince's most ardent aims had been to ward off revolutions, but, just as he had aided capitalism in spite of itself, so in spite of himself, an institution which he had fostered helped the great revolutionary to develop ideas on the nature and use of technology. These became embodied in the planned science and technology in the new socialist states inspired by Marx.

The rise of the new socialist states with planned science and technology has in turn been one of the most important stimuli to the comprehensive expansion of science and technology at South Kensington, which is taking place in the second half of the twentieth century.

The Seventh Duke of Devonshire

1808–1891

This William Cavendish married Louisa O'Calaghan, a daughter of Lord Lismore. He died through an accident while driving, leaving three young children. When his eldest son, who was to become the seventh Duke, was of appropriate age, he was sent to Eton, and then to Trinity College, Cambridge.

He was a quiet reserved young man, and a brilliant student. He took the honours examination in mathematics in 1829, and gained the second place. In the subsequent examination for the Smith prizes he gained first place; the man who had beaten him in the degree examination was second.

Charles Babbage, who was then Lucasian professor of mathematics, was one of his examiners. He spoke highly of his mathematical talent, and described how pains were taken to avoid any prejudice in his favour on account of his aristocracy. Babbage arranged that his papers should be independently assessed by a second examiner, who did not know what marks Babbage had given; the marks in both cases were found to be substantially the same.

William Cavendish scored his success in one of the earliest of the Cambridge degree examinations in which printed questions were set to candidates. He was therefore one of the first to do well after the Cambridge mathematics examination had begun to take a more modern form.

As a Cavendish, William was a strong Whig, in fact, as a young man he was to the left of the Whigs, and more a Liberal. The Cambridge Whigs and Liberals invited him to stand, together with Palmerston, for the Cambridge University seats in the General Election of 1829. Charles Babbage was one of the most enthusiastic and energetic political campaigners for his talented and aristocratic pupil. In the intense political struggle working up to the Reform Bill of 1832, Cavendish and Palmerston won in 1829.

In the same year, he married Blanche Georgiana Howard, the fourth daughter of the sixth Earl of Carlisle. He was a taciturn man, with no taste for public speaking, but after his election to the House of Commons, he made one brief but weighty speech in favour of reform. He said that although he differed in opinion from a very considerable proportion of his constituents, many of whom were Tories, yet he gave an unqualified support to the whole of the Government measure for parliamentary reform. No one was more sensible than he that in many respects this country was fortunate beyond the ordinary lot of nations; but he was quite at a loss to see how that could depend on the existing borough system.

There was another consideration of paramount importance. Without the confidence of the country it was certain that the Government could not go on. There could be no stability unless the great majority of the people supported the Government. At present, the House was not the genuine representative of the people, and as long as that state of things continued, the dissatisfaction of the public would continue to increase. That dissatisfaction might be smothered for a moment, but whenever any circumstance occurred to call it forth, it would burst out with redoubled violence. As for those who said the Reform measure was only a stepping stone to further concessions, he could not see any weight in their argument, the tendency of which was, in fact, to throw obstacles in the way of all improvement. He was surprised at the clamour of revolution which had been raised against the Bill. It was his decided opinion that if revolution was to be apprehended in the country, it was not from that Bill, but from the continuance of a system which was completely at variance with the general interests. Nor would the measure promote the downfall of the aristocracy. It was true that it would deprive the aristocracy of a portion of their immediate power; but it would induce them not to rely on their boroughs, but on that which always ought to be the source of their legitimate influence—viz., their own talents, and their means of conferring happiness on the people.

The Cambridge University electors did not like this, so, in the General Election of 1831, they rejected him, and Palmerston also. The Cavendish connection soon found him a new seat, first at Malton in Yorkshire, and then at North Derbyshire, where he was elected in 1832.

In 1834 his grandfather died, and he inherited the Earldom of Burlington. Thenceforth he sat in the House of Lords, but rarely spoke.

His wife died in 1840, and he was left with three sons and one daughter. He personally undertook their education. He devoted a great deal of time to this, and was a good teacher. His eldest son, the Marquis of Hartington, became a distinguished Liberal statesman, and prime minister. His second son, Lord Frederick Cavendish, M.P., then Chief Secretary for Ireland, was murdered in Phoenix Park in Dublin, in 1882. His daughter Laura married the Hon. F. Egerton, M.P., the son of the Earl of Ellesmere.

The sixth Duke of Devonshire was a bachelor, an able but deaf and unhappy man. He engaged Joseph Paxton to build the giant conservatory at Chatsworth; this experience led Paxton to conceive the great iron-and-glass building for the Exhibition of 1851, which was the parent of modern steel-and-glass architecture.

The sixth Duke died in 1858, without issue. His heir was the Earl of Burlington, a first cousin at one remove, who accordingly became seventh Duke in that year.

III

The Iron Duke

THE new Duke, now aged fifty, found the Cavendish estates heavily encumbered. He extended the careful personal management he had applied to his own estates to his new inheritance. Among his real estate projects was the conversion of three straggling villages, three miles to the east of Beachy Head, into the modern seaside resort of Eastbourne. He had a house there, which was one of his favourite residences. When he died in 1891, he left a fortune of £1,790,870.

His retiring disposition did not change after he had inherited the dukedom. He was rarely seen in London society, and seldom spoke in the House of Lords. He was almost of the same age as Gladstone, and for long was a supporter of his policies. He strongly supported his Irish Church Bill in 1869 in the House of Lords. 'I regard this measure as indispensable for laying a foundation for the removal of that estrangement and alienation with which Ireland has so long regarded England. If this Bill should be rejected, what reason would there be, supposing its rejection could be permanent, for expecting that Ireland in the future would be anything different from what it has been in the past; and in such case could we contemplate such a prospect without utter despair? I believe this is the first step for the removal of one of the most frightful sources of discontent in that country; and as such I support it as one of the most just, and beneficent measures ever presented to my consideration, since I have had a seat in your Lordships' House.'

He became as strongly opposed to Gladstone's subsequent policy of Irish Home Rule. Through his Boyle descent he had large estates in Ireland, which, like his other estates, were well managed. He encouraged the construction of railways on his Irish estates. While he welcomed the extension of religious rights for the Irish, he did not relish the prospect of Irish management of economic affairs, which would have come with Home Rule. He accepted the presidency of the Irish Loyal and Patriotic Union, formed to fight against the granting of Irish Home Rule. Those who supported their policy became known as Unionists, and at the end of the nineteenth century became the allies of the Conservatives, and were subsequently absorbed by them.

Like other intelligent landlords in the first half of the nineteenth century, he had taken a keen interest in scientific farming. He supported the founding of the Royal Agricultural Society in 1839, and became its president in 1869. He contributed to the foundation of the Agricultural College at Cirencester, and he persuaded the University of Cambridge to pursue the scientific study of agriculture. He was personally interested in the breeding of shorthorn cattle, a herd of which he kept for fifty years.

His great industrial contribution arose through the discovery and exploitation of high-grade iron ore on his estates near Holker. In the course of this development, the small fishing village of Barrow was converted into one of the chief centres of iron and steel production, and the manufacture of armaments, in the world. The Duke said he could remember the time when Barrow had only a hundred inhabitants. In 1847 it had 325; when he died in 1891, its population was 57,000. One of the admirers of this development was Gladstone. In the midst of it, in 1867, and before the Duke differed from him on Irish Home Rule, he took part in a banquet at Barrow, in which he proposed 'The Town and Trade of Barrow'.

Iron-smelting at Barrow was started by H. W. Schneider, who had taken a lease to mine iron ore on the neighbouring Cavendish estate. The project encountered many difficulties, and in 1850 he was threatened with the termination of his lease. This prompted redoubled efforts which led to his striking the rich Park Mine of haematite ore. The Barrow Haematite Steel Company was founded to smelt it. The Duke was the chairman, and the company took over Schneider and others, who became directors. It became one of the largest Bessemer steel works of the day.

The Park Mine was 500 yards in length and 120–240 yards wide. The ore was overlaid with 10 fathoms of drift, or earth; and went down to a depth of 70 fathoms below the surface. It yielded 8,500,000 tons of haematite in 35 years, which, up to 1886, provided £535,000 in royalties.

Barrow had originally been scarcely accessible, except from the sea. The Furness Railway, 134 miles long, was built under the initiative of the Duke and Sir James Ramsden, to transport the ore and other goods, which soon ran into millions of tons. Docks were constructed to deal with the new trade. In 1867 the Devonshire and Buccleuch Dock was opened. It covered 60 acres, had a stone quay 1½ miles long, and a hydraulic crane which could lift 100 tons. Subsequently the Ramsden Dock of 200 acres was added.

The owners had the vision of Barrow becoming a major port which could compete in general trade with Liverpool, but this did not materialize.

When the Iron and Steel Institute was founded in 1869, the Duke was elected the first President. The second General Secretary of the Institute was J. S. Jeans.

In his first Presidential Address, the Duke said that for many years an increasing degree of importance had been assigned to those branches of knowledge which were of essential service to the iron-master. Proposals had been under consideration for promoting a more systematic cultivation of experimental science, several branches of which had already exercised great influence, and were, in all probability, destined to exercise a still greater influence, in promoting improvements in the processes and operations carried on in their furnaces and ironworks.

The new institute would encourage these developments. It would follow the Institutions of Mechanical and Civil Engineers, local mining societies, the Royal Agricultural and other societies in helping the 'promotion of science in its practical applications'. The application of chemical science was of especial importance for the iron industry.

Referring to the history of the iron industry in England, he said that her production of iron in 1740 had fallen to less than 20,000 tons, while, not very long before, it had been 200,000. She had, in consequence, become a large importer of iron. The decline was due to the consumption of the forests for fuel. The introduction of coal smelting enabled production to rise again. The invention of the hot blast by Neilson in 1829 led to a very important economy in fuel.

'As a further illustration of the scientific character of this manufacture, I may mention that it has been proposed to determine the exact point of decarburization in the Bessemer process, by means of the spectrum analysis, a discovery which has already revealed to us the fact that iron is one of the forms of matter existing throughout the universe. If this suggestion should ultimately prove of practical value, it will rank among the most interesting applications of pure science to practical purposes.'

He referred also to Whitworth's invention of high pressure steel casting. Finally, he commented on the social influence of iron; through the construction of railways, guns and agricultural implements.

When the Duke's portrait was presented to the Iron and Steel Institute, Sir Lothian Bell, the iron-master, said that 'His Grace himself, as was well known, ventured of his own free will into an arena where neither ancestors nor lineage could procure any advantage, and then, by the exercise of his own intelligence and industry, he obtained the highest meed of approbation and honour which it was in the power of their Universities to bestow.'

After the death of the Duke of Wellington, who, through temperament and military achievement came to be popularly known as The Iron Duke, this title, for more concrete reasons, was transferred in some quarters to the seventh Duke of Devonshire.

While initiating and superintending all this business, he was personally active in promoting the development of the universities. Besides being Chancellor of Cambridge University, he actively helped Owens College at Manchester, and the Yorkshire College of Leeds. As President of Owens College, he said in his inaugural address in 1873 that a university should teach not only some few selected subjects, but every great and important branch of human knowledge. At Owens 'we find that the importance of combining literary and scientific studies has been from the first recognized both in principle and practice'.

The Duke had been Chancellor of Cambridge University for

nine years when, in 1870, he offered to provide funds for the construction of a laboratory for experimental physics. The reforms in science teaching and research recommended during the chancellorship of the Prince Consort required to be carried out. The Duke thoroughly understood the need for the systematic teaching of the kind of science, such as heat and electricity, in its experimental as well as theoretical aspect, in the new industrial age; he was a great industrialist himself. He had the means and also the generosity to contribute to its realization.

Clerk Maxwell, as examiner in mathematics, had begun the introduction into the honours examination of questions on heat and electricity. These could not be properly answered without a previous training in experimental physics, which the University had not yet begun to teach systematically. The Duke offered £6,300 for the construction of the buildings and the provision of equipment. This does not seem a large sum today, but compared with the provision for experimental physics before 1870, which was virtually nothing, it was vast.

Parallel with the Duke's offer, the University created a professorship of experimental physics, so that the new professor could design and superintend the construction of the new laboratory, and launch in its systematic teaching and research in experimental physics. William Thomson and Helmholtz were approached to occupy the chair, but they were not prepared to leave Glasgow and Berlin, so Clerk Maxwell was appointed; a greater man than either, though this was not widely recognized at the time.

Maxwell designed the laboratory, and thought out its courses and intellectual policy in detail. He endowed it with its wonderful tradition. Besides doing this, he astonished many of his contemporaries by devoting a great deal of time to the editing of the papers of Henry Cavendish, the founder's famous scientific kinsman. Like so much of his research in physics, this was also a profound and highly original contribution to learning. There is no other instance of the work of one major physicist being edited in such a manner by another.

The professor of experimental physics came to be known as the Cavendish professor. The subsequent history of the Cavendish Laboratory and its professors can be regarded as the result of progress in the adaptation of Cambridge University to the needs of the industrial age. The seventh Duke, by virtue of his position as Chancellor and head of the University, his status as a leading industrialist, and member of the traditional ruling class, and his knowledge of the University as a distinguished student both of mathematics and classics, became the leader of the adaptation of Cambridge science to contemporary social needs.

IV

The Devonshire Commission

THE Royal Commission on Scientific Instruction and the Advancement of Science was set up in 1870, to report on their state in England, and make recommendations for their improvement. The seventh Duke was appointed president, and the other members were the Marquis of Lansdowne, John Lubbock, J. P. Kay-Shuttleworth, B. Samuelson, W. Sharpey, T. H. Huxley, G. G. Stokes, and H. J. S. Smith (who replaced W. A. Miller on his decease). The Secretary was J. Norman Lockyer.

The Commission's enquiries covered a wide range. Many eminent leaders of scientific education and scientific research were interrogated at their numerous meetings, in the process of collecting evidence. The Duke was regularly in the chair, and personally opened the interrogations.

The Commission started by investigating the condition of scientific and technical instruction, especially the results of the movements stimulated by the Prince Consort and the Exhibition of 1851.

The Science School

They investigated the complex of scientific institutions which had been established at South Kensington. They found that still, after about twenty years, there were many deficiencies. The Royal School of Mines and the Royal College of Chemistry formed practically one School of Pure and Applied Science; but as such it was not efficient. It had no chair of mathematics; no laboratories for physics and biology; and the Royal College of Chemistry had poor premises.

They recommended that the two colleges should be consolidated. A chair of mathematics should be added, and sufficient laboratories for practical instruction in physics, chemistry and biology should be provided. The consolidated institutions should be called the 'Science School', and be governed by a Council of its professors; one of them to act as Dean. It should be accommodated in the projected School of Naval Architecture and Science at South Kensington.

There were great advantages in the concentration of institutions at South Kensington. The Royal School of Mines, the Geological Survey, the Mining Record Office, the Museum of Practical Geology, and the Royal College of Chemistry all came under the Director-General of the Geological Survey and Director of the Royal School of Mines.

The important rôle of geology in the stimulation of technological education and research in England is striking, and was related to its connection with the increasing exploitation of coal, minerals and ores through the development of industrialism.

Technical Education

The second Report contained a review of technical education. It was observed that before 1859, elementary instruction in science was scarcely attainable by the working classes. Some of the principal Mechanics' Institutions in the towns had popular science lectures. Even these were restricted to the great towns, such as Glasgow, Edinburgh, Manchester and Liverpool, and one or two institutions in London. In the smaller manufacturing and rural districts there was almost none.

The establishment of the Science and Art department in 1853 had led to the organization by that department in 1859, of a system of teaching elementary science, and of teaching teachers of science. In 1860 there were 9 schools with 500 pupils being taught science; in 1870 there were 799 schools with 34,283 pupils receiving such instruction.

In 1869, Guthrie, Michael Foster and T. H. Huxley were engaged to give lectures to science teachers on the art of science teaching. In 1870 they were joined by Frankland on chemistry. The science teachers were paid by results. They received £1 for each of their pupils who gained a second class, and £2 for a first class in their examination.

In 1870 the ages of the pupils ranged from eight to sixty years; the average being about thirteen years. Five of the eight-year-old pupils were successful, but both of the two sixty-year-olds failed. In this year one of the teachers made £227 10s. from the successes of his pupils, but the average extra payment secured by the teachers was £35.

A total of 16,515 pupils were examined. They took altogether 34,413 papers, and secured 18,690 passes in them; 50·6 per cent passed the examination successfully.

The Commission recommended the creation of a more efficient teaching system, with grades of science teachers. It said little about the need for building and equipment.

Oxford and Cambridge

The Commission's third Report gave 'a full account of the present state of scientific study' in Oxford and Cambridge. The evidence revealed deficiencies, 'but also much that is suggestive of hope for the future'. In reporting it, 'we desire at the very outset to guard against a possible misconception. Our use of the term Science in this Report is limited, by the scope of the duties assigned to us, to the Sciences of Organic and Inorganic Nature, including under that general designation the Science of Number and Magnitude, together with those which depend on Observation and Experiment; but excluding the Mental and Moral Sciences, as well as all those parts of human knowledge and culture which are not usually regarded as having any scientific character. . . . In dealing with the relations of the Universities to Science, we shall use the word in this restricted sense; and we can refer only in a very secondary manner to the equally important duties which such academical bodies owe to literature and learning, and to education in other than purely scientific directions. Nor must it be supposed that in referring only incidentally, as we shall have to do, to subjects which justly form a large part of the business of a University, we intend in any manner to underrate them, or even to suggest any comparison between the place which they occupy in University Education and that which has hitherto been assigned, or which ought hereafter to be assigned, to training in the methods of Science. Least of all should we wish to imply that there is any antagonism between the literary and scientific branches of education and research; it is rather our

THE SEVENTH DUKE OF DEVONSHIRE

conviction that neither branch can be neglected without grave detriment to the other; and that an University in which the Mathematician, the Experimental Philosopher, and the Biologist are actively engaged in the endeavour to advance human knowledge, in their own provinces, is not on that account less likely to be productive of original labours in the fields of Literature and Learning.'

The Commission dealt with the state of science in the ancient Universities under six headings: the course of study and examination; the professoriate; the scientific institution within the universities; the colleges; the relation of the universities to technical education and the education of the professions; and the duties of the universities with regard to the advancement of science.

At that time Oxford and Cambridge had no matriculation examination, which students must pass before entering the university. Thus the fitness of candidates for university study in science was an important subject of discussion.

The eminent men from whom evidence was taken on this question had very varied views. Some were in favour of a preliminary examination, others were strongly against. 'A young man may have a fair share of rough untrained ability', and he should not be excluded because he had not previously received any formal training. 'If secondary education in England were more satisfactorily organized than it is,' this problem 'would not be so bad'.

Remarkably outspoken views were expressed by Mark Pattison, the professor of logic at Oxford. He was opposed to any matriculation examination, and the requirement of any knowledge of the classics. J. C. Adams, the Cambridge astronomer, on the other hand, held the view that 'literary culture is extremely important, that without it the mind is apt to become narrowed, especially if it be exclusively devoted to material objects, and that in consequence even physical studies themselves are likely to be pursued with less success'.

The Commissioners concluded that 'it is essential that some evidence of literary culture should be required by the University from every student; and in the interests of science itself', it 'should not be too low', but, in 'a like manner, evidence of corresponding scientific culture should be required from the student of Classical Literature or of Theology'.

Benjamin Jowett, the Master of Balliol College, Oxford, expressed in his evidence the view that he 'should be inclined to require from everyone a certain amount of Science before he took his degree'.

The Commissioners thought that 'it is much more probable that the literary tests now required from scientific students [before they can sit for their degrees] will be lowered, it may be even beyond what is desirable, than that any new requirement of a *minimum* of scientific knowledge will be imposed on Students of Classics, or Divinity, or Laws'. They said that 'it is impossible not to recognize a tendency in the direction of that complete freedom of study which is so ably advocated in the evidence of Mr. Pattison; nor can we escape the conclusion that this tendency will receive yet further development'.

In this delicate question of the relations between Science, and Literature and the Classics, and what should be expected of their respective students, and what general education they should receive, the President's possession of high qualifications in classics as well as in mathematics was highly important, and added much to the impartiality and weight of the Commission's recommendations.

It was recommended also that steps should be taken to ensure that every schoolboy should have been afforded some opportunity during his work at school, 'of acquainting himself, to a certain degree, with the objects and methods of more than one of the typical branches of human knowledge'. Otherwise, he would not know what to do when he entered the university.

The Commissioners recommended that University Scholarships in Natural Science should be founded at both Oxford and Cambridge. There should be one in physics, one in chemistry, and one in biology at each university. Like the Commissioners of 1852 on Cambridge and Oxford, they commented that professorial lectures were of little use to candidates in the Cambridge degree examination, and they said that 'whether the influence which this examination exerts on the studies of the students may not be excessive, is a question which seems to deserve the serious attention of the University'. Evidently, they thought that the progress which had been made during the last twenty years on these matters was inadequate.

They compared the science courses in the University of Berlin with those in the ancient English universities. They noted that there were no lectures in the philosophical faculty at Berlin on any part of electricity, that is, on electrical science as distinguished from its applications. They thought, however, that Berlin gave good courses in science for liberal education, and on recent advances in science.

They were also impressed by the large staffs in the departments of mathematics, physics and chemistry, headed by Weierstrass, Helmholtz, Hofmann, and other scientists of the first rank. The courses on chemistry were particularly complete. Roscoe in his evidence said that 'a plurality of teachers is an indispensable prerequisite both for breadth and depth of instruction'. The Commission commented that the science teaching in English universities was 'inadequate in amount'.

At Oxford 'some further subdivision of the subjects must be introduced . . . for the purposes of general culture an acquaintance with the principles of Biology is of more importance than a knowledge of special Physiology'. At the earliest opportunity Oxford should found two chairs of physics, two in chemistry, one in pure mathematics and one in mathematical physics. There should also be a chair in Applied Mechanics and Engineering. The biology chairs should be redistributed, with five independent professorships.

At least three chairs of chemistry were needed in place of the existing one. Experimental physics and civil engineering should have at least three chairs. One chair of physiology should be founded. Pattison in his evidence said that he believed twenty to thirty chairs of science were needed to equip Oxford adequately for the contemporary age. Some witnesses suggested that more skilled assistants for existing lecturers rather than more independent lecturers were required. The professors of geology and botany had no assistants.

The Commissioners commented that 'A Natural Science Professor should have, in the first place, sufficient skilled assistance to relieve him from all mere drudgery in the preparation of his lectures. In the second place, he should have such further assistance as may be necessary to enable him to carry on original researches. And, thirdly, although no professor would wish to hand over the superintendence of the practical teaching in his laboratories entirely to others, he should be enabled to discharge this duty of superintendence without an undue sacrifice of time. The work should be done under the professor's eye, but its details should be entrusted to competent demonstrators appointed by and responsible to him.'

The Commissioners in this and many other instances contributed in detail to the formulation of the methods of science teaching in the universities which were to become standard practice in the next generation. They said that 'University Teachers, who might be termed Adjoint Professors or Readers, should be appointed to undertake the instruction in special branches'.

New chairs should have the same academical status as the existing chairs, and there should be a Central Board or Council, representing the Scientific Faculty, and having definite functions. They noted that non-residence of professors had been abolished.

They were against a complete separation of Original Research and Teaching. 'A professor who should undertake the direction of a laboratory in which advanced students were to be trained in the methods of scientific research would be very far from holding a sinecure office, and would be rendering the highest, as well as the most direct, service to scientific education.

'The object of a University is to promote and to maintain learning and science, and scientific teaching of the highest kind can only be successfully carried on by persons who are themselves engaged in original research. If once a teacher ceases to be a learner, it is difficult for him to maintain any freshness of interest in the subject which he has to teach, and nothing is so likely to awaken the love of scientific inquiry in the mind of the student as the example of a teacher who shows his value for knowledge by making the advancement of it the principal business of his life.'

The Commissioners followed this classic statement with the observation that they 'should regret to see any scientific office whatever established in either of the Universities without its being understood that it is expected from the holder that he shall do what is within his power, not only for the diffusion but also for the increase of scientific knowledge'.

They broadly agreed with H. J. S. Smith that the boards for election of professors should consist of, first, representatives of the local scientific element; second, of the outside scientific world; and third, of some impartial and simply businesslike element.

They were of the opinion that professors at Cambridge should receive at least £450 a year, exclusive of income from college fellowship. The conditions of university appointments should be such as to attract the best men.

'It is of great importance in the interest of the Universities that these places should be such as to render them attractive to the most eminent scientific men that can be found to take them, and it may be doubted whether the amount which has been named is sufficient for the purpose. When an office is offered to a man, the duties of which are to form the business of his life, it is certainly right that the remuneration accompanying it should be such as to enable him to marry and maintain a family in a suitable manner.'

They would therefore 'wish to see a well-considered system of retiring pensions instituted in the Universities'. They believed that this would be conducive, not only to the comfort of the professors, but also, 'which is of more importance, to the maintenance of an uniformly high standard of instruction'.

The only quarter which, so far as they could see, could supply the extra finance for these reforms were the colleges. The contrast between this point of view, and that which obtains today, when most of the finance for Oxford and Cambridge comes from the State, is very striking. In 1871–2, the incomes of the universities, apart from that of the colleges, was £31,718 19s. 4d., and £23,206 18s. 2d. respectively.

They drew attention to the meagre supply of museums, libraries and laboratories for students of science. In this, the English universities were far outdone by many institutions in Europe. At Cambridge, 'the new Museums contain no sufficient provision for the study of Experimental Physics. This want, which of late years has been strongly felt, has been met by the establishment of a Physics Laboratory, now being erected at the expense of the Chancellor'; that is, the Cavendish Laboratory founded by the Duke and President of the Commission.

The Commission investigated the number of college scholarships at Oxford and Cambridge. At Oxford in 1872 there were 75 scholarships, of which 6 were for science, 13 for mathematics, and 55 for classics. There were 370 fellowships at Oxford and 350 at Cambridge. Of the Cambridge fellowships, only 120 were held by men resident in the university; 230 were held by non-residents, many of them clergymen and lawyers.

Pattison in his evidence said he was in favour of suppressing 260 Oxford fellowships, but feared to express this opinion, as it might 'throw ridicule on the whole proposal'. Jowett, on the other hand, said that he thought 'that a number of highly educated young men are able to go to the bar or to some other profession, having leisure and being free from pecuniary anxiety, and not being compelled to slave for the press, or lose their time for the sake of making money for seven or eight years of their life, seems to me to be a very great national good'.

The Commissioners emphasized that it was 'most important that a certain number of fellowships should be appropriated to the Direct Promotion of learning and Research in various directions'.

Lord Salisbury observed in his evidence that 'Research is unremunerative: it is highly desirable for the community that it should be pursued, and, therefore, the community must be content that funds should be set aside to be given, without any immediate and calculable return in work, to those by whom the research is to be pursued.'

Jowett said it was impossible to get a man for money to make a discovery, but 'you may enable a man who has shown a special capacity for research to exert his powers; and we are of opinion that, unless an effort is made to do this, one of the great purposes for which learned bodies, such as the Colleges, exist, may run the risk of being wholly lost sight of. Scientific discoveries rarely bring any direct profit to their authors, nor is it desirable that original investigation should be undertaken with a view to immediate pecuniary results.'

A graduated system of offices was required. There should be three classes of fellows: senior, permanent and non-celibate; seniors elected from juniors; and juniors elected for 14 years, seven of which might be non-resident.

In the last twenty years at Oxford only twelve fellowships had been awarded for science, out of more than 200. There was a fear of offering fellowships and scholarships for science, because there were few candidates, and hence inferior winners. This in turn meant few senior scientists, which in turn meant still fewer juniors.

The Commissioners were against a Natural Science College. The position of natural science 'in relation to the various branches of learning is not one of separation or antagonism; it should rather be regarded as running through the whole of human knowledge, and as inseparably linked with every part of it'.

They pointed out that other studies were just as much neglected as science. There was no public lectureship in English language and literature at either of the universities.

A balanced system of learning was required. In the past, magnificent libraries had been provided. Now, laboratories were required for the Sciences of Observation and Experiment.

The main function of a university was to maintain the position of science in a liberal education. It should supply highly educated Teachers of Science.

The tendency of a great deal of the evidence heard by the Commission was 'to show that the Universities ought not to undertake to give direct professional or technical instruction'.

With regard to the provision of Libraries, Benjamin Brodie said that he was 'really inclined to think that in former days a more real and earnest desire must have existed to preserve knowledge as a valuable national commodity for its own sake than exists now'.

The dangers today were different from those in the Middle Ages. 'The growing perception of the practical importance of knowledge' caused 'a very great draught indeed to be made upon the scientific intelligence of the country'. Teaching, sanitation and manufacture provided 'the only ways through which an income can be obtained, the pursuit of scientific truth being an absolutely unremunerative occupation. . . . The real perfection of science is shown only in scientific enquiry.' Appreciation of this had been established in Germany. There, research degrees were a great spur to scientific investigation. No such degrees existed in England.

The Universities should have (1) a complete scientific professoriate; (2) fellowships for original research; (3) laboratories; (4) museums for research, and (5) a doctorate in science.

William Thomson (Lord Kelvin) was critical of examinations. 'That in some degree, competitive examinations produce an elementary smattering of science I have no doubt whatever, but I cannot see that they produce much beneficial influence; and in the higher parts especially they have, I fear, a very fatally injurious tendency in obstructing the progress of science.'

Perhaps Thomson also had wry memories of the Tripos examination of his year. He was incomparably the most gifted candidate, and universally expected to be first. It has been said that Thomson shared the universal confidence, and on the day of the announcement of the result, he sent his servant to find out who was second. Being questioned on his return, he replied: 'You, sir.'

Parkinson, the man who beat Thomson, was said to have owed his success to getting up some of Thomson's own original papers on the evening of the examination. On the following day he was able to answer questions on it, while the author was unable to recall under examination conditions what he had previously discovered. Perhaps Parkinson's success was 'fatally injurious' to his career as a discoverer. He did not publish much original work, but he became one of the best-known Cambridge teachers of his generation; they also serve who only stand and teach.

In their Fourth Report, dealing with Museums and Public Lectures, the Commissioners recommended adequate provision for the Natural History Collections, and adequate staff to deal with them. They recommended that there should be a Collection of Scientific Instruments. This subsequently materialized as the Science Museum in London.

They said that the Government should promote science lectures in all centres of population. They should be on the General Principles and Facts of Science, and for 'the Working Classes on the Application of Science to the Arts and Industries of the Country'.

The Fifth Report dealt with the London and some other University colleges. Government aid for University and King's Colleges was recommended, but they did not think it would be necessary or desirable 'to give the Crown a voice in the appointment of the Professors, or any control over the management of the Colleges' other than visitational jurisdiction on accounts. King's College was to abolish all religious restrictions on the selection of professors on receipt of public money.

The Commissioners gave striking figures on the finances of Owens College at Manchester, which had within twenty-five years achieved such academic distinction. In 1871, the Senior Professor of Natural Philosophy, Balfour Stewart, received £400 a year. The professor of civil and mechanical engineering, the great Osborne Reynolds, received £300, and H. E. Roscoe, as professor of chemistry, £150 a year. The total salaries paid by the College of *all* the science professors, seven of them, was £1,565 per annum.

In addition to their salaries, the professors received fees

from students, In the case of chemistry, these amounted to £1,213 6s. 6d., natural philosophy £297, and engineering £109 8s. 0d. Altogether, professors and lecturers received £3,199 8s. 10d. in fees, and £3,767 6s. 10d. further fees for evening classes. The Commissioners recommended that Owens should receive State aid.

Their report on the National University of Ireland was hostile, on account of its being under clerical control.

The Sixth Report, issued in 1875, was on the Teaching of Science in Public and Endowed Schools. Lockyer was made an Assistant Commissioner to assist in its preparation. The Commissioners reported that 'We are compelled, therefore, to record our opinion that the Present State of Scientific Instruction in our Schools is extremely unsatisfactory . . . we cannot but regard its almost total exclusion from the teaching of the upper and middle classes as little less than a national misfortune.'

Stokes dissented from their recommendation that in all Public Schools science should be taught throughout the school course.

The Seventh Report dealt with the Scottish Universities. The Commissioners recommended Government aid for Edinburgh, Glasgow and St. Andrews Universities, but not for the Andersonian Institution in Glasgow, or for Dundee. The grant for Queen's University, Belfast, should be increased. Their recommendations for these institutions were generally more conservative than for English institutions. They were anxious not to offend Scottish pride in the educational and scientific facilities of Scotland, and deferred to the opinions of Scotsmen prominent in these fields.

The Commissioner's Eighth, and last, Report dealt with Government and Science. This subject was raised particularly by Colonel Alexander Strange, who had had much to do with bringing the Devonshire Commission into existence, and though his name is not well known, is one of the most, perhaps the most, outstanding British Statesmen of Science in the second half of the nineteenth century. For these reasons the next chapter will be devoted to Colonel Strange, and the Eighth Report of the Commissioners.

Alexander Strange

1818–1876

I

Almost Forgotten

THE virtual disappearance, during the first half of the twentieth century, of the name of Lieut.-Colonel Alexander Strange, F.R.S., described by Professor R. V. Jones as one of the 'almost forgotten' men of British science, is symptomatic of the weakness which had silently penetrated British thinking on science during that period. He was the most far-sighted of all those who considered how science in Britain should be fostered. He perceived the scope and scale of State action which would be necessary for this purpose. Though his ideas were fundamentally correct, he and they were put out of mind by the British world of science, in a kind of Freudian forgetting, because they were contrary to the individualistic conception of scientific activity then dominant. Even his friends and admirers described them as 'somewhat impracticable'.

Alexander Strange was a son of Sir Thomas Strange, a distinguished British jurist in India, and Chief Justice in Madras. Sir Thomas was descended from a Scottish Jacobite family, though he became a strong Whig. He was educated at Westminster School and Christ Church, Oxford. The college possesses a portrait of him, after he had become a judge, by Sir Martin Archer Shee. He was a handsome man who preserved his interest in scholarship, and published an important work on the *Elements of Hindu Law.* He was also an effective man of action in dealing with disturbances in Madras.

He was married twice. His first wife died early, and when the widowed judge was forty-eight, a second wife was found for him by the mother of the Duke of Wellington. This was Louisa Burroughs, then eighteen, the daughter of an impecunious Irish gentleman and lawyer, who recouped his fortune, lost in gambling, by lucrative briefs in the Madras Court.

They had twelve children; their last when Sir Thomas was

seventy-five. Alexander Strange was Sir Thomas's fifth son. He was born in London on April 27th, 1818. There was a wide difference of age between the quiet dignified judge and his talented son.

Lady Strange became 'a fine linguist, a musician, an artist of uncommon merit, and an exquisite needlewoman'. Unlike most of the Englishwomen then in India, she was deeply interested in the crafts, works of art and natural history of India. She did not pursue her artistic interests seriously until she had borne her twelve children, and then she had the strength of mind to make serious studies in early French art.

Alexander showed great ingenuity and skill in construction as a boy, and was never without occupation. He was sent to Harrow, but he was withdrawn at the age of fifteen, 'under the idea that he was too idle to profit by the instruction given there'.

As a consequence, he was put into the Indian army when he was sixteen, as a cadet in the 7th Madras Light Infantry. When he arrived in India 'he turned at once to scientific pursuits, especially astronomy—making telescopes, and repairing and altering instruments, and thus attracting the attention of Lord Hardinge, who placed him on the service of the Trigonometrical Survey. . . .'

After studying at the observatory in Simla he was appointed second assistant in the Survey. He carried out the triangulation of the arc of longitude from Sironj in Central India to Karachi, equivalent to 670 miles in length, one of the longest ever made up to that time. He performed the triangulation with the highest skill, taking it across 200 miles of desert, and then the plains of Sind.

After much anxiety, and having overcome almost insuperable difficulties, the triangulation was completed in 1853. The Surveyor-General reported that the remarkable energy and rapidity with which it had been done reflected the highest credit on Alexander Strange.

He was appointed to the headquarters office of the Surveyor-General in 1855. Two years later he was struck down with jungle fever, or malaria. In 1859 he was promoted major, and retired, with special thanks from the Government of India. He returned to England in 1861, at the age of forty-three, with the rank of Lieutenant-Colonel, and a pension.

In the following year he persuaded the Government of India

to establish a department for the supervision of scientific instruments. There were many of these set up independently for various purposes in different parts of that large country. Strange wished to organize the individual and systematic use of the instruments, and their manufacture on a planned basis.

He was appointed organizer of the department. He abolished the existing patterns of instruments, and encouraged the invention of new designs by competition. He himself designed large and ingenious surveying instruments. He recommended the use of aluminium bronze in instrument construction.

He had a special observatory erected at the Store Department of the India Office, in Lambeth, for testing the design and construction of the instruments. About 7,000 of about a hundred different kinds passed through his hands, and he acquired 'great technical knowledge of opticians' and engineers' workshops'.

Strange designed his theodolites on the 'flying micrometer plan'. His zenith sectors were portable and designed to give the maximum power for the minimum weight. They were about half the weight of those designed by Airy, and Captain John Herschel reported that they turned out at least twice as much work as comparable instruments.

They were at the time the most perfect and powerful geodetical instruments ever constructed. Their manufacture was carried out by Troughton and Simms, with the advice of Cooke, under Strange's supervision.

Strange's authority as a designer of instruments, and his superiority in this instance to Airy is of importance in relation to his views on Babbage's calculating machines. Unlike Airy, who reported against them, Strange was one of the few to believe in them, and in Babbage.

Strange became a fellow of the Royal Society, and served on its council from 1867–9. He was a leading member of the Royal Astronomical Society, and served on its council from 1863–7, and was its foreign secretary from 1868–73. He wrote the obituary notice of Charles Babbage for this Society, which was perhaps the only true contemporary perception of Babbage's character and genius.

Strange devoted himself to the scientific life of London, and of the day. He worked and lectured enthusiastically for many societies. He was a disinterested man who could always be counted on to further any worthy scientific cause. His numerous connections, goodwill and intelligence gave him persuasive influence. He acted as a Juror at the International Exhibition of 1862, and at the Paris Exhibition of 1867. He spoke French fluently, 'both as to diction and accent'. As a lecturer, he always spoke with knowledge and lucidity. He was a capable artist and an excellent performer on the violin.

Strange died on March 9th, 1876, at the early age of fifty-seven. *The Times* said that his death left a void in the scientific world which would be very difficult to fill, and also 'a void in the hearts of all who knew him. His varied and remarkable talents may well have drawn forth these public encomiums—but he himself, affectionate, generous, liberal, truthful, pre-eminently agreeable, was loved with no common love.'

Strange left four children. His only son, Alexander Burroughs Strange, became a civil engineer, and served on the railways in Madras.

The novelist, Nora K. Strange, a grand-niece of Alexander Strange, who has studied the archives of her family, has discussed why it did not retain its position in British life. It seems that its former Jacobite tradition left it with 'uncompromising consciences, lack of initiative, a limitless and foolish pride in refusing to cultivate friends at Court, a faculty for sponsoring and following lost causes. . . .' But she concluded that 'as a family, we have been the victim of our virtues rather than our vices'.

The emergence of Alexander Strange as one of the more significant men of the nineteenth century is no doubt due in part to those 'virtues', and an 'uncompromising conscience' about the need for State organization of science.

Coutts Trotter in the *Dictionary of National Biography* says that as 'a lover of science for its own sake, he long preached the duty of government to support scientific research, especially in directions where discovery, though enriching the community, brings no benefit to the inventor. To his advocacy was mainly due the appointment in 1870 of the Royal Commission on this question (presided over by the Duke of Devonshire), which adopted and recommended many of his suggestions.'

Strange's membership of the British Association, and of the councils of the Royal and the Royal Astronomical Societies in the years immediately preceding 1870, increased his opportunities for persuading eminent scientists and official bodies of the need for such a Commission.

COLONEL ALEXANDER STRANGE

In 1869 he had proposed to the British Association an enquiry into the question whether there existed in the British Isles sufficient provision for the vigorous prosecution of Physical Research, and if not, what measures were needed to secure it. The Association appointed a committee to consider this, whose members were W. Thomson, Tyndall, Frankland, Stenhouse, Mann, Huggins, Glaisher, Williamson, Stokes, Strange, Fleeming Jenkin, Hirst, Huxley, Balfour Stewart, Lyon Playfair, Lockyer, and Alfred Tennyson, the poet, who was also a fellow of the Royal Society.

The Committee concluded that the provision was 'far from sufficient'. It was universally admitted that 'scientific investigation is of enormous advantage to the community at large', but 'these advantages cannot be duly reaped without largely extending and systematizing Physical Research'. Greatly increased facilities were undoubtedly required, but they did not define these because 'Any scheme of scientific extension should be based on a full and accurate knowledge of the amount of aid now given to science, of the sciences from which that aid is derived, and of the functions performed by individuals and institutions receiving such aid.'

The Committee had not the means and powers to acquire this knowledge. Formal enquiry and inspection of records and examination of witnesses was essential, as the whole question of the relation of the State to Science, at present in a very unsettled and unsatisfactory position, was involved. They therefore urged that a Royal Commission alone was competent to deal with the subject.

The Committee held that the subject was sufficiently important to the nation 'to demand the use of the most ample and most powerful machinery that can be brought to bear upon it'. They therefore recommended the appointment of a Royal Commission to consider:

1. The character and nature of existing institutions and facilities for scientific investigation, and the amount of time and money devoted to such purposes.
2. What modifications or augmentations of the means and facilities that are at present available for the maintenance and extension of science, are requisite; and,
3. In what manner these can be best supplied.

The Association's recommendation, as has been seen, was duly acted upon by the appointment of the Devonshire Commission, some of the chief members of which had been prominent in the British Association's committee.

Strange followed up his original initiative by delivering a lecture to the Royal United Service Institution 'On the Necessity for a Permanent Commission on State Scientific Questions', after the Commission had begun to sit, and a year later, in 1872, gave extensive evidence to the Commission itself.

At his lecture, the chair was taken by Col. W. F. Drummond Jervois, C.B., R.E., Deputy Director of Works for Fortifications. The concern of these scientific soldiers with the problems of the organization of science is of considerable significance. To a considerable extent, the practical recognition that science must be organized was due to scientific soldiers, who in the course of their main profession had become thoroughly familiar with the need for organization in utilizing human ability on a large scale.

Strange started his lecture by stating: 'The duty of the Government with respect to science is one of the questions of the day. No question of equal importance has perhaps been more carelessly considered and more heedlessly postponed than this. And now that a hearing has been obtained for it, neither the governing class nor the masses are qualified to discuss it intelligently. The governing class, because it is for the most part composed of men in whose education, as even the highest education was conducted thirty to fifty years ago, science occupied an insignificant place; and the masses, because they may be taken to be virtually destitute of scientific knowledge. Those who wield, and those who confer, the powers of government being alike incapable of dealing with this question, it devolves on another section of the community to urge its claims to attention.

'The section qualified to do this is composed of scientific men, properly so called, of professional men, such as engineers, and certain manufacturers who are engaged in applying science practically, and of a limited number of officers in the naval and military services. This section is without much political influence, but its intellectual power has never been so strongly exerted, or so decidedly acknowledged as at the present time.'

He described the problem that the Commission was expected to solve as being of very great complexity, delicacy and difficulty. 'It has to survey the whole world of scientific thought, and to construct a chart on which the districts that it is the duty of State to occupy, shall be clearly delineated, with boundary lines so drawn as not to trench upon tracts which may be best left to individual or corporate management. It has then to devise a form of government of which not a trace at present exists, fitted to administer the affairs of the newly acquired territories. Instruction in science is one thing, and, I admit, an indispensable thing without which there can be no foundation for future scientific progress; scientific investigation is another and perfectly distinct thing, constituting the end to which instruction is the means. . . .' It was for the Commission to point out 'how far and by what agency, the Government may beneficially aid each'.

Strange argued that the problem set to the Commission was 'How should the State aid Science?' He proposed in his lecture to deal with the totally different, though allied problem of 'How can science aid the State?' His reply was perfectly concrete. It was 'By means of a permanent scientific commission or council, constituted for the purpose of advising the Government on all State Scientific questions.'

He analysed his proposal under four headings: the scope implied by the term State scientific questions, and their importance; how such questions were at present dealt with, and with what results; what the constitution and functions of the proposed council of science should be, and alleged objections to the proposal.

He included every aspect of military science, such as armaments; sanitary and medical services; and the employment of military staff on explorations and other activities 'tending to advance purely scientific knowledge'.

Civil science included all those scientific activities which affected the well-being of the community, such as sanitation, telegraphy, meteorology, astronomy, survey, and 'the physical sciences generally', so far as they are promoted by the Government. Fiscal and commercial questions which have a scientific basis should also be included.

With regard to armaments, most improvements could be made only by attention to scientific principles, and 'so long as human knowledge advances, in other words so long as the world lasts, there will be an incessant demand for improvements in these things'.

With regard to civil science, 'the health, welfare, commercial and intellectual progress of the community' depend on it. In fact, 'in the present stage of human progress, science is indispensable to national greatness'. In a nation that neglects science, 'the arts cannot flourish, trade cannot prosper, knowledge cannot advance, and war cannot succeed'. A 'nation that is not foremost in science cannot be foremost in civilization'.

It was therefore not rash to assert that 'State Scientific Questions' are of immeasurable importance. How were these at present dealt with? When not absolutely neglected, 'desultorily, inefficiently, irresponsibly'. This included 'ALL Administrations', and applied equally to those of all political parties. 'I am not aware of a single attempt on the part of any Government that has ever existed in England to define its duties with regard to science, or to model any administrative agency for dealing with it in a rational, efficient and comprehensive manner.'

Yet the number of questions involving science are innumerable and never ending. In the national advantages of greater wealth, more extensive mineral resources, and larger manufacturing power, no people could then vie with Britain; yet there were no official arrangements by which the nation could take the maximum benefit from these gifts by the application of science.

The official arrangements for science were still the same as in the pre-scientific era, in spite of the enormous advances of the previous forty years. Not a single step had been taken to create an *organization* capable of concentrating and directing the scattered independent efforts. The Government was at its wits' end on how to deal with the demands of scientific inventors. It tried to do this by guesses in each particular case.

At present State scientific questions were dealt with by three principal methods. First, by subordinates in the departments; second, by temporary and special committees; and third, by consultation with eminent scientists and scientific bodies.

He omitted Parliament 'because no scientific question was or ever will be solved by such an assembly'; and the Press, because so influential in other ways, it was quite unreliable in such matters.

The objection to these arrangements was that subordinate officials had other duties, and no time for scientific research; that science and especially State scientific questions were so complicated that they could not be grasped by a single mind, and lastly, that subordinates were disqualified as advisers, because 'no inferior can be expected to urge distasteful counsels on a powerful superior, and no superior can be expected to abandon his own preconceived ideas in consequence of the timid and feeble remonstrances of an inferior under his own orders.'

He instanced the recent disaster to the man-of-war *Captain*. It had been constructed on novel lines, according to the ideas of an ingenious and energetic naval captain. This 'typical independent inventor' had in his design offered a solution of what was essentially a scientific question. This was accepted without proper Government scientific investigation, and the ship went to the bottom in an average squall.

One objection to temporary advising committees was that its members were selected by ministers, who were generally not qualified to select scientists, and even worse, select scientists to suit their purposes. The selection of scientists 'is in itself a scientific question'. Another objection was that the problem discussed by a temporary committee must be taken up again from the beginning, and a lot of the previous work repeated, when the problem has to be again investigated. 'Permanent arrangements alone can deal with the unbroken continuity and unceasing change of scientific development.'

A third objection was that when there are many temporary committees at work, several committees will cover some or all of the same ground, wasting much effort through overlapping; he gave a current example of overlapping and confusion in the discussions on the merits of the Martini-Henry rifle.

With regard to the consultation of eminent scientists and scientific bodies, this was conducted 'without any system whatever'. It was objectionable in principle, because an independent individual or society has no responsibility. 'A great, powerful and opulent nation like England' should not be 'reduced to such makeshifts as private societies,' such as the Royal Society, for advice on matters of 'such tremendous national moment'.

The existing arrangements being quite inadequate, what system should be established? It was plausible to suggest that each ministry should have its own complete set of scientific advisers. Objections to this were that a very large number of scientists would be necessary, and there would be bickering between the ministries on scientific matters, because each set of scientific staff and advisers would consider themselves as good as any other. There would be no 'final court of scientific appeal to reconcile discordancies and give certainty to the action of the executive'.

He concluded that 'one permanent great Council for advising and assisting the Government on all State scientific questions' was necessary. The Council should be purely consultative, and not executive. All ministries could seek assistance from it. It should not initiate questions, though it might propose investigations to the Government. The Government should not be bound on all occasions to accept its advice, but it would in either case be 'absolutely responsible for all consequences'.

The Council would consist of a sufficient range of scientists to cover every branch; he thought it should contain about fifty.

The Council would conduct its business by means of working sub-committees. Their reports would be discussed by the whole Council, which would take the responsibility for passing the advice to the Government. 'This mode of working would insure dispatch of business, special aptitude in the investigators, and large views derived from a great variety of attainments and habits of thought. Decisions thus matured could not fail to command public confidence.'

The Council would advise the Government on all scientific questions arising out of routine administration; on special questions, such as the founding or abolition of scientific institutions, the sanctioning of scientific expeditions, 'and applications for grants for scientific purposes'. It should advise on inventions tendered for use by the State. It should conduct or superintend the experiments necessary to enable it to carry out all of these duties.

Among the recent instances illustrating the lack of such a system, were the difficulties experienced in obtaining Government support for a Solar Eclipse Expedition. 'The men of science went first to one department and were snubbed by it; they then tried another, from which they did not receive even a snub, their communication being totally ignored. Ultimately, a private individual obtained by personal influence an interview with the Chancellor of the Exchequer, and succeeded in inducing that Minister to sanction an object with which his particular department had no concern. Had there been a Department of Science, none of this fumbling would have occurred. . . .'

The provision of laboratories, equipment and funds for the

Council to pursue the investigations necessary to the performance of its duties would be 'absolutely indispensable'. The members of the Council would have to be very highly qualified, and give all or most of their time to the Council's work. They should therefore 'be handsomely paid'.

It would be idle to expect members to work 'from pure love of science and of their fellow-creatures'. The delights of philosophical speculation are one thing, but 'downright official routine work is quite another'.

'It has hitherto been too much the custom to treat men of science as exceptions to all other professions; to assume that whilst it is quite proper to enrich and ennoble soldiers who fight for pay, lawyers who evade or apply the law according to circunstances, physicians who kill or cure as seemeth best to them, and even divines, whose mission to save souls might be deemed a sufficient privilege . . .' the man of science 'should work for love, and die, as he too often does, in poverty'. He suggested the salary should be £1,500 per annum.

Strange said that three objections were commonly made to his proposals: because they were centralized; liable to jobbery; and too costly.

With regard to centralization, he considered it an advantage, not an evil. 'Those who are scared by centralization forget that it constitutes the very basis of civilization and of stable efficient government. In primitive savage life there is no centralization, no united effort for a common purpose. Each individual struggles single-handed for his rights. Civilization teaches us to set apart certain members of the community for purposes beneficial to the whole, to form them into distinct bodies, having definite duties to be executed, under the direction of a head central authority.'

He instanced the Army, Navy, Post Office, as examples of such bodies. 'The body we are considering will have to perform duties of a strictly imperial character, contributing directly to the efficiency of the defensive power of the empire, and to the security and well-being of every member of the community.' Such a body could not exist except in a centralized form.

With regard to jobbery, he did not see why a scientific organization should have any more of it than already exists and is tolerated in the Army, Church or Parliament.

With regard to costliness, one had only to look around to see the enormous waste that occurs through lack of science. 'Nothing is so ruinous as disregard for the laws of nature, and nothing so profitable as intelligent obedience to them. Science, looked at in the dryest commercial spirit, must, in the long run, *pay*.'

He did not suggest that the system he had outlined was more than a part of what was necessary. There was one other part which was so important that he felt he must name it: 'I mean the appointment of a Minister of Science. He need not necessarily be exclusively devoted to science; he might, perhaps, with advantage, have charge of education and the fine arts also; but some one in Parliament representing the scientific branches of the national services has become absolutely indispensable. . . .'

He also suggested that there should be a High War Council, to advise the Government 'on the highest problems of strategical science'.

'When we have all Scientific National Institutions under one Minister of State, advised by a permanent, independent, and highly qualified consultative body to advise the Minister of War and Marine in strategical science—then the fact that, in accordance with our marvellous constitution, these Ministers must almost necessarily be men without pretension to a knowledge of the affairs which they administer, need cause us no alarm. When these combinations have been, as they assuredly will be, sooner or later effected, the wealth, resources, and intelligence of the nation, having due scope, will render us unapproachable in the arts of peace, and unconquerable in war—but not till then.'

The Council of Science would invoke no new administrative principle. The Council of India—a *standing commission*—was such a body. He therefore proposed only to extend the use of an accepted principle in administration; 'to substitute concentration for scattered effort, system for chance, organization for disorder'.

He proposed neither to exact new duties from the Queen's advisers, nor fix new responsibilities upon them. The aim of his proposals was 'to lighten their labours and anxieties by putting into their hands better arms than those with which they now vainly strive to uphold the power and the glory of the nation'.

A year later, in 1872, the Devonshire Commission considered the question of Government and Science virtually under the headings raised by Strange. The chief items of the agenda of their Eighth and last Report were:

1. Scientific work by departments of Government.

2. Assistance given at present by the State to Scientific Research.
3. Assistance that it is desirable that the State should give.
4. The Central Organization which is best calculated to enable the State to determine its action on all questions affecting Science.

Strange gave extensive evidence on these topics to the Commission.

II

The Cultivation of Science from a National Perspective

STRANGE explained to the Commission that during the previous ten years he had paid much attention to the cultivation of science from a national point of view. The postulates on which he based his proposals were:

'1. That science is essential to the advancement of civilization, the development of national wealth, and the maintenance of national power.

'2. That all science should be cultivated, even branches of science which do not appear to promise immediate direct advantage.

'3. That the State or Government, acting as trustees of the people, should provide for the cultivation of those departments of science which, by reason of costliness, either in time or money, or of remoteness of probable profit, are beyond the reach of private individuals; in order that the community may not suffer from the effect of insufficiency of isolated effort.

'4. That to whatever extent science may be advanced by State agency, that agency should be systematically constituted and directed.'

He gave a list of fourteen institutions under six Departments of State, illustrating their insufficiency and want of system. For instance, astronomical observations in England, Scotland and India were under the Admiralty, Office of Works and India Office respectively.

The observatories had been originally made many years ago, 'chiefly, if not entirely, for the avowed purpose of assisting navigation'. Since Greenwich was founded, an entirely new astronomy had grown up, of which Solar Physics was an important part.

The new Astrophysics should be separated from gravitational astronomy. Another type of mind was needed for its prosecution. 'Researches cannot be carried on with the same fullness and power by a private individual as they can by the State, nor do I think that the State should look to agencies of that sort for doing what is national work.' The element of continuity is wanting in private effort.

It was desirable that some meteorological observatories should be near London, as it was 'the centre of all intellectual activity'.

He pointed out that the observations then carried out by the Meteorological Office were insufficient to provide a basis for forecasts; 'Prediction I conceive to be the great object of meteorology, and that is not attempted by the Meteorological Office.'

In connection with meteorological observations, he remarked that State funds should not be controlled by an unpaid body. Meteorology must be based on national and international observations, with standardized instruments.

With regard to physics, there was no State physical laboratory. *All* branches of science should be promoted or encouraged by the Government. This cannot be done by private individuals. 'I think that the whole of our naval and military and social economy is dependent upon investigations such as would be carried on in a physical laboratory.'

Independent but associated physical and chemical laboratories were required, which should not be for educational purposes. 'I look upon science . . . as a matter of business principles, and to be considered as a work to be done. . . .'

'Nothing is so wasteful as to employ men highly distinguished for their capacity for investigation in teaching the elements of knowledge. I call that a positively criminal waste of intellect.'

He had suggested to the British Association that the staff of the laboratories should deal with: 1. research of direct use to the State; 2. telegraphs; 3. sanitary and social progress; 4. original research; 5. help private persons without means to pursue researches; 6. give instruction to a small number of research students; and 7. deliver public lectures.

It was essential that 'there should be a body capable of issuing credentials to the men of science who should have these advantages placed at their disposal'.

In other parts of the country there would have to be other institutions in the great centres of industry. It was right to grant aid to anyone who could contribute to the extension of knowledge.

The director of each laboratory should carry out researches for the State, with the moral duty to use the equipment for carrying out original research. Directors should be members of a body which gave suggestions for research. With regard to encouragement of research, it was true that 'you cannot pay a man to discover, but you may put him in a position favourable to discovery'.

He commented on the lack of provision for standards of measurement. No private person had the right to ascertain a standard measure, and compare it with his own. There was still no standard thermometer in England. A proper system of scientific standards was required. He pointed out that the International Commission on Standards originated in Russia, not England.

On the provision of scientific advice to the Government he said: 'It has sometimes been suggested to me that the Royal Society is a body already in existence which might very well be constituted as a standing adviser to the Government on all scientific questions. . . . Being a private and in no sense an official body it would or would not undertake enquiries as it saw fit. That will not do for business arrangements, and I am talking about science as a matter of business.'

Strange related how he had consulted the Royal Society on the problem raised by the differences in the Greenwich and the Kew tests of thermometers and barometers. The Society had refused to undertake it, and had told him to take his choice as to which of the two standards he preferred. 'It left me,' he said, 'a State official, to create my own authority. Now, that is a responsibility that should not devolve upon me.'

There were more chemical than physical laboratories in England because the direct application of chemistry to manufacturing was more obvious than that of physics. But 'more public money is spent in England in certain departments of natural history than on all other branches of science put together'. (Natural history was one of the particular interests of the pre-industrial age of exploration, whereas the need for physics had become pressing only after industrialism had reached an advanced stage.)

He was himself nominally the inspector of scientific instruments for India. In fact, he was really the inventor of such instruments for India. He did not rate English instrument-makers very highly. They were tradesmen, and their purpose was to make fortunes, not to advance science. He had had to re-design every English instrument to suit Indian conditions.

The design of scientific instruments should be systematically improved. As a rule, scientists were not good designers of instruments. A collection of scientific instruments should be made (A Science Museum) to aid in the development of design. 'I find very few persons who have really studied what I will venture to call the physiology of instruments and apparatus.' In general, mechanical engineers were more advanced in design of machinery than instrument-makers were of instruments.

The scientific education provided on the Continent led to more sound principles of construction. The Government of India had established the India Civil and Engineering College because British engineering education had been found to be 'excessively faulty'. They took men from England, and then gave them an engineering education in India, which was generally better than they could obtain at home.

Finally, he brought forward again the idea of a scientific centre in London. (The Prince Consort had enthusiastically advocated it.) Strange suggested it should be furnished with libraries in various branches of science, congregated together. There should be a public central hall. The centre should be open at night, and light refreshments should be available.

Continuing his evidence, Strange quoted a speech by Gladstone at the Annual Dinner of the Institution of Civil Engineers on May 7th, 1872, as a classical example of the failure to appreciate the need for organization, owing to a mistaken social philosophy. 'It was in the growth of individual and local energy,' said Mr. Gladstone, 'and in freedom from all artificial and extraneous interference that the secret of the greatness of this country was to be found. That danger of centralization which had been a formidable and fatal difficulty in other lands had not yet obtained serious dimensions among ourselves, but it had lifted its head in this country also, and Englishmen would show at once their wisdom and their fidelity to the traditions of their forefathers by taking care not to hand over to the executive the discharge of functions which would be much better performed by themselves. . . .'

The Times commented that the Institution of Civil Engineers had 'fought their way and been the founders of their own fortune', and so their president had had the pleasure of telling the Prime Minister, that they 'have been and are independent of all governments whatever'.

Commenting on this ideology with respect to science, Strange said that according to his notion there are four stages in the progress of science: collecting, observing, experimenting and discovering. It was the same with nations as with individuals. As a *nation* (*not* as a private individual) England was in the first of these stages, and at the beginning of the second.

He was 'told over and over again that such things as great laboratories will not be allowed, but are out of the question; and that there are principles of economy now working in the Government which are totally opposed to such an idea; in fact, that it is madness to think of it.' But that did not deter him from saying that it ought to be done.

He then put forward his proposal for a Council of Science, which he had described to the Royal United Services Institution. He thought that the members of the Council would have to give up original work and devote all their energy to administration.

As for scientists engaged in the proposed new laboratories, 'if there are men of high originality and great genius, they are very often better left to themselves, and it is so no doubt; but still public business cannot always conform itself to the peculiarities of individuals. They would have to be directed and have to do as they were told, just as the assistants at Greenwich Observatory have to make particular observations, of particular stars in a particular manner. . . .'

He quoted Baden-Powell's opinion in favour of 'A Council of Science, with extended powers, properly elected, and adequately remunerated, would be the appropriate adjunct of the Government of a country, all of whose resources are so powerfully developed in extensive dependence on the application of science.'

Strange said that the great strength of the British private scientific societies was very valuable, but they had the inherent limitations of private societies. Sabine, then President of the Royal Society, had told him that Palmerston had said the Society could have £10,000 if it wanted it. He told Sabine that he had a great deal to answer for in not asking for it. It was preposterous that thirty fellows of the Society should spend a whole afternoon discussing how a sum of £400 was to be spent.

III

A Ministry of Science

STRANGE gave his reasons for the establishment of a Ministry of Science in his evidence in May 1872. He said: 'It seems to me that in the first place there should be some means of bringing science fully before the nation through Parliament. I know of no means of doing this that is in accordance with our constitutional procedure, except through a minister of state; and therefore assuming science to be a matter of enormous national importance, I think it is essential that it should all be brought under one minister of state, who should be responsible to Parliament for everything which is done in the name of the nation to advance science, and who should frame his own estimates and keep them distinct from those departments which have little or nothing to do with science.

'What I should be glad to see would be a minister for science, but I dare say that if proper assistance were given to such a minister, he might superintend other departments as well; for instance, as on the continent, he might superintend education and the fine arts. I think it would be preferable that he should be for science only. . . .'

He thought there would be considerable difficulty in defining the boundaries between science and education. One section of a composite ministry would relate to education, 'which is quite a distinct thing from national research'. He thought their mixing up was a great evil. Education was 'the means, the other the end; instruction I conceive to be the mode of growing a certain number of persons fit to investigate'.

Strange dealt with a number of points which had stimulated

his ideas. Regarding finance, he explained that when, a few years ago, he had first taken up the subject of Government science, he had 'endeavoured to get at the aggregate amount of money voted annually for science'. He found this quite impossible without personal enquiry. The votes were scattered through many departments.

The Government estimates did not provide the information, so he thought 'that there should be an estimate for science', just as there was for the military services. 'It is a distinct subject, which should be brought under a distinct head of finance, and to do that it would be necessary to have a Minister of State.'

Asked whether the science of artillery should be removed from the control of the Admiralty and War Office, he replied: 'No; the great difficulty in those questions is to bring the professional mind and the scientific mind into contact, and machinery must, I think, be created which would have that object in view.'

The first essential was the establishment of a Ministry of Science. The next step would be permanent staff for administrative purposes. 'The question of the under-secretary is one that requires a little attention, for the minister of science might be, for instance . . . a peer.'

There should be a permanent under-secretary to prevent fluctuations due to changes of ministry. There should be the usual ministerial, administrative and executive organization; and a Consultative Council on the lines he had previously described.

G. B. Airy, at the time President of the Royal Society, as well as Astronomer Royal, pointed out in his evidence that the idea was not new. The Royal Society had proposed a Council of Science in the Report of the Government Grant Commission in 1857. It had been said in the Report for 1855, that if such a Council were established so as not to interfere 'with the ancient and recognized relation between the Royal Society and the Government', it appeared that such an official advisory board for the Government on research and publication, and on public scientific appointments, might be advantageous. It was desirable 'that scientific officers be placed more nearly on a level in respect to salary with . . . other civil appointments'. so that scientific posts became as attractive as ordinary civil service posts to the 'ambition in educated men'. It should be something like 'the old Board of Longitude, but with improvements'.

'The Board of Longitude was a very useful body for a time, when the struggle was rising about accepting the theory of gravitation, and generally introducing it, especially into the formation of the lunar tables for the aid of nautical astronomy. . . .' He was of the opinion that the experience of these bodies showed that it would be best for 'the Government, when occasion requires it, to get the best advice it can'.

Airy found every opportunity for opposing the proposals for the extension of organized Government activity in science. He said that 'the Government are already pushed very hard in their estimates. The screw is always put on them, "Cannot you reduce the estimates a little more?" And then it would always come to a question of extensive feeling in the House of Commons, and of popular feeling out of the House of Commons, and I am confident from what I have seen that those two bodies would not in every respect support an extension.'

Airy said that he looked to Cambridge for improvements in scientific education, but they were too much confined to pure mathematics. A Cambridge man sits in his room all evening and thinks of abstract problems which have no bearing on natural philosophy. He produces matters of great ability. 'but they are not of any use for the science of the world'. He thought that 'the best thing that could happen to the University would be to have a good deal of foreign blood in it'.

He had been in the habit of relying on the Government for very little, except money. The best thing would be for the Government to call specially upon persons in whom it has learned to have some confidence. He saw great difficulty in promoting science through such a Commission as this.

He was against anything like a paid Academy. It was 'very much opposed to the genius of this country. I believe it has been found necessary in Russia, for instance, where, without it, there would be only a set of barbarians. . . .' Here 'it is quite the spirit of things' for persons to work individually.

With regard to the observatory, science had been introduced into it 'from its connection with a utilitarian subject, and I am inclined to think, from all I see of the history of the observatory, that it is the best fate that can happen to an observatory. It is supported in a better and more healthy condition from being connected with a subject of social utility than if it were left wholly to the abstract science of astronomy.'

The evidence that Strange's ideas were not entirely new was no doubt meant to weaken the case for them, but it also strengthened the case for those who wished to recommend them as not fanciful.

Strange said that the proposed Council should deal only with important problems, and with all departments of state. It was necessary to have an organization which would bring the professional mind and the scientific mind together. It would then not be necessary to have a minister or head of the department who was both a scientist and a professional politician. 'If you wait until you find a competent man, who is also a parliamentary man, a man of property, and so on, you may wait for ever before you get him.'

Every State scientific institution should be under the Minister of Science, and the Council should consider inventions.

He said that if he had limited himself to what well-informed people had told him the Government might concede to science, he would have troubled the Commission much less than he had done. He had been told over and over again that big laboratories were out of the question; that there were principles of economy then operating in the Government which were totally opposed to such an idea; in fact, it was madness to think of it. But that did not deter him from saying that it ought to be done.

A large Consultative Council could be subdivided into committees, standing or temporary. Even a small Council of six would be a tremendous step forward. There were innumerable subjects which required continuous attention. For example, a permanent arrangement for the study of metals should be established. Metals will be studied 'as long as the world lasts'.

If the Government had had such a scientific organization as he proposed, it would 'have had the means of sound scientific advice constantly at hand, of which experience proves they are in daily want on every emergency, and which they obtained by asking the gratuitous services of men of science, and the crown would have possessed the means of making a graceful acknowledgement of the services, and paying a just tribute to the genius of men devoted to the higher branches of the abstract sciences which are of a nature incapable of themselves of affording any kind of remuneration, or in the ordinary course leading to any of those honours or preferments which await eminence in other professions.'

The Commission devoted their Eighth Report substantially to the topics that Strange had raised. They dealt with them under four headings: Scientific Work by Departments of Government; Assistance given at present by the State to Scientific Research; Assistance that it is desirable the State should give; and the Central Organization which is best calculated to enable the Government to determine its action in all questions affecting Science.

They said that imperial investigations covered too much time and space to be carried out by private bodies and societies. For example, topographical and hydrographical surveys; in 1874–5 these cost respectively £132,000 and £121,033. The cost of Astronomy was £9,703; the Geological Survey, £22,920; Meteorology, £12,082; Botany, including Kew, £21,470; and the Standards Department of the Board of Trade, £2,063.

With regard to the Central Organization, the majority of witnesses recommended either a Special Minister of Science or a Minister of Science and Education. In most cases, witnesses were of the opinion that such a Minister should be advised by a Council.

Richard Owen had said that 'the recommendation by Bentham in the last century of such a minister can hardly fail to be practically adopted before the close of the present century, and that the necessity of having a minister for such a purpose will be recognized.' William Thomson, already at the height of fame, said:

'It would be quite necessary to have a Minister of Science; it is indeed, I think, generally felt that a minister of science and scientific instruction is a necessity . . . specially of Scientific instruction; and not under any national education board, but a minister of science and scientific instruction. The minister would necessarily be in Parliament and a political man, but it would be very rare that he could also be a scientific man, and perhaps not desirable that he should be a scientific man, but he must have able scientific advisers at hand. . . . If there is to be a minister, it must be a minister of science and education. There might be a minister of science and education, with a chief secretary or under minister for national and elementary education, and another for the advancement of science and for the higher scientific instruction. But naturally the minister of education must act for the masses; that must be his great duty, and however much he might wish to act for science, he has still a great duty to the masses. On the whole, I think it would be preferable to have a distinct minister of science and scientific instruction. A minister of science and scientific instruction, as a subordinate to a chief minister of science and education, might probably be a very good arrangement . . . the minister of science administers knowledge to the whole country. . . .'

Warren de la Rue, the noted printer and physicist, joint inventor of the first envelope-making machine; the first user of electro-typing on a manufacturing scale; inventor of the Daniell cell with neutral solutions; and a pioneer in the photography of celestial bodies, said that even if £10,000 were given to the Royal Society to aid investigations, he did not think that ought in any way to interfere with 'the consideration of the establishment of a science minister whose functions would be altogether larger and much more important. We want science really cared for in England by the State, and we want all State questions relating to science properly considered by a body capable of dealing with them.'

General Strachey, an Army engineer, a fellow of the Royal Society, and a friend of Strange, with Indian experience, said that 'The principal reason that I have for thinking that such a body as the Council of the Royal Society is not suitable for the purpose [of acting as an official consultative Council on Science] is, that it cannot have that specific responsibility put upon it which should be put upon' such a body. The Royal Society 'is got together for totally different purposes and objects. The Council of the Royal Society has to manage the business of the Royal Society, and is not at all selected to advise the Government on matters connected with the advancement of science, or the application of science in the operations of the public departments.

'The minister would have a perfect right to repudiate any scheme which they put forward, or any advice they gave; I mean that he would be justified in doing so on the ground that he was not responsible for their selection.

'I understand that the Treasury give a thousand pounds a year to the Royal Society to spend in their own way on scientific objects. I think myself that this system is essentially vicious; to make a homely comparison, it is as though I desired to absolve myself from all responsibility in connection with the suffering and poorer class of the community, by giving the first beggar I met sixpence. The Chancellor of the Exchequer hands over a thousand pounds to the Royal Society, and thinks he has done all that is necessary for the promotion of science.'

Captain Galton suggested an administrative Council under the Privy Council, perhaps nominated by the Prime Minister. Its function should be similar to the India Council, to which the Secretary of State for India must minute any differences of opinion with it.

The Commissioners remarked that in spite of General Strachey, Colonel Strange and others, the India Council had failed to cope with many problems, for example 'the Efflorescence of Soda on Irrigated Land'.

C. W. Siemens said that the Government should not direct research, but direct enquiries to be made on matters of national importance. He had no doubt that there were 'Political Men of highly cultivated minds, or even with a great knowledge of Science, who would be quite capable of taking such a position'.

W. R. Grove was 'not very sanguine as to the working of such a Council', but thought 'the experiment worth trying. . . . A large or highly paid Science Council . . . would lead to intriguing for place; and not the best men of science but the ablest men of the world would succeed. . . . Scientific men moreover, are not, as a body, suited for the work. . . .' He thought that the continuation of the Devonshire Commission on a permanent basis, but with different, modestly paid individuals, would be the best arrangement.

H. E. Roscoe recommended a Council organized on the lines of the Commission. The lay members should be nominated by the Government, the scientists by the scientific societies.

William Thomson said that 'the main object of such a council would . . . be to advise the Government on all scientific questions which might come under the attention of the Government, and all scientific works actually undertaken.'

A. W. Williamson wanted such a council to make 'a complete report on the national resources available for scientific instruction and research', and keep it up to date.

Airy was almost alone among the scientific witnesses in his negative attitude. Asked whether he needed the assistance of a Ministry of Science or Education with reference to Greenwich

Observatory, he replied: 'No; we are naturally connected in these respects with the Admiralty.' Asked whether he saw any inconveniences arising from the several scientific institutions that are more or less connected with the Government being under different departments, he replied: 'Not that I am aware of.'

While the scientific witnesses were almost unanimously in favour of a Government scientific organization, some were less forthright than others. Such men as T. H. Huxley and H. E. Roscoe came out less impressively. They were professors, and were no doubt more interested in the teaching and educational side of science, and in academic research. Huxley questioned Strange on salaries for members of the proposed Council. 'Take the case of the late Mr. Faraday, for example. If you had offered him £10,000 a year, I do not believe he would have taken one of those posts?' Strange replied that a member would have to sacrifice his scientific work to some extent. Public duty had also its demands.

Roscoe's tentativeness was perhaps influenced by his close relations with the political party in power. Generally speaking, Huxley, Roscoe, Grove and others do not seem to have thought out the problem of the organization of science very far. William Thomson's forthrightness and definiteness were all the more impressive, especially in view of his very great scientific eminence. Perhaps his practical experience in such matters as the Atlantic cable had clarified his mind on large problems of scientific organization.

The political witnesses were generally against the proposals. Lord Derby, the Chancellor of the Exchequer, was against a Council of Science. 'The conduct of administrative business and the management of men is an entirely different thing from the conduct of scientific research.' Those who took the lead in managing such a Council would be those whose time and attention were least devoted to scientific work. The Council of the Royal Society could not be this body because it was 'appointed by a process with which the Government has nothing to do'.

Lord Salisbury said that the Government could always get better opinions by going to the best scientist. The India Council was in reality simply a bureau of administrators. The House of Commons would never feel itself prevented from reversing the decision of a Council of Science of that kind. He preferred increasing the grant to the Royal Society to any new-fangled

Scientific Council, because 'we know how it works, and it would be pretty sure to go on working as well as it does now.'

Sir Stafford Northcote agreed with Lords Derby and Salisbury, but not to taking counsel from irresponsible advisers.

Salisbury showed himself well aware of the ideological problems involved. Asked whether the State could legitimately give aid for the advancement of science, he replied that it was 'a very orthodox doctrine to hold, and one which could be supported if necessary by quotations out of Adam Smith'. Its essence was that the State was justified in stimulating that kind of industry useful to the State, that will not provide a reward to the efforts of individuals.

Derby said that, as a general rule, he was 'very strongly in favour of private effort, and very decidedly against the application of State funds to any purpose that can be accomplished without them', but he thought that if there was an exception to this 'sound and wholesome rule', it was 'in the case of scientific research, because the results are not immediate, they are not popular in their character, and they bring absolutely no pecuniary advantage to the person engaged in working them out', but they are 'a benefit to the whole community, and in a certain sense to mankind in general'.

The Commission concluded this part of their Report by observing that the assistance given by the State for the Promotion of Scientific Research was inadequate. The Government grant to the Royal Society should be increased. A Ministry of Science and Education should be established. 'We consider the creation of such a Ministry to be of primary importance.' There should be a 'Council representing the Scientific Knowledge of the Nation'. It should consist of nominees of the Government, the Royal Society, and other scientific societies.

IV

Problems, Laboratories and Salaries

THE Commission collected evidence on problems which were being neglected through lack of laboratories that could only be provided by the Government, and opinions on the kind of laboratories required. They also collected some views on the Payment of Scientific Workers, which brought out the contrast between what they received and what they ought to receive.

The lack of Government laboratories was particularly felt in scientific engineering research, because such institutions were largely beyond the means of private resources, and their results were of immediate practical importance.

William Froude dwelt on the fallacy of engineering experimenting on the full scale, 'on the scale of 12 inches to the foot', instead of with small-scale inexpensive models. F. J. Reid, M.P., complained that the Admiralty were accepting ship designs based on inadequate hydraulic and marine engine research.

John Anderson, the Superintendent of Machinery at Woolwich, wanted a 'grand laboratory'. He said that the experiments of Joule, which were fundamental for the improvement of the efficiency of steam engines, and 'which he carried out for himself were the sort of thing which I think the Government should have done for the sake of the country'. William Thomson pointed out the need to examine standards every 10, 50, 100 or 500 years.

The Commissioners remarked that 'as there are no Public Laboratories available for the Researches of Private Investigators, it may be said that in many Branches of Experimental Science, the State affords no permanent material aid to such Investigations'.

In 1849 Lord John Russell in a letter to Lord Rosse, then President of the Royal Society, had offered £1,000 per annum for the support of researches. The Commission gave an analysis of the outcome of the expenditure of £20,000 from this source during the last twenty years. It made a wonderful list, including researches by Thomson and Joule, Clerk Maxwell, Cayley, Balfour Stewart and Crookes.

Frankland in his evidence stressed the need for Government promotion of scientific research, in order to produce that science from which industrial inventions could be made, and thus ensure industrial advance. 'In my opinion there could not be any doubt but that the nation which neglected science must suffer in the end, because although it could buy scientific inventions from the other country, yet it still would always be behind, as it were, in the market. . . . It is also much more difficult to establish new manufactures upon new inventions in a country which neglects science because you cannot have either workpeople or managers competent to conduct those processes which depend on scientific principles.'

Thomson said that 'There are many investigations which can only be done by the nation as a whole, and viewing the Government in one sense as acting for the nation, as it were a committee of the whole nation, there are very many investigations not merely of importance with reference to promoting scientific discoveries, in which the whole nation takes pleasure, and from which the whole nation derives as great benefit as anything material can possibly produce. Investigations for which a large expenditure of money is necessary, and which must be continued through long periods of years, cannot be undertaken by private individuals. Generally speaking, I believe that if the Government is well advised in respect to science it will be for the good of the nation that the Government should make it part of its functions to promote experimental investigations in science.'

Thomson was in favour of five Government research laboratories near London, covering physics, astronomical physics, chemistry and physiology. There should be no teaching, except instruction in research to young men.

Strange proposed a complete system of Government laboratories. 'It may be necessary for a manufacturer to prosecute only such particular investigations as promise direct and speedy profit. A great nation must not act in that commercial spirit. All the laws of nature are so intimately interwoven, that it is impossible to say beforehand that a given line of research apparently unproductive may not throw light in unsuspected directions, and so lead to untold and undreamt of treasures.'

Frankland thought that such men as Joule, Perkin, Lockyer and Grove would find such institutions as those recommended by Strange very helpful.

Thomson was in favour of astronomical observatories in various parts of the world. Balfour Stewart said a thorough study of the sun was necessary. 'We ought to remember how greatly the accurate observations of Tycho Brahe contributed to the generalizations of Kepler.'

Thomson referred to the researches of Joule and himself on Tidal Observations. Continuous observation of sea levels and tides was needed. 'With regard to the sea level, there have been reports from time to time with regard to the inroads of the sea on our coasts, but sufficient steps do not appear to have been taken to ascertain the facts in these cases. It seems to me very important to be acquainted with any alterations in the configuration of the earth which may be taking place, however minute those alterations may be.' In 1872 an application by Thomson to the Treasury for £150 for the extension, improvement and harmonic analysis of tidal observations was rejected.

On the subject of the payment of Scientific Workers, Lord Salisbury observed 'how very much more rapid the progress of research is where there is a commercial value attached to the results of it'. The electric telegraph had stimulated electrical research, and coal-tar dyes organic chemistry. He thought senior scientists should receive £1,000–£1,500 a year, corresponding to similar positions in the Church, and with a retiring pension. He thought direct salaries should be paid for research.

Lord Derby said it was part of the public duty to relieve men of eminent capacity for original discovery from engaging in work below their talents in order to gain a livelihood, but he did not descend to particulars as to how this should be done.

Thomson said 'that men should be enabled to live on scientific research is a matter of most immediate consequence to the honour and welfare of this country. At present a man cannot live on scientific research. If he aspires to devote himself to it he must cast about for a means of supporting himself, and the only generally accepted possibility of being able to support himself is by teaching, and to secure even a very small income, barely sufficient to live upon, by teaching, involves the expenditure of almost his whole time upon it in most situations, so that at present it is really only in intervals of hard work in professions that men not of independent means in this country can apply themselves at all to scientific research.'

The Commission even collected Joseph Henry's views, while he was on a visit to Europe. He said: 'My idea would be that if the funds were sufficient, and men could be found capable of advancing science, they should be consecrated to science, and be provided with the means of living above all care for physical wants, and supplied with all the implements necessary to investigation.'

The Commission concluded that there were three ways of assisting scientists; by grants of money for investigations; by providing laboratories for the services of the State and in the Universities for the use of scientists; and laboratories erected by the Government for private investigators.

V

Men of Insight

STRANGE'S grasp of the necessity of a comprehensive organization for the development of the potentialities of modern science helped him, virtually alone for nearly a hundred years, to understand Charles Babbage. The inventor of the computer was regarded almost universally as an unpractical, egotistic, disappointed inventor.

When Babbage died in 1871, Strange, who was Foreign Secretary of the Royal Astronomical Society, wrote his obituary notice for that Society's journal. Babbage had been one of the most active founders of the Royal Astronomical Society in 1820, and in 1823 was the first recipient of its Gold Medal, now a famous award, for his invention of his first calculating machine.

Strange's prophetic conception of the organizational needs of British science was influenced by his knowledge of Babbage, and of what had happened in the development of his calculating machines. He said that a study of the documents showed that the Government's failure to give proper support to Babbage 'arose mainly from the fact that there was no provision in the Government for the proper consideration of such a question—no minister, no department, no official advisers, who could properly be made responsible for thoroughly investigating the matter, and for pronouncing a well-weighed decision upon it. The consequence was, that in the press of party politics, no one minister would give the requisite attention to such a matter. . . .'

He regretted that, at the time of writing, 'the deficiency in our administration, which operated unfavourably in this famous case, still exists'.

Strange, an inventor in the sphere of instruments and in the organization of science, was particularly well-qualified to understand Babbage, the inventor in the sphere of machines and the application of scientific methods to manufacture. He said that Babbage 'had the faculty of endearing himself to those who knew him'. He was full of human sympathies, and mixed habitually during his busiest years 'in the society and even in the gaieties of the metropolis'. His conversation was so easy and genial, that wherever he went he was a centre of attraction, particularly among the ladies. He was a 'patient and deeply interested listener' to skilled artisans who had something interesting to impart. Those who 'imagine him to have been a mere peevish visionary, require to be told that no man ever more truly loved his kind, and few men have devoted transcendent powers like his with such disinterestedness, such tenacity, and such noble self-sacrifice, to what he believed to be the profit and the elevation of humanity'.

Strange thought that the indirect effect of Babbage's labours could not be adequately estimated, and would 'probably never be duly appreciated but by a few. The discoveries and improvements introduced by him in the art of metallic construction are innumerable. The shaping of metals by automatic machinery, now so well understood, was an art in its infancy when Babbage was first compelled, by the necessities of his designs, to turn his attention to it.'

The foreman in the workshop of Joseph Clement, where Babbage's machines were made, was Joseph Whitworth, who subsequently became famous as the founder of the machine-tool firm at Manchester and the developer of precision and standardized mechanical engineering. Babbage was once asked whether the improvement in the precision of machine tools and of the instruments used in scientific laboratories was mainly due to his attempts to complete the calculating machine, and he replied: 'You are quite right, it used to be said by the men in my workshop, Mr. Babbage made Clement, Clement made Whitworth, and Whitworth made the tools.'

In due course, in 1855, Babbage supported Sir Joseph Whitworth's proposals for the introduction of standardized engineering measures and gauges.

The parts of Babbage's calculating machines had to be made to a higher order of accuracy than had hitherto been achieved in that branch of mechanical engineering. He and his mechanics had to devise more accurate and versatile machine tools, the principles of which were applied in the construction of machine tools for other purposes. He anticipated modern methods of mounting cutting tools, and he used diamond cutters for very fine and accurate finishes.

The assessments of Babbage by Strange, and by Airy who

confidentially reported on the calculating machine as 'worthless' and thus caused the discontinuance of Government support for its development, illustrate the difference between the man of insight and the supremely competent man without it.

Among other outstanding figures in the Devonshire Commission was its scientific Secretary, Joseph Norman Lockyer. He was born at Rugby in 1836, the son of a doctor, and died in 1920. He was educated privately, and on the Continent, so that his mind was not formed in the usual British institutions. He acquired an interest in science from his father. He entered on a civil service career as a clerk in the War Office, and in 1865 became editor of the *Army Regulations*. Like Strange he was thoroughly acquainted with the ideas of organization through his military connections.

He studied astronomy in his spare time, and engaged in observations with his own telescope. In 1866, he attached a spectroscope to it, and observed the spectrum of sun-spots. He observed no bright lines, but thickened dark ones. Then he studied solar prominences by the same technique. On the same day, in October 1868, he, and P. J. C. Janssen in Paris, published their discovery of what Lockyer subsequently named the sun's chromosphere. In the same year, he detected a line in the sun's spectrum, which he called 'helium'.

By 1870 he had become an eminent scientist, as well as a capable official, and consequently was excellently qualified to be Secretary of the Commission.

Lockyer's scientific insight led him to foresee that the enhanced and super-enhanced spectral lines of the elements had a deep physical significance. They later became part of the evidence for the quantum theory of the atom. His notions on the bearing of new physical ideas on stellar evolution were equally far-sighted.

When the Royal College of Science was founded in 1890, largely as a result of the Commission's findings, he was appointed director of a new Solar Physics Observatory attached to it. He also started the Science Museum.

His understanding of the significance of science for the public inspired him to found the famous journal *Nature* in 1869, with the publisher Alexander Macmillan. He founded the British Science Guild in 1905, to promote the study of the social implications of science.

He engaged Richard Gregory as his assistant. Gregory succeeded him as editor of *Nature*, and continued and extended the attention to the bearing of science on human affairs, which Lockyer had promoted with so much vision.

Lockyer had splendid insight both in science and in its meaning for mankind. He combined these qualities with orderliness and an incisive style. The Commission owed a great deal to him. His enthusiasm for astrophysics, which he had so actively advanced, was, however, a handicap in a secretary. The Commission, through his pressure, gave too large a share of its attention, and too much prominence, to the subject in which he was so passionately interested. If his own particular scientific interests had not been given such a prominent position in the Commission's deliberations, its findings as a whole might have had more influence.

Lockyer regarded the great Commission as a failure. Its most fundamental recommendations were not implemented even in his long lifetime. But this failure arose far less from shortcomings in its members and staff than from the social ideology which was dominant at the time, in Government, and in private capitalism.

When the Duke of Devonshire died in 1891, *Nature*, Lockyer's journal, briefly said: 'He acted as Chairman of the Royal Commission on Scientific Instruction and the Advancement of Science, whose reports might have marked an era in our national progress if there had been a scientific department of the Government to give effect to them.'

Richard Burdon Haldane

1856–1928

I

The Intermediary

THE agitation for the incorporation of science in the national life, and the foundation of universities with strong science faculties in the great provincial cities, had been led by Brougham in the first half of the nineteenth century. Playfair and others promoted adequate conceptions of scientific organization in the middle of the century. The main features of higher scientific and technological education, ministries of science, and advisory councils of civil and military research, had been conceived and recommended for adoption by the State.

By the end of the century some progress had been made towards their creation. Colleges for higher education had been founded in Manchester, Leeds, Liverpool, Birmingham and other cities, where students could obtain instruction which qualified them to pass the examinations conducted by London and other university examining bodies. The colleges and institutions at the Prince Consort's South Kensington complex had developed and extended.

But even by 1900, these colleges had not become independent civic universities, and there was still no institution fully equivalent to a technological university. There was still no State organization of science, either for civil or military purposes.

The British statesman who first brought these developments from the nascent into the actual stage was Richard Burdon Haldane. He was a lawyer who reached the head of his profession. He was twice Lord Chancellor, on the second occasion holding that office in the first Labour Government in 1923–4. Following Francis Bacon and Brougham, he was the third Lord Chancellor to have a major influence in carrying science into the national life. Like them, he also had exceptional misfortune as well as great success in his career, though his misfortune was not as serious as theirs. It seems that the combination of law and science, though it may have valuable results for mankind, has not hitherto been a happy one for the individual. While it may contribute to ultimate reputation, it hinders immediate success.

Haldane had the decisive rôle in bringing the civic universities into independent existence, and in the formation of the Imperial College of Science and Technology, an advance in the direction of a British technological university.

In the course of reorganizing the British Army as Minister for War, and making it efficient and prepared for participation in the defence of Belgium and France before the outbreak of the First World War, he founded the first advisory committee on the scientific aspects of military affairs, which started the realization of one of Alexander Strange's proposals. Subsequently, he recommended a similar advisory committee for civil science, helping to realize Strange's proposal in this field also.

The development of government research departments about the time of the First World War, and the establishment of Advisory Councils in Military and Civil Science after the Second World War; followed by the great extension of universities, and such institutions as the Imperial College of Science and Technology, may be regarded as the beginning of an adequate realization of the proposals broached a century or more before.

Haldane became active in the period between the creative scientific organizers of the middle of the nineteenth century and those of our own time. He was the chief British statesman of science in this intermediary period.

Haldane was enabled to achieve this rôle through his Scottish intellectual background and his German higher education, in combination with his natural talents. Like Brougham and Playfair, he was a Scottish intellectual and politician, with the practical characteristics of his nation. He was industrious, and patient in negotiation. It is a striking fact that Haldane made no reference to Brougham and Playfair in his autobiography, though he must have known Playfair in the House of Commons. He makes very little reference to his predecessors in the statesmanship of science; no doubt his ideas in this field were original to himself, and he was not very keenly aware of what his predecessors had contributed.

Haldane was not educated in England. His parents wanted him to go to Oxford, after some study at Edinburgh University, but he chose to go to Göttingen, owing to a youthful crisis in his views on religion. This led him to acquire a knowledge of the German system of higher education, which subsequently extended to technology as well as the arts and sciences, and an understanding of the German talent for organization in civil and military aspects of national life.

He adopted law as his profession, and had such success that he could afford to enter politics. His abilities enabled him to rise in both these fields, and he brought with him a knowledge and understanding of German organization in education and science which was unique in the leading British political circles.

This combination of qualities and circumstances enabled him to perform a unique service to the nation. At the same time, it prevented him from taking the first place in British public life, and indeed led to his being hounded out of it for a while.

He was not fully identified with any British type. His German higher educational background prevented him from becoming the leading Scotsman of his day, and even more the leading man in England. Unlike Asquith, he was neither an English nor an Oxford man, and unlike Lloyd George, he was not a manifestation of the spirit of his own people.

So, in spite of reorganizing the British Army, and laying the foundations for British military success in the First World War, he was relieved of political office from 1915 until 1924, and taunted publicly that Germany was his 'spiritual home'.

Haldane attributed his lack of popular appeal to defects of personality and ungainliness. It arose more from his incomplete identity with any particular party, or with British intellectual life. He said that 'it is impracticable to produce much effect unless one works with a party'. Because of his German education he looked at British ideas with a cool, comparing detachment. This enabled him to see their limitations, and make suggestions for their improvement, which was invaluable, but not endearing. His combination of detachment and intellectual interest enabled him to appreciate intelligent men in other parties. While he was a Liberal minister, he was friendly with the Conservative statesman Balfour and the Socialist statesman Sydney Webb. He used his friendships with the political Right and Left to forward higher educational reform, in which his own Liberal Party was less interested. This caused him to acquire a reputation for intrigue.

His writings on philosophical subjects did not appeal to

English readers, for they lacked clarity and force, and appeared to reproduce the obscurity of German philosophical literature. His normal style was rather diffuse and verbose, and apt to raise remembrances of one of the favourite sayings of one of his favourite authors: Goethe's 'Die Zeit ist unendlich lang!'

Yet under the spate of words Haldane tirelessly elucidated the facts of his problems. He contended that 'it is the energy which is directed by close research that in the end gives the most stable and rapid results'. He was correct, but in the meantime, and until a considerable interval after the results were achieved, he got little credit for them. It was almost inevitable that in his case this must be so, because the very qualities which enabled him to contribute so much were just those which prevented the immediate appreciation of his achievement.

Schuster, the Permanent Secretary to the Lord Chancellor's office, said that those who worked immediately with him found him an ideal chief. He was full of youthful zest; he delegated responsibility, and he had a temper which was naturally sweet, unsoured by public obloquy.

II

Theological Travail

RICHARD BURDON HALDANE was born in Edinburgh on July 30, 1856. He belonged to a Scottish family which had had a small estate at Cloan in Perthshire for centuries. His father was a writer to the signet, or solicitor specializing in the legalities of land transactions. He worked in Edinburgh, but spent a good deal of the year at the ancestral home. Haldane's own life always retained roots in Cloan.

His father was a strict and earnest Baptist. His paternal family had connections with India, and one of his great-uncles conceived the mission of converting Hindoos to Christianity. He was frustrated in his intention by the East India Company, who feared that it might be bad for trade, so he and his brothers turned their attention to evangelizing the Swiss and South Germans. He spent what was then the enormous sum of £70,000 on forwarding this movement, which came to be known as Haldanite. When Haldane visited Germany after he had become well known, he was reminded of it. It is worth recalling that his nephew, J. B. S. Haldane, became an Indian citizen and died in India.

Haldane's mother was a remarkable woman, descended from George III's formidable Lord Chancellor Eldon. Her personality increased with age, and she died in her 101st year. Her brother was the eminent physiologist Sir John Burdon Sanderson, professor at Oxford. Haldane's younger brother, the physiologist John Scott Haldane, was given his first names after Eldon. John Scott Haldane went to Oxford to work with his uncle, and when his son was born, he was named after him: John Burdon Sanderson Haldane, and became an eminent biologist.

Richard Burdon Haldane's mother was her husband's second wife, and bore him a second family of five children. Haldane's father was consequently rather old; he was affectionate, but distant in years and thought from his second family.

The earnest atmosphere and talented family stimulated study. Haldane's sister Elizabeth became the translator of Hegel, and biographer of Descartes and George Eliot. His brother John became the father of Naomi Mitchison as well as J. B. S. Haldane.

Haldane went to the Edinburgh Academy after some tutoring and preparatory education. He did not find school interesting, though he had a classical master at the Academy who, in his exposition of the Bible, indicated by his manner that he did not believe much of what he read. This unsettled Haldane's beliefs. He was sent to Edinburgh University when he was sixteen. He had not been sufficiently well-taught at school to appreciate most of the professorial lectures. He sat for the London Matriculation Examination at about the same time, and only just got through. He became friendly with fellow students, who included Andrew Seth the philosopher, and W. A. Haswell, who later collaborated in a famous textbook of zoology.

He enjoyed the country life at Cloan, and was physically strong, besides being mentally active. He could remember going for a walk of seventy-three miles, accomplished in twenty-three hours. Subsequently, when Minister of War, generals became footsore in trying to keep up with him.

The religious doubts which troubled him continually increased. His father wanted him to proceed to Balliol College,

Oxford, though he feared that it was permeated by an insidious Anglican influence. Haldanc consulted Blackie, the Edinburgh professor of Greek, who was interested in his spiritual troubles. He advised him that the German philosopher Lotze of Göttingen could probably help him best, and he persuaded Haldane's parents to send him there, instead of Balliol.

Haldane sailed for Hamburg from Leith in a freighter laden with iron, in April 1874. He knew little German, the environment was rough, and he felt depressed. Then he discovered a Scottish youth on board who was studying chemistry at Göttingen. His new friend most kindly showed him the ropes at Göttingen, and eased his entry into the new atmosphere of the strange foreign university. Göttingen town was then rather primitive and dirty.

He found a learned German lady, a retired schoolmistress, who coached him in the language and taught him much about German history and literature. Lotze set him to read Fichte, and started the course of study that led to the resolution of his troubles.

While the professoriate were eminent, Haldane found the students uneven in quality. It was difficult even to keep clean. The usual thing was to bathe in the river Leine, into which Bismarck had formerly jumped in order to escape his creditors. The Leine was not too wholesome, for the staple industry of Göttingen was tanning.

Haldane retained his connection with Göttingen. Later, the University conferred honorary degrees upon him and von Tirpitz on the same occasion.

A few months at Göttingen had transformed Haldane, both mentally and physically; it permanently focussed his life. His depression had gone, and he was convinced that the truth was to be found through the philosophies of Berkeley, Fichte and Kant, and the literature of Goethe, Shakespeare and Wordsworth. He had become very thin, grown a moustache and long hair. His family could scarcely recognize him. Nor could the University of Edinburgh, after he returned to it; he collected degrees, medals and scholarships in swift succession.

Notwithstanding his age and the unfolding of his intellect, his father was exceedingly disturbed by the fact that he had not yet been baptized. Haldane was alarmed by his father's mental distress, so he consented to undergo the rite, in spite of his disbelief in it. As he 'rose dripping from the font,' he expounded to the large congregation his philosophical reasons for disagreeing with the doctrine. Among those who were present was a Scotsman learned in German literature, who was so impressed that he bequeathed to him his library, rich in German books.

III

The Law

WITH the legal tradition on both sides of the family, Haldane was destined for the law. Indeed, it was said that when he was six years old, his nurse had sat him on the Woolsack when the House of Lords was in recess, as an earnest of his future.

Haldane applied himself to the law with determination, in spite of feeling that he was handicapped by an unimpressive presence and a poor voice. He succeeded in making up for his deficiencies by intellectual grasp, strong memory and tireless persistence.

After 1877, when his father died, he began to work in London, but Cloan always remained his home. He was called to the Bar in 1879.

He tried to remedy his lack of social charm by taking dancing lessons. He was joined in these by Dr. Elizabeth Garrett Anderson, who felt that she also suffered from similar shortcomings. The lessons were not very successful, and were soon discontinued. Apart from the law, his friends were mostly in the circle of his uncle, the physiologist John Burdon Sanderson, then at University College, London.

At this period he collaborated with his friend Andrew Seth, who later took the name of Pringle-Pattison, in bringing out *Essays in Philosophical Criticism.* This was published in 1883, and contained a remarkable article written by himself and his younger brother John, the physiologist, on the Relation of Philosophy to Science. The brothers dealt in a forthright way with the philosophers on the one hand, and the scientists on the other.

'Kant's great mistake was . . . the assumption that the sphere of imagination was co-extensive with that of knowledge up to and including the relations of mechanism, and that all beyond this, that which was for him the subject of judgment as distinguished from perception was unreal. . . .'

For 'a more advanced theory of knowledge, space and time become themselves indistinguishable in kind from other relations in experience and consequently the different aspects of experience are regarded as differing not in kind but in degree. . . .' Forty years later, Haldane found in these ideas clues to the problems raised by Einstein's relativity theories.

The brothers thought the 'Natur philosophie' of Hegel 'somewhat unintelligible', but while they found Kant and Hegel worthy of correction, they considered the Laplacian and nineteenth-century mechanists beneath contempt.

The essay contains the principles of the biological philosophy which J. S. Haldane subsequently elaborated. They concluded that 'in fine, the relations of life are not capable of reduction to the relations of mechanism'. Such notions as functions, purpose, self-conserving system, and development could be apprehended only 'through higher categories than those of spatial and temporal arrangement'. Life could be explained only in conceptions drawn from itself. Living wholes were qualitatively different from an organization of their constituents.

They made the same criticism of the State as a mere aggregate of individuals. The social organism of which a man is a member is a whole of its own kind. 'In the light of such a conception the shortcomings of the abstractedly individualistic doctrines of the Manchester school in political economy become apparent.'

They thought that 'the work of philosophy in the near future must pass into the hands of specialists in science who are at the same time masters of philosophical criticism'. This was necessary because the mere man of science 'perpetually raises difficulties insoluble for himself in his own department by the dogmatic application of mistaken categories'.

This early essay was more trenchant than Haldane's later writings, and clearly owes much to his brother. It contains the essence of Haldane's later views on philosophy and science, and even foreshadows his disposition towards relativity.

Meanwhile, he devilled for his seniors at the Bar. Haldane's first great case came to him through the accident of his senior, the distinguished lawyer Horace Davey, being summoned to the House of Lords five minutes before he was to argue a very important case, concerning the Government of Quebec, before the Privy Council. The members of the Judicial Committee saw on the one side an array of famous lawyers, and on the other a youth whom they had never previously seen or heard of. They wondered whether it would be seemly to proceed, but decided that at least they might hear what the young man had to say. They did so, and were impressed. Haldane won his leave to appeal.

In the first three years of his practice he had earned very little. Now he was sought out in his garret, and offered valuable briefs. He became particularly successful in arguing cases involving the law of the dominions and colonies before the House of Lords and Privy Council. He said that within a fortnight he had to deal with Buddhist law from Burma, Maori law from New Zealand, French law from Quebec, Mohammedan and Hindu law from India, Roman-Dutch law from South Africa, Jersey law and Scottish law.

While Haldane was labouring at the Bar he became active in Liberal politics. He founded the '80' club in 1880, which consisted of young Liberals who were particularly interested in the Empire. About two years later he met Asquith, who was also a young barrister; they began to sit next to each other when dining at Lincoln's Inn. After an illness, Haldane went to convalesce with Asquith and his first wife in their Hampstead house.

By 1885 he felt sufficiently prosperous to stand for Parliament. He fought the traditionally Conservative seat of East Lothian, and won it for the Liberals. He arranged that his friend Asquith should stand for East Fife, and so enabled him to enter Parliament, in 1886.

Meanwhile, through this intense legal and political activity, he pursued his reading in German literature and philosophy. His three-volume translation, with John Kemp, published in 1883–6, of Schopenhauer's works, earned him the nickname of 'Schopenhauer' in political circles. His loyalty to philosophy prevented him from ever being a completely accomplished politician. However, he considered that his twenty years in the House of Commons mitigated the effects of the tendency of his mind towards abstract thought.

His combination of legal and political interests led him to

participate in legal cases of political importance. The greatest of these was the Taff Vale case, which inspired the Act promoted by Keir Hardie, that made trade unions immune from prosecution for strike action. He was leading counsel for the trade union involved.

While his intellectual interests hindered his political career, they assisted him in sides of the law requiring special aptitude for mastering technical matters. This led the Nobel firm to engage him in a case against the Crown concerning their patent for a slow-burning propellant made from nitro-glycerine and nitro-cellulose. After this, the Crown retained him in a related case against Maxim. These cases caused him to read the chemistry of explosives, and drew his attention to the scientific problems of armaments and warfare.

His knowledge of these subjects was presently put to political use. While travelling up to London in the train during the South African War, the Secretary of State for War, Lord Lansdowne, happened to get into his compartment. In the course of conversation Haldane remarked to him that the British explosives were defective, and were ruining the guns. Lansdowne listened to him, and suggested he should be chairman of an Explosives Committee to look into the matter. Haldane said he should follow the example of the French, who had appointed their great chemist Berthelot chairman of such a committee, Lansdowne then asked him to name a corresponding British scientist, so Haldane proposed Lord Rayleigh. The committee was in consequence set up under Rayleigh, and besides Haldane included W. Crookes, W. Roberts-Austen the metallurgist, and Andrew Noble the artillery expert. This committee continued to meet weekly for several years.

From this beginning, Haldane gradually extended the application of science to various aspects of British military problems, establishing the approach which was to have effect in the First World War, and great effect in the Second.

IV

Higher Education

HALDANE was particularly interested in the influence of German literature and philosophy on the reform and organization of German education in the early part of the nineteenth century. With his friend Hume Brown, who had been tutor to the Haldane family, and later became professor of history at Edinburgh, he embarked on a comprehensive biography of Goethe.

They made regular visits to Germany, with Weimar as their headquarters. They searched for materials in many places, including his old university of Göttingen, and discovered new material, unknown to German scholars.

These investigations led Haldane to appreciate modern German literature more and more, and especially the organization of German higher education, which at that time was unique. He thoroughly studied the work of Wilhelm von Humboldt and Stein, who had been its chief founders.

Hume Brown died before his life of Goethe was finished. Haldane and his sister completed it, and published it in two volumes.

Haldane's direct knowledge of the German system of higher education made him keenly aware of the deficiencies in the corresponding British system. He felt this all the more because of his special interest in the future of the British empire. The superior German higher education threatened British science, industry and imperial power with ultimate supersession. His Liberal political associates were not much interested in the scientific and educational aspect of this problem.

He examined the initiatives in progress in Britain for advancing higher education, especially the movements for expanding civic colleges into universities, and gave them enthusiastic support. He addressed Liverpool business men in 1901 on the need for a modern university in the city, if they were to hold their own in the increasing competition from the highly educated and scientifically based new German industry and business.

He explained to the Liverpool business men that when Goethe

had said that 'Der Engländer ist eigentlich ohne Intelligenz,' he was not, as Matthew Arnold had pointed out, saying anything really derogatory. He was referring only to a certain insularity, a want of suppleness in his mind, springing indeed from his very strength, which caused him to accept the conventional as the law of nature. He needed a dose of German *Geist* to enlarge his outlook and understanding.

Haldane followed Arnold in contending that the British middle and governing classes could acquire the necessary *Geist* only through the extension of the higher education system.

It was not surprising that the United States, with their vast natural resources, had overtaken the volume of British industrial production, but it was 'startling that we have also been beaten in this particular race by Germany'. If Britain were to retain an appropriate position, 'she *must* continue to increase her commercial output'. It was the foundation on which her finance, fleet and empire rested. She must not only maintain her trade, but increase it, in order to meet the increasing demand for expenditure.

He quoted two industries to illustrate what was happening. He chose brewing first, because its recent history was less well known. In the middle of the nineteenth century the Germans did not export beer. It was surprising to realize, in view of the modern reputation of German beer, that this was because it was not then good enough. Two leading brewers went to England to learn the best practice, and on their return to Germany organized a brewers' association for research. By 1871 it had begun to function effectively under the motto: *Die Wissenschaft ist der Goldene Leitstern der Praxis; ohne sie nur ein blindes Herumtappen in dem unbegrenzten Reiche der Möglichkeiten* (Science is the golden guiding star of practice; without it [there is] only a blind groping about in the unlimited realm of possibilities). It led ultimately to the production of superlative beer. The brewers set up laboratories, where the problems of quality and keeping were solved. Schools of brewing were established, where students received technical education appropriate to the various parts of the industry. The same kind of development occurred in other industries.

Germany had already a comprehensive and effectively compulsory system of secondary and technical education, whereas Britain had not. This provided a large flow of students qualified to enter the universities.

The student entering the brewing school had to be over seventeen, and the average age was twenty-four. His qualification for a post in the industry depended on his diploma, awarded on his examination results and term work.

Thus the direction and staff of the breweries became scientifically and technically competent. German beer became superior, and saleable abroad.

Haldane drew the attention of his Liverpool audience to the advanced methods of the Germans in another of his special interests: explosives. The German firms, though competing with each other, combined to finance a research laboratory to investigate fundamental problems of explosives. The British had nothing of the kind, yet they hoped to retain their sales to such important consumers of explosives as the South African mining industry.

Haldane then dwelt on the effects of the size of the science departments of the German universities, and the technical high schools, or technological universities. In Berlin the student could find a whole range of professors of chemistry, according to the part of the subject in which he was interested. At Edinburgh or Glasgow there was only a single professor, giving a general course to students, whatever their aims in life might be.

He described the Technical High School in Berlin, which had been built in 1884, and had 4,000 students studying science and engineering. There were already ten of these technological universities in Germany, and not one in Britain. They had been built because the Government believed them to be a good investment, and contributed nearly three-quarters of the cost.

Students flocked to them, in spite of having to pay fees, because they helped them to gain a better position in life. The industrialists and the professoriate worked closely together, watching promising students, and offering them good openings when they had completed their courses.

Haldane gave figures on the number of scientists and engineers of various grades which were being produced by the German higher education system, showing how much larger they were than the British, and thereby providing a far more competent technical staff for German industry.

Thus the German ordinary and technological university system promoted pure culture on the one hand, and the application of science to commercial enterprise on the other. The complete system was supported by heavy taxation, believed to be in the national interest.

The German educational system not only produced a more competent industry, but more competent soldiers of every rank, from private to general.

What the German Government was doing by organization, American millionaires were doing by expenditure. They were busy founding universities and technical high schools, as an alternative to churches to saving their souls. The results were good for business, too.

But 'the British people are not yet a decaying race'. It was remarkable that the absolute volume of British trade continued to be as high as it was. During the previous ten years, income had risen by 20 per cent, while population had increased by only 10 per cent.

Why should not Britain have a university system to rival the German? Oxford and Cambridge were rooted in splendid traditions, which should not be disturbed. But why not create another kind of teaching which they were not adapted to give, and which was nevertheless a national necessity? Why should not Liverpool and Manchester have independent universities, which they certainly would have, if they were German cities? Why not Leeds, and Birmingham and Bristol? Why should the Scottish universities, 'owing to the sluggishness and want of ideas of their governors', be of little use from the point of view of the application of science to industry? Why should not the University of London, converted from an examining into a teaching university by the Act of 1898, become the educational centre of the British empire? New Zealand had suggested that the best memorial to Queen Victoria would be the establishment in the University of a post-graduate research college, for students from all parts of the empire. Haldane welcomed this as a new link of Imperial Federation, of the only kind which was likely to survive.

London itself, with its huge industrial population, offered special scope for the teaching of the application of science to industry; and for the development of institutions for this purpose which would be difficult to equal elsewhere.

Only those who had struggled with the 'apathy, the ignorance, and the jealousy' which retard such enterprises, realized how far Britain was from having an appropriate university system. The truth was that it could be instituted only by large support from the State, contrary to the political tradition of the day.

The effort required was far beyond the strength of local or private enterprise. It was in fact a salvage expenditure, for it was what was needed to create the sources of the nation's future: continually increasing knowledge and science, and their application to the national needs and life.

Liverpool duly founded its university.

Haldane subsequently became Chancellor of the university founded at Bristol. He was chairman of the Royal Commission on London University, which deliberated on its reform for four years. He accomplished an enormous amount of work for the Commission, in spite of other very heavy duties. He had the chief part in converting London University from being in the main an examining body into a university of the usual type, taking initiatives in teaching and research. Haldane recommended the University to develop on the Bloomsbury site.

The influence of Haldane's more particular views was long-lived. Though he greatly admired the German universities and technical high schools, he thought they should never have been developed as separate types of institution. Accordingly, when he sought to promote the development of an institution corresponding to a German technical high school, he aimed at doing this under university auspices. He promoted the plan of combining and extending certain of the colleges at South Kensington into a new entity, to be called the Imperial College of Science and Technology. He was supported in this by Edward VII, who, as a son of the Prince Consort, had a filial interest in the extension of his father's great ideas. It was to be the central British high school for the British empire, but incorporated in the recently reformed University of London.

He was of the opinion 'that it is only in the larger atmosphere of a University that technical education of the finest kind can be attained'. This arrangement was accepted. Haldane was assisted in working out the details of the scheme by Francis Mowatt, the head of the Treasury, and Sidney Webb. He took the lead in securing large endowments for the new institution from Wernher, Cecil Rhodes, Rothschild and Cassel. Mowatt secured increased financial support from the Government.

Thus the Imperial College of Science and Technology came into existence, a further realization of the Prince Consort's plan.

Haldane's insistence on the Imperial College being within the University of London did not work out as happily as he had expected. He had assumed that the influence of the university spirit would undoubtedly be good for the College. It apparently had not occurred to him that an inadequate university spirit might have a retarding effect on the College. In fact, the development of the College was later hampered by opposition from other sections of London University to its large demands for funds. Technological higher education is much more expensive than the traditional university subjects, and the other sections of London University did not see why the College should have more than a proportionate share of available funds.

Tizard has said that this contributed to the shelving of the plan for a large extension of the College, drawn up in 1935.

The big extension of the College in the 1960's became possible because the concepts of university education had changed, and become much larger than formerly, in response to the modern social and scientific situation.

Haldane was chairman of the Royal Commission which laid the foundation of the University of Wales. His plan for Wales was still influencing policy in the 1960's. His Commission had recommended that Wales should have one university, with colleges in the main centres at Aberystwyth, Bangor, Cardiff and Swansea. When a commission recommended in a majority report that the colleges should now, in the conditions of the 1960's, become separate universities, it was rejected in favour of a minority report recommending the retention of one university for Wales. Welsh national feeling supported the minority report, and quoted the views of the Haldane Commission in support of the retention of the existing organization.

Haldane's work for the Imperial College brought him into frequent consultation with Edward VII. This in turn influenced the direction of his subsequent activities in politics.

Among other university institutions which he helped to create was the London School of Economics. He collaborated with Sidney Webb on this project in 1895.

Haldane conceived that science had just as important a place in organization and administration as in the laboratory. 'What is true of Commerce and Industry is not less true of the Art of Government. This art is founded on science. When the clear conceptions which science alone can give are absent, confusion is the result. . . . Our best reformers in such subjects as Poor Law Administration, in Education, in Local Government, in the region which belongs to the Labour and Commercial sides of the Board of Trade, in Public Health, and, last but not least, in Railway Administration, are yearly insisting more loudly on the necessity for the trained mind. . . .' he wrote in 1906.

He arranged that military officers should receive courses in administration at the London School of Economics. He clearly conceived the scientifically managed modern society and state.

He promoted the scheme of extra-mural studies, by which universities provided lectures and teaching to the public in their neighbourhoods.

In 1905 W. S. McCormick was made a member of the new Advisory Committee to the Treasury on grants-in-aid to the universities. Haldane supported this body, which gradually developed under McCormick's skilful leadership into the University Grants Committee, that now provides most of the finance for British universities, and their large modern expansion.

Haldane collaborated with Mansbridge, Laski and Tawney in the development of the Workers' Educational Association. He helped in the founding, and the collection of endowments, of the British Institute of Adult Education, and presided over it for a number of years. He supported the development of Birkbeck College, and was head of its governing body until his death.

V

Reforming the Army

THE course of the South African War had raised profound disquiet about the technical efficiency of the British Army. Haldane had detailed knowledge of one aspect of this from his membership of the Explosive Committee.

The Conservative Government, which had been responsible for the conduct of the war, became very unpopular. They had not done well that thing upon which they particularly prided themselves: military affairs. Their opposition to social change became all the more obnoxious. Consequently, they were severely defeated in the election of 1906.

Haldane had hoped to become Lord Chancellor in the new Liberal Government. He was offered only the post of Attorney-General, which carried no seat in the Cabinet, and was in fact not as high in legal prestige as his own private status at the Bar. The lord chancellorship had already been given to another eminent lawyer.

The Prime Minister, Campbell-Bannerman, wished Grey to be Foreign Secretary. Grey, however, for various reasons, was not anxious to have the position. Grey and Haldane, who were very close friends at the time, agreed between themselves that Grey would accept the foreign secretaryship only if Haldane were offered the War Office, with a seat in the Cabinet. Campbell-Bannerman gladly agreed to this, for none of the more radical pacifist, nor the ambitious, influential Liberal politicians wished to have anything to do with the discredited War Office.

Haldane started his work as Minister for War by asking his predecessor to recommend some competent man to act as his secretary. The very capable Colonel Ellison was recommended. Ellison had studied military science in Germany. Haldane and he at once began to read Clausewitz and the other German military masters. Presently, when the British generals asked him what sort of an army he wanted, he replied: 'A Hegelian Army,' after which the discussion languished.

Haldane found that the Committee of Imperial Defence, which had been set up by the former prime minister, Arthur Balfour, to bring more order and unity into British military organization, though excellent in principle, had not been adequately developed. He increased its power and versatility, and inspired it to consider the scientific aspects of defence.

The prime military question for the British was the defence of their island. Was it liable to be invaded, and from where? The Committee of Imperial Defence had shown that the Navy could successfully prevent invasion, on condition that northern France remained in friendly hands. It was therefore necessary to organize an Expeditionary Force of adequate strength, which could be rapidly mobilized and transported into that region. The contemporary threat came from Germany, so this force would have to be in the field within fifteen days, if it was to be effective.

The existing troops were of a scratch character; units were

small, and weapons and medical services defective. Before the end of 1906, Haldane and his assistants had drafted the plans for a fully equipped expeditionary force of eight divisions, which could be put into northern France within a fortnight.

Haldane initiated scientific general staff conversations with the French.

Then, as the plan for the expeditionary force was worked out, the question of reserves, for protecting the home country after the force had departed abroad, became pressing. This led to the conception of the Territorial Army. Haldane appointed Haig to the General Staff to work on these plans.

He now set out to learn what he could directly of the German military organization at work. His desire was transmitted to the Kaiser, who invited him to attend the annual manoeuvres, but Haldane said he would prefer to see the German War Office.

The Kaiser received him in public. He was aware of what was going on from the German secret service. He arranged for Haldane to inspect the German War Office. He was being shown round by von Moltke, who told him that the Army had no plans for the invasion of England. Haldane asked him whether that applied also to the German Admiralty. Von Moltke replied that the German Admiralty had considered it, but concluded that the outcome would be uncertain, while damage to the commerce of both countries would be great, which would be to the benefit only of the United States.

Haldane inferred that the German Army was thinking of invasion through northern France, and he returned with the redoubled intention of organizing the Expeditionary Force into a state of instant readiness.

During his visit he had met the chief German military leaders, and he formed the opinion that they were a less able body than the German staff of 1870. A feature of the German military organization which particularly impressed him was the sharp separation of the command from the administration, thus reducing the possibility of confusion.

While Haldane was working away at his army reforms, the chief Liberal leaders governed in the spirit of Victorian Liberalism and the old Industrial Revolution. They conducted Cabinet business without proper procedure, and had little interest in higher education, especially in relation to industry. They believed that Free Enterprise and Free Trade were sufficient to guarantee the progress of industry.

They were therefore little interested in the promotion of industrial research by the State, and many even believed that this would be a retrograde tendency. No notice was taken of Haldane's advice to increase expenditure on higher education by a million pounds, and promote researches at institutions like the National Physical Laboratory, in order to assist manufacturers in the application of science in industry.

Their attitude towards the application of science to social questions was quite different. The emergence of the Labour Party had revealed the political importance of these questions. In response to the new social pressure, the Liberal Government founded the Development Commission in 1909; and the Medical Research Committee, the forerunner of the Medical Research Council, in 1911. It was financed out of the National Insurance Act of that year, which contained a clause that one penny a year for each person insured in the United Kingdom should be devoted to research.

The Department for Scientific and Industrial Research was not founded until 1916, during the First World War, when the inefficiency of British industry, especially in the manufacture of scientifically advanced armaments, had nearly brought the country to defeat.

By then, Haldane had been driven from office by reactionary clamour, but this did not prevent him from serving on the committee for the new D.S.I.R., as one of its most industrious members. It was due to him and McCormick that the D.S.I.R. was set up as an independent department with Heath as secretary. Nor did he refuse to serve as chairman of a committee on the Machinery of Government, which led to the more efficient conduct of Cabinet business, and many other parts of the constitutional machinery, especially those concerned with the administration of justice.

In Haldane's view, one of the causes of the decline of the Liberal Party was due to its failure to recognize the rôle of State organization in a more technical age. He forecast that the Conservative Party would decline in the same way unless it recognized this, and modified its policies accordingly. Haldane was particularly interested in the organization of the British Electrical Grid for the national distribution of electricity. He was a member of the Cabinet committee of the first Labour Government which promoted this scheme. Haldane found that the Liberal majority in the pre-1914 Parliament was too much concerned with the question of religion in education to be able to have large views on the development of the educational system.

Meanwhile, the diplomatic operations with Germany continued. Haldane was prominent in the Kaiser's visits to England in 1907 and 1911. On the latter occasion he entertained him in his flat in Westminster, to which the Kaiser referred as his 'Doll's House'.

Almost immediately afterwards the Kaiser provoked the Agadir crisis. Haldane had, however, got the arrangements for the Expeditionary Force in full working order. The Agadir crisis passed, but when it became evident in August 1914 that the German Army was about to invade Belgium, the arrangements were set in operation, on the day before formal mobilization. The telegrams of instructions, already drafted, were taken out of the store. The place of concentration on the Belgian frontier and the commander-in-chief had been designated years before. The operation went off without a hitch.

The British Expeditionary Force, though excellent in quality and speed, was too small to exert more than a delaying action on the great German Army. In the condition of Liberal opinion in the pre-war period, a larger force was out of the question.

The retreat of the British Expenditionary Force was inevitable, but not appreciated by British public opinion. A scapegoat was sought, and Haldane was fixed upon. Was he not a friend of the Kaiser? Did he not esteem German culture more than British? Was it not obvious that he had been impeding the British effort in favour of the German? His political position was soon made very difficult. He did not possess the aptitudes to make the popular appeal which could dispel such prejudices. Without the gift of rhetoric or concise expression, he appeared to the uninformed a prodigious and unpatriotic bore. Asquith dropped him from the Woolsack, to which he had translated him in 1912, on the formation of his Coalition Government in 1915.

On the very day of his demission Haldane projected his treatise on *The Reign of Relativity*, with the aim of combining the results of his lifetime's study of philosophy with the implications of the recent work of Einstein. He started to work on it in solitude.

When victory was celebrated in 1918 by a huge parade in London, led by the King and the Commander-in-Chief, Haig, Haldane spent the evening alone in his London flat. While he was sitting solitarily, he was informed that an officer had called to see him, but would not give his name. Haldane had become cautious about visitors, but his servant had developed judgment in this matter, and thought that in this case it would be all right. The officer was shown in, and turned out to be Haig, who had called after the parade, and said he could stay only a moment. but wished to leave a book.

After he had gone, Haldane opened it and found it was a bound volume of Haig's dispatches, with the inscription: 'To Viscount Haldane of Cloan—the greatest Secretary of State for War England has ever had. In grateful remembrance of his successful efforts in organising the Military Forces for a War on the Continent, notwithstanding much opposition from the Army Council and the half-hearted support of his Parliamentary friends.'

Six years later than this, and nine years after he had been forced to relinquish the lord chancellorship, he was recalled to be the head of the law, as Lord Chancellor in the first Labour Government in 1924. When he returned to this great position, it was noted that 'he was surprised at the warmth of the welcome he received from all parties'.

VI

Military and Civil Research

In the course of carrying out the army reforms which received such magnificent justification, Haldane laid the foundations of the proper application of science to British military affairs.

His contribution in this direction has been described by Tizard in his Haldane Lecture of 1955, in which he expressed the opinion that Haldane had had a greater and more lasting influence than any other British statesman of recent years 'in bringing science to bear on national affairs'.

The Explosives Committee founded on Haldane's suggestion, under the chairmanship of Rayleigh, met many times, and its proceedings have never been published. Tizard says that it was the first definite move to use science in the modern manner in British military affairs. One of its known results was the foundation of a Chemical Research Department at Woolwich Arsenal in 1903.

After Haldane became War Minister in 1906, he was visited by many inventors, including those of the new heavier-than-air flying machines, which were just becoming successful. He perceived at once the military importance of these inventions, but the inventors whom he interviewed seemed to him only clever empiricists. If British development was left to this type, they would be at a profound disadvantage compared with the Germans, who were building up their air service on a foundation of science.

The Committee of Imperial Defence appointed a subcommittee on Aerial Navigation, with Haldane as chairman, to consider the matter, but he could not persuade it to sanction systematic scientific research on the problem. He therefore acted alone on behalf of the War Ministry, and took development of military aircraft out of the hands of the Ordnance department, and had a new department for aeronautical research founded at the National Physical Laboratory, and financed by the War Ministry.

Haldane then set up an Advisory Committee on Aeronautics to guide the research. He turned to his old friend and colleague, Rayleigh, to act as chairman. He arranged that the committee should report to the prime minister, so that generals would not be able to interfere.

He also brought the Balloon Factory at Farnborough under the guidance of the new committee, and placed Mervyn O'Gorman in charge. O'Gorman subsequently told Tizard that when Haldane visited the factory he was more interested in talking to the intelligent young men than in looking at gadgets, and that when he was taken for a flight in a dirigible balloon, he insisted on going up in his silk hat.

As the factory became involved in aeroplane design, Haldane changed its name to the Army Aircraft Factory. This was the first official use of the word 'aircraft' in the English language. The institution has since grown into the famous Royal Aircraft Establishment.

The 'intelligent young men' at the Army Aircraft Factory in whose conversation Haldane used to delight, were joined during the First World War by F. A. Lindemann, later Lord Cherwell. At about the same time, Tizard joined the experimental section of the Central Flying School of the Royal Flying Corps, which was closely associated with Farnborough.

Thus the two most influential British statesmen of science in the Second World War began to qualify themselves for their future achievements in a military scientific research environment of which Haldane was the chief creator.

When Haldane was appointed Lord Chancellor in 1924, he became chairman of the Committee of Imperial Defence, and presided over the meetings of the Permanent Chiefs of the Staffs of the Navy, Army and Air Force. He recommended to them the maxim: 'thinking costs nothing'. and he recorded that 'we accomplished a good deal of defence work of a permanent character in this period'.

Under Haldane's leadership the Committee of Imperial Defence began to study the scientific aspects of military problems. This development, together with that of the aeronautical research committee founded by Haldane, led ultimately to the creation of the Defence Policy Research Committee set up in 1946.

The Advisory Council on Scientific Policy, set up at the same time in 1946 to deal with civil science, evolved from proposals made by Haldane in the first Labour Government in 1924. His plan was described in a minute to Ramsay Macdonald, but before any action was taken, the Government fell. Balfour found the plan in the files when the succeeding Conservative Government came into office, and launched a Committee of Civil Research with the same aims. It was to consider the development of economic, scientific and statistical research in relation to civil policy. It was not very effective, and was superseded by the Economic Advisory Council in 1930.

The enormous extension of the application of science during the Second World War, with its military effects, and its extension in industry, created the environment for a more effective realization of Haldane's proposal, with the foundation of the Advisory Council on Scientific Policy in 1946.

Thus, at last, the beginning of a comprehensive State organization of science, guided by two advisory councils, one for military and the other for civil science, were started.

The vision of Alexander Strange, and the labours of Haldane began to bear appropriate fruit.

VII

The Reign of Relativity

THE work which Haldane conceived on the day of his demission from the Woolsack in 1915 was to be the philosopher's response to what had just happened to him. He was to incorporate the experience in his lifetime's study of philosophy; one more event to be placed in its proper perspective in the history of his mind, and of the evolution of his mind's conception of the history of the universe and reality.

His exclusion from office as an alleged pro-German, when he was conscious of having to a large degree saved his country through his creation of military preparedness, appeared from one point of view a personal tragedy; but from the perspective of history and understanding, it appeared to be objectively interesting and highly instructive. It all depended on the point of view from which it was looked at; it was a question of relativity. 'What is truth from one standpoint may not of necessity stand for truth from another.'

While Haldane was meditating on the significance of his experience, in the light of his philosophical learning, news arrived in England of Einstein's General Theory of Relativity, which was published in Germany at the end of 1915. He was soon following the expositions of it by Eddington, and other English scientists.

He appreciated that Einstein had shown that the principle of relativity went very much further in physics than had hitherto been understood, and that it implied that the accepted conceptions of space and time must be modified.

His own political experience of the relativity of fame put him in a frame of mind to appreciate the revolutionary discoveries of Einstein. Both impelled him to undertake a new examination of the bearing and extent of the principle of relativity in every direction; in science, philosophy, art, religion, politics and life.

Aware, as he said, that there were others who could do this as well as, or better than, he could, he nevertheless undertook the task, because he felt that it was an essential one. He believed that the recognition of the far-reaching extent of the principle of relativity led to the discovery of principles of unity underlying differences and controversies which had hitherto appeared insoluble.

He contended that the aspirations and achievements of mankind, what he called 'the soul of the people', are not developed by 'the mere men of affairs', but by creative thinkers in art, religion, science and philosophy. For this reason, 'men of science, and our thinkers generally, should remember that they are under a responsibility to society at large. Where they have failed to realize this, the reason for their failure seems to have been something that was wrong with themselves.'

He pushed on with the work, and published it under the title *The Reign of Relativity* in 1921. About a quarter of the book is devoted to an exposition of the Special and General Theories of Relativity, as seen by a non-mathematician. He referred with particular pleasure to the contributions of Gauss, Riemann and Minkowski to the mathematical background of the theories. They were great men of his own University of Göttingen, and he wrote of them with an appropriate knowledge of their lives as well as mathematicians.

The effect of relativity theory in science was to promote 'the disposition to search for, and drag to light unconsciously-made assumptions'. This applied to biology as well as physics. He echoed the essay he had published with his brother in 1883. Life could not be explained in terms of mechanistic principles, and biology must be developed in terms of its own principles.

The theory might have 'tremendous consequences' on earth, and bring forth 'unexpected and practical transformations'. He quoted a Berlin engineer to show that 'the business world is just beginning to ask questions about this'. Relativity theory indicated that matter consisted of enormous concentrations of latent energy. How soon will the great scientific discoverer appear who will release atomic energy?

'It may be a long time, but we do not know. Genius, when it appears, has wings with which it mounts in a fashion that astounds us. Newton and Einstein are examples from which we do well to take heed. We shall be wise if, as a practical nation, we listen to the new warnings which science is now giving us in however general a language. We cannot foresee what new developments knowledge may bring for industry. We have to watch and study and experiment. . . .'

He thought that Einstein's theory of space and time might be more important even than Newton's had been. He again recollected his thoughts of 1883, and discussed its effect on the philosophy of Kant, which is based on the acceptance of the Newtonian conception of space and time as independent and absolute. He remarked that Hegel's theory of space and time fitted relativistic theory better, and he complained of the current misinterpretations of his philosophy. His chapter on Hegel is one of the best in the book. It is written with more clarity and conciseness than is usual in his works. It reads almost as if he had composed it to spite the common opinion that Hegel is obscure.

'As I interpret him, he broke definitely and finally with Kant's attempt to treat knowledge as an instrument which we can hold out and look at as something capable of being critically dissected *ab extra* into constituent parts. For Hegel knowledge in its comprehensive meaning was the foundation and source of all that was, is, and can be. . . .' He describes how Hegel expounded his conception in his first great book, finished in 1806, amid the rattling of sabres. Napoleon had just entered Jena, where he had written his last pages. Hegel wrote to a friend: 'I have seen the World Spirit, it was on horseback.'

Haldane dwelt on the relation of science to the period in which it was done, and hence on the influence of social and historical forces in shaping it. He considered man in relation to the state, and in relation to the universe. He explored man's relation to God, and when he had arrived at the answer in Hegelian terms, found that Emily Brontë had already expressed it in English:

With wide-embracing love,
Thy spirit animates eternal years,
Pervades and broods above,
Changes, sustains, dissolves, creates, and rears.

Though earth and man were gone,
And suns and universes ceased to be,
And Thou wert left alone,
Every existence would exist in Thee.

There is not room for Death,
Nor atom that his might could render void,
Thou, Thou art Being and Breath,
And what Thou art may never be destroyed.

Haldane suffered from diabetes in his last years, but his life and activity were prolonged by the scientific discovery of insulin by Banting and Best. Science enabled him to serve science and learning to the end.

Haldane received the honours customary to his eminence. Among these, he was elected a fellow of the Royal Society in 1906. He was appointed a viscount in 1912. He was elected a fellow of the British Academy in 1914, and a member of the Order of Merit in 1915.

He never married, though he made a proposal which was not reciprocated when he was a young man. He and his learned sister Elizabeth shared the flat at 28 Queen Anne's Gate in Westminster.

When he could, he resided in his family home at Cloan, and he died there on August 19th, 1929. He was buried at Gleneagles; the procession being led by pipers of the Black Watch, and a large contingent of soldiers.

Henry Thomas Tizard

1885–1959

I

Background of a Scientific Strategist

TIZARD had an outstanding part in shaping the British strategy in the military use of science in the Second World War. He foresaw which new scientific weapons and methods would be of importance. He had great success in encouraging their development through research, and in persuading the fighting forces to use them.

This gives a true impression of the weight of his contribution. Tizard did not, however, wear a uniform. He was a civilian guiding the development and use of science for military purposes; a statesman of military science. As such, he made a major contribution to the winning of the Second World War, and so his work has already had an important influence on the destiny of mankind.

Tizard was of medium height, with reddish-brown hair, and a grizzled aspect. His neck was short and his broad jaw low and prominent. He looked formidable and was quick-tempered. He was often cutting; this was painful or amusing, according to the point of view. His criticism was often mixed with quizzical humour.

Early in the Second World War, before the fall of France, two leading French scientists came to England on a mission to promote Anglo-French scientific cooperation. After one of them had delivered a long and earnest discourse, out of touch with reality, Tizard murmured: 'Good Gawd! We shall lose the war!' The French did lose their war.

Tizard was not a particularly good organizer or administrator in the conventional sense. His uncertain temper, which seemed to be connected with nervous trouble exacerbated by experiences as an experimental air pilot in the First World War, limited his popularity. Apparently he had difficulty in disciplining his mind. This was reflected in his work and writings. His imagination shot off in many directions; he had a flood of original and incisive thoughts, which he often seemed unable to develop systematically, except in connection with military affairs. He appeared to require the pressure of external authority to spur him to his greatest achievements.

Some people thought that he was better at influencing senior officers than in leading subordinates, and that he did his greatest work before the Second World War started.

Tizard was born at Gillingham in Kent on August 23rd, 1885. His father, Captain Thomas Henry Tizard, was a distinguished scientific sailor. Captain Tizard was born as long ago as 1839. He joined the Navy in 1854, as a Master's Mate. Some years passed before he became a fully commissioned officer.

In those days navigating officers, and any kind of technician, were looked down upon. Questions of status became impressed on Thomas Henry Tizard. It seems likely that this had an influence on his son, for Henry Thomas Tizard acquired much of his social outlook from his father, and this social outlook was probably the largest factor in the conflict that he was later to have with Frederick Alexander Lindemann, later Lord Cherwell.

Tizard's father served in the Baltic in the Russian War of 1854–6. He joined the Surveying Service in 1860, and spent several years charting the South China Sea. After being invalided home in 1867, he laid a submarine cable between 1868–72. He surveyed the Gulf of Suez preparatory to the opening of the Suez Canal, and he solved the problem of the current which flows through the Straits of Gibraltar. In 1872 he was appointed commander of the famous *Challenger* Expedition of scientific exploration. Then he spent three years at the Admiralty writing the narrative of the voyage, and its oceanographic and hydrographic results. He investigated the meteorology of Japan, and established the existence of the Thomson Ridge in the Faroe Channel, which separates the cold from the warm water in the north-eastern Atlantic.

The boy who had started as a Masters' Mate in 1854 was elected a Fellow of the Royal Society in 1901. He became Assistant Hydrographer to the Navy in 1907. He surveyed the British coasts, and wrote a treatise on the Tides and Tidal Streams of the British Isles.

Of particular interest among his achievements was his report for the Admiralty on the Tactics employed by Nelson at Trafalgar. This was published in 1912, and contains the most exact information on the subject. Henry Thomas Tizard had a father who was an authority on tactics.

Captain Tizard had a reputation for habitual caution and good judgment, and great power of concentration of thought and application. He was described as a genial companion and messmate, with a keen sense of humour.

His portrait suggests that his very strenuous and fruitful life also established rather severe habits of discipline and sense of duty. He seemed to pay so much attention to work that his material conditions suffered. He received a Greenwich Hospital pension besides his ordinary pension.

Henry Thomas Tizard believed that his family was of Huguenot origin, and had settled in Weymouth. His grandfather was a shipowner and coal-merchant in that port. His mother, Mary Elizabeth Churchyard, was the daughter of a civil engineer who was engaged in the dockyards at Malta and Pembroke, and included among her ancestors Sir Paul Rycaut, an early fellow of the Royal Society, who was born in 1628, two years after the death of Francis Bacon, and was elected to the society in 1666. He was an author and traveller.

Tizard was the middle child and only son in a family of five children. His naval and scientific background was fundamental to his career and achievement. He was born into the very combination of science and military considerations which he was destined to develop. It was in this field that he exhibited the intuitions of genius. In it he could draw upon relevant attitudes which had begun to be formed in him by his parental background in his infancy, even before he could speak. In other fields his best achievements were more those of an unusually able man.

Tizard was never closely concerned with the conduct of ordinary business and industry. He was not at ease with profit-seeking and exploitation, which he regarded as the canker at the heart of modern society.

He remarked near the end of his career that he had 'been intimately concerned with that peculiar business called war'. Even when he was Secretary of the Department of Scientific and Industrial Research, and Rector of the Imperial College, he was more deeply concerned with military science than with industrial research or scientific education.

The formation of his officer-outlook and interest in military technique began in his boyhood. He played around the dockyard at Chatham, watching warships being built. The dockhands and sailors were kind to the officer's lively little son. Few environments are more interesting and stimulating to a small boy than a dockyard, and few are more effective than a naval dockyard in establishing the characteristic patterns of class behaviour between members of the ruling and the working classes.

Tizard's father was appointed Assistant Hydrographer to the Admiralty in 1891, and moved his home to Surbiton. Tizard, then about six years old, was sent to his first school, which was run by three maiden ladies in this suburb. It was a good one, with a particularly good teacher of mathematics, who gave him a thorough grounding in the subject. He ever afterwards approached mathematics with confidence and facility, and he attributed much of his subsequent achievement to the excellence of his early mathematical teaching.

For instance, Tizard was able in committees to examine on the spot proposals involving mathematics. People who do not know mathematics cannot, of course, do this; and many good mathematicians do not like to make calculations under such conditions. Such a facility is often of great assistance in quickly detecting whether a technical proposal is mistaken or impracticable, and thus to the swift progress of the committee's business.

It was taken for granted that Tizard would follow the tradition and become a naval officer, but when he was about fourteen, it was discovered that he had a blind patch in one of his eyes. This defect of sight disqualified him for entry into the Navy, so he had to prepare for some other career. His father, like many members of the officer class, had only a comparatively modest salary to support his social position and considerable family.

His son would normally have entered one of the colleges for educating naval cadets, but now it was necessary to send him to a school of the same kind of social standing, but where prior naval connections would be of no particular benefit. An ordinary fee-paying public school education would have been too expensive, so Henry was sent to compete for a scholarship at Westminster School. His good mathematical training helped him to gain an exhibition, which gave him entry, but not so much financial help. If he had not soon after been awarded a scholarship which was more valuable, he might not have been able to continue at Westminster.

In this school, the thousand-year-old ancillary of Westminster Abbey and the Church, Tizard was exposed again to a complex of conservative traditions in social and intellectual ideas.

He had good teachers in mathematics and chemistry, but not in physics. He thought of competing for one of the special scholarships at Trinity College, Cambridge, restricted to candidates from Westminster School. It seems that he was persuaded by his housemaster not to do so. He was told that they were not open to scientists. It looks as if the housemaster had been trying to reserve these valuable places for arts men.

Tizard later regretted that he had not gone to Cambridge, for it would have brought him into the inspired atmosphere that existed there about and after the discovery of the electron. In his conscious mind Tizard was extremely independent and courageous, but unconsciously he was inclined to obey authority. Instead of competing at Cambridge on his own initiative, he sat for a demyship, or scholarship, at Magdalen College, Oxford, which he duly won. Yet again he entered a conservative wing of the contemporary educational system.

He went to Oxford in 1904, and commenced to read mathematics, taking a first-class in the first examination in the following year. Then he dropped mathematics.

Tizard seems to have lacked self-confidence as an intellectual. He said in later life that he gave up research because he lacked intellectual stamina. This was surprising to an observer, because his innate intellectual ability appeared to be greater than that of many scientists who surpassed him in research.

The causes of his lack of intellectual self-confidence were complex. One of them was the atmosphere of authority in which he was born and grew up. He seems in his youth to have taken it for granted that he should follow any line only under the auspices of some authoritative guide. His naval background, Westminster and Oxford contributed to this intellectual conventionality.

He decided to specialize in chemistry, in which he had been well-taught at school. Chemistry had begun to rise underneath the official university surface at Oxford. Chemists of great ability were at work in comparative obscurity. Tizard found in this atmosphere the intellectual support he needed. He decided to study chemistry, and found N. V. Sidgwick as his tutor. Sidgwick was then not well known, and had not published the works which subsequently brought him a wide reputation.

Tizard immediately responded to his intellectual powers, and was profoundly influenced by him.

When Tizard was a student, chemistry was in a condition which could exist only in a university like Oxford, where there was then a rather distinct division between what belonged to the university, and what to the colleges. The university professor was old, with his main scientific activity finished. University lectures were dull, and the university laboratories in a bad state. In most universities, such conditions would have frustrated any serious study, but in Oxford, with colleges possessing their own buildings and finance, it was possible for young men of talent to make independent arrangements.

Able enthusiasts in Balliol, Magdalen and Trinity Colleges set up laboratories in college buildings and cellars. With these modest material resources, and plenty of brains, flourishing chemical researches developed, especially in physical chemistry. The famous modern Oxford school of physical chemistry arose in this way.

Tizard sat for his degree in chemistry in 1908. He took the theoretical papers first, and answered them to his satisfaction. These were followed by a practical examination lasting a week. At the beginning of this he had a high fever, and had to be removed to a nursing home. His temperature was brought down by the crude methods of the day, and he was allowed to return and attempt a subsequent paper, supported by a nurse. He was not well enough to proceed, and the examiner sent him back to bed. On following days he succeeded in doing more. In spite of this, he was awarded a first class on the examination as a whole.

Tizard suffered from these sudden fevers on several occasions in his life. They seem to have had nervous aspects.

He followed the new Oxford interest in physical chemistry, but as opportunities for pursuing it there were still circumscribed, he was advised by Sidgwick to spend a year in Nernst's laboratory in Berlin. Sidgwick obtained for him the offer of a place, and he went there on small financial resources, having only £130 raised from his college and his father.

Berlin was then the centre of the scientific world, with Planck, Einstein and Nernst in their prime. Nernst had recently discovered his Heat Theorem, which was to become established as the Third Law of Thermodynamics. His laboratory offered a range of intellectual abilities and material facilities not paralleled anywhere at that time in the study of physical chemistry. Outside the laboratory, Berlin offered an unequalled range of scientific activity and life.

Tizard did not prosper in Nernst's laboratory, or in Berlin. He was seriously unwell, and made no progress on the two research problems proposed to him. He became acquainted there with F. A. Lindemann, who later was to cause him tribulation.

They were at first very friendly, and remained so for about ten years, in spite, of one or two incidents. Lindemann was a scientifically exceptional, and socially very exceptional, student. Tizard admired his scientific abilities, which had much more immediate success than his own, but the extreme difference in their financial and social position, besides great contrasts in personality, prevented their friendship from growing on any firm foundation. It was an unstable structure, which ultimately collapsed spectacularly.

After his unsatisfactory year in Berlin, Tizard, on Sidgwick's advice, returned to Oxford, and started research on the kind of physical chemistry which was being pursued there. He published several papers on the sensitivity of chemical indicators.

In 1910 he met his future wife, Kathleen Eleanor Wilson. Nearly five years passed before their marriage in 1915, which was delayed through financial stringency.

He had been elected a fellow of Oriel College in 1911, and for the first time his financial situation improved. His income was about £500 a year, with the usual college privileges, and still he did not marry. Tizard had strong natural feelings, so not surprisingly, in 1912 he had another of his fevers. He was evidently internally perplexed, for he said that he found Oxford life too comfortable, and he must ultimately earn a living in the harsher world outside. Perhaps this was a remnant of a guilt complex from his Protestant Huguenot ancestors.

In 1914, by a happy accident, he went to the meeting of the British Association, held that year in Australia, in spite of the outbreak of the First World War. The Australian Government invited a hundred distinguished scientists as guests, and one of these, who was unable to go, suggested that Tizard should take his place.

Sidgwick was one of the party, and another, in particular, was Rutherford. Tizard met, and immediately became friendly with Rutherford. He conceived a passionate admiration for him.

Rutherford became for him, as for many others, a paternal figure. He had the supreme confidence and authority, and natural psychological healthiness which made him the perfect intellectual parent.

No doubt through Rutherford Tizard found his complexes assuaged. He was very fond of speaking about Rutherford, and wrote several articles on him. These are really more revealing about Tizard than about their subject. Their essence is Tizard's remark, in his Memorial Lecture on Rutherford, that 'for my part I feel cheerful when I think of him'. Rutherford acted as a release to Tizard's spirit, perhaps from the mould made by his father, the strenuous and dutiful naval captain.

Tizard had a similar feeling of release when he spoke of the distinguished scientific engineer Bertram Hopkinson, under whom he worked in the First World War. He was more analytical about Hopkinson than Rutherford, but even with Hopkinson he conveyed more the impression of what Hopkinson had meant to him, rather than what Hopkinson was.

Yet again, in his nervous troubles after the First World War, Tizard found comfort in the personality and advice of Richard Threlfall, a noted academic and industrial scientist, one of the original members of the Advisory Council on Scientific and Industrial Research, who had been a famous athlete in his youth, and in later life a keen shot and freshwater fisherman. Tizard benefited from his healthy intelligence.

From the analytical point of view, his biographical notice of Sidgwick is of particular interest. Tizard wrote of him with deep insight, for it seems that though they were very different men, they also had common problems.

Sidgwick belonged to a distinguished family, and had had a difficult father. He grew up with an inhibited or repressed personality. He had been educated at Rugby School, where, in his day, science was suppressed in favour of classics. He was very gifted intellectually, and at Oxford was outstandingly successful as a student, taking a first class in science, and then in classics and philosophy, a very rare achievement.

In spite of his extraordinary intellectual capacity he did not advance quickly in science, or in influence in Oxford life. Then, as with Tizard, he met Rutherford on the ship to Australia in 1914. He was already forty-one, but from this time his science acquired a new life. Rutherford released him from the inhibitions, both of his personality and of Oxford science. He began to apply the new atomic conceptions to chemistry, and he formed 'a determination to synthesise the sciences of physics and chemistry'. He had made such progress by 1922 that he was elected a Fellow of the Royal Society, an honour for which he had hungered, but which, for so gifted a man, had been delayed until the late age of forty-nine.

Sidgwick gradually achieved his synthesis of the two sciences in his book on *The Electronic Theory of Valency*, which was published in 1927, and his vast *Chemical Elements and their Compounds*, which appeared in 1950. He is one of the few chemists who acquired a great reputation after the age of fifty. It seems that in his earlier years he suffered from paternal frustrations, and then from the conditions of his early education and of Oxford science in the first years of the twentieth century.

Tizard arrived back in England from Australia in the autumn of 1914. He and the great physicist H. G. J. Moseley went together to obtain commissions in the Army. Tizard was posted to the Royal Garrison Artillery. He had to train territorials in the use of anti-aircraft guns, but soon concluded that he would be better employed on something in which his scientific training was of value. He secured a transfer to the Royal Flying Corps, to join in experimental work at the Central Flying School at Upavon, in Wiltshire.

II

The First World War

TIZARD'S work at Upavon was concerned with the testing of the performance of military aircraft. The commandant of the school was a naval commodore, who was not a scientist, but appreciated the scientific approach.

One of the problems which were being investigated was the error in the dropping of bombs caused by the resistance of the air which diverted the bomb from a true parabolic path. Tizard concluded from the work so far done, that the error arising from bad flying of the aircraft was far larger. He therefore asked for permission to learn to fly, in order to investigate this. It was granted, on condition that the normal teaching work of the school was not interrupted; he was to use aircraft only when the weather was too rough for the cadets to proceed with their usual flying lessons.

In learning to fly under such conditions he seriously risked his life. He learned to fly in less than six hours. He became a fully qualified pilot, and in 1916 flew to France to investigate the effects of bombing. There he met General Trenchard.

The rapid development of aircraft made them more versatile, and their use in new ways more practicable. Besides dropping bombs, they could be used to attack enemy aircraft. This raised the problem of the fighter aircraft, which would require qualities different from those of the bomber. Its speed, rate of climb, and height to which it could rise would require to be known accurately. These would have to be measured accurately, not by pilots' estimates, but by reliable, specially devised instruments.

The possibilities of aerial reconnaissance increased, which raised demands for aerial photography, and radio communication, and suitable equipment for carrying them out. Flying near and in clouds became important because of the possibilities of concealment, both in fighting and reconnaissance. But cloud-flying presented problems of its own, which required meteorological investigation.

Tizard stimulated the development of the instruments needed for these various purposes. G. M. B. Dobson, subsequently a distinguished meteorologist, was a member of his team, and devised instruments for measuring the rate of climb of an aircraft, and its fuel consumption.

Tizard felt, however, that the military authorities had not grasped the conception of the aircraft as a weapon; they regarded it as an ancillary device, like a telescope, or motor-truck with wings, rather than a potential fighting machine.

He came in contact with Bertram Hopkinson, the professor of mechanical sciences at Cambridge, who had joined the Department of Military Aeronautics at the War Office, to direct the design and supply of bombs, guns and ammunition, specifically for aeronautical warfare.

Hopkinson had the grasp of a good scientist, and at the same time the practical judgment and capacity for handling men of a good engineer. Tizard was profoundly impressed and influenced by him.

Besides his intellectual and personal qualities, Hopkinson had the engineer's supreme gift of being able to choose the best among many alternatives. For instance, in designing a bridge, it is necessary to choose which, out of many different types, will best serve the needs. Then, among many different designs of the same type, to choose which is the best among several, all of which are apparently about equally suitable.

The example of Hopkinson assisted Tizard to develop his own remarkable judgment in foreseeing which potential weapons would become most important, and in what order of priority their development should be pursued. The chair occupied by Hopkinson had been founded through the pressure of the Cambridge reformers, reflected in the Royal Commissions of 1852 and 1870. Thus their influence bore fruit in military service, which even those far-sighted men did not foresee.

Hopkinson saw that experiment and research ought to be separated from the teaching activities at Upavon. He therefore had the experimental flying with aeronautical armaments moved to Orfordness in Suffolk. The aircraft test flying was moved to Martlesham Heath nearby, with Tizard in charge of the research and experimental work.

Tizard now enjoyed one of the best years of his life. His first son, to whom his friend Lindemann became godfather, was born in 1916, shortly before the move to Martlesham, and his second son in 1917, shortly after. He found flying exhilarating, and was confident that he could make an effective contribution to military aeronautics. He observed from flying experience that the development of the internal combustion engine promised far quicker improvement in aircraft performance than more sophisticated aerodynamics. A big increase in engine power per pound weight enabled the pilot to deal with many subtle flying difficulties by brute force, before the complete scientific answer had been worked out.

To compare experience in a different direction, the same thing was observed in agriculture in the Second World War. The development of the tractor had far more effect in increasing production than the application of more sophisticated scientific discoveries.

Tizard's flying experience impressed on him the very great

importance of the development of the aero engine. This stimulated his interest in the science of the internal combustion engine, in which he later carried out notable research.

In the course of one of his flying tests, he came in contact with a formation of German bombers which were raiding London. His fighter was armed with guns and ammunition which had not been previously tested. To find out their merit he rose behind the German formation and attacked one of its near planes. He fired his gun in a short burst, without any visible effect. The guns then jammed. Not being able to make any further attack, he followed the planes and made notes on their performance, which was not then known.

In the latter months of 1917 he began to feel ill. He thought it was due to repeated flights above 15,000 feet without oxygen. It may also have been connected with the kind of nervous trouble which seemed to affect him at other times. He had lost interest in testing, which had been reduced to a routine. The future of the Martlesham Station was uncertain, and because of this he moved his family to Oxford. Anxiety about the future seems at all times to have weighed considerably with him.

However, he was asked by Hopkinson to become his deputy as controller of Research and Experiment at Headquarters in London. He had arrived at the kind of position most suited to his talents. By 1918 he had been promoted to Lieutenant-Colonel; he was then thirty-three.

He also found himself working in the higher ranks of Winston Churchill's ministry, for aircraft production had been transferred to the Ministry of Munitions.

In the course of his visits to experimental stations, which he usually made by flying his own aircraft, he had one bad crash. Though apparently not particularly evident at the time, this was probably still another heavy strain on his nervous system.

One of his most important pieces of scientific work at this period arose out of the German submarine campaign. The sinking of tankers had caused a serious shortage of fuel for aircraft engines. This had been made from Pennsylvania petroleum, which was found to be particularly good for the purpose, though the reason for this was not known.

Tizard had tests made on mixtures of aircraft fuel and benzol from gas works. This was found to give even better results than the aircraft fuel. As Pennsylvaniania petroleum consisted of aliphatic or paraffin hydrocarbons, while the benzol contained aromatic hydrocarbons, the improvement appeared to be due to the latter.

The benzol mixture was not satisfactory, however, in flight, for the benzene in the benzol solidified at the low temperatures at high altitudes. Different aromatic compounds which did not freeze under flying conditions were required, so toluene was tried. This was available in Burma petroleum, which was not in such short supply. The pursuit of this line of research led ultimately to the discovery of 'anti-knock' substances, which prevent the knocking, due to premature explosion of the mixture, that sometimes occurs in internal combustion engines.

Just before the end of the war, Hopkinson, who had also learned to fly in order to acquire practical knowledge of aircraft, and to travel from place to place, was killed in a crash. Tizard described this as a 'national calamity'. It was a disaster for British aeronautical science and engineering, for it had been intended that Hopkinson should be the director of a National School of Aeronautical Engineering.

It was also a profound personal blow to Tizard. He had to succeed a man who had made a profound formative impression on his psychology and life. In addition to this, Tizard contracted the notorious influenza of 1918.

He returned to civilian life in 1919, after having undergone severe stresses.

III

Between the Wars

TIZARD resumed his former academic life at Oxford. He picked up the research which he had dropped at the beginning of the war, returning to the investigation of chemical indicators.

His most important academic activity at this time was probably his part in helping to secure the election of his friend Lindemann to one of the physics chairs at Oxford. The other physics chair was occupied by Townsend, with whom Tizard had collaborated on research into the conduction of electricity in gases. Townsend had had a difference with J. J. Thomson, and took a detached view of Cambridge physics. In his book on *Electricity in Gases* he gave a notably dispassionate account of the history of the discovery of the electron. Tizard may have been influenced by Townsend's attitude. Though he had a passionate regard for Rutherford, he was a profoundly Oxford man. This characteristic was a factor in his support of Lindemann's candidature; the desire to raise Oxford physics.

Tizard's detached view of Cambridge physics became noticeable again after the death of Rutherford. He was inclined to favour a change in the line of Cambridge physics. He doubted whether it was good for British physics that so much talent should be concentrated in one line; it might be better if another line were given priority for a time, and thus lead to a more balanced development of British physics.

The change of priority at Cambridge from atomic physics to the structure of materials has been followed by a remarkable development in molecular biology, in which Cambridge physicists have had a very distinguished part.

The work on aircraft fuels that Tizard had begun at Martlesham during the war provided him with the best opportunity for further personal research. The chemical properties of petroleum were evidently of great importance for their use in aircraft engines. The petroleum industry became deeply interested in the science of the internal combustion engine, which was stimulating such a demand for oil. It supported a laboratory for engine research directed by H. R. Ricardo. Tizard participated in the work, and brought with him D. R. Pye, who had been with him at Martlesham. During the war Ricardo and Tizard discussed plans for a research engine, in which the compression could be varied while the engine was running. The effects of changes in compression could thereby be investigated and elucidated.

Tizard suggested that a second engine should be made, which performed one stroke, and then stopped at the top of the dead centre, just before the ignition of the compressed mixture. This engine, which was called the 'Sphinx', was used for investigating the unstable conditions which occur just before ignition.

At Oxford, Tizard and Pye made a comprehensive study of the physical characteristics of a large number of comparatively pure hydrocarbon constituents of petroleum, and other combustible substances that might be used as fuels. After accumulating these data, Tizard joined Ricardo in investigating the behaviour of these various substances in the experimental engines.

By working with single chemical substances, and not with mixtures, it became easier to identify the fuel characteristics of each substance. The investigation of the chemical changes during the combustion process was simplified, for only one fuel substance was present. It became easier to understand which particular constituents gave commercial fuels desired properties.

The experiments confirmed that the most important single factor in limiting the performance of the petrol engine was the incidence of detonation. Tizard introduced the Toluene Number for expressing the anti-knock quality of fuels. American investigators subsequently introduced the Octane Number.

The investigation showed that for a given compression ratio, the maximum power developed was comparatively independent of the nature of the fuel. This was because of the dissociation of carbon dioxide at the high temperatures. The best fuel was that which showed least tendency to knock. The efficiency of the engine was highest with a weak mixture.

Tizard was appointed University Reader in Thermodynamics at Oxford early in 1920. He was invited to join the Aeronautical Research Committee. At about this time he was invited to become an Assistant Secretary of the Department of Scientific and Industrial Research, which had been founded four years before. He decided to accept this position in the Civil Service. He was assailed by his lack of intellectual self-confidence, feeling that he would never be an outstanding scientist, and, like his father, suffered from financial anxiety on behalf of his family. He feared that if he stayed in Oxford he would not be able to earn enough to educate his children adequately.

He left Oxford for London in the summer of 1920, and again had severe influenza and a kind of nervous prostration. Delayed effects from his flying experiences in the war may have been a contributory factor. Again he found solace in the sympathy and advice of an older, widely experienced man; Threlfall recommended him to take up fishing. In 1922 he was ill once more. He was told that he was suffering from anxiety on behalf of his family. After this, he remained comparatively well until he was elderly.

When Tizard joined the Department of Scientific and Industrial Research in 1920, one of his major tasks was to conduct four boards which had been set up, to coordinate military with civilian science. Their subjects were chemistry, physics, engineering and radio. Their aim was to facilitate exchange of scientific information, reduce overlapping, and ensure efficient single financial control on all fundamental research which was of civilian as well as military interest.

Tizard did not agree with this organization. He believed that each service should have its own director of research, who should have a great deal of authority. He fought fierce battles to raise the status of such posts. His efforts to raise the status of science within the ranks of government organization were among his most important contributions.

Tizard was elected a Fellow of the Royal Society in 1926, and in 1927 he became the Secretary of the Department of Scientific and Industrial Research.

In 1929 he left the D.S.I.R. to become Rector of the Imperial College of Science and Technology. Here again he was a conscientious and capable director, but the character of the College did not change very much during the period of his rectorship. He believed that it would become the first British technological unisity, and he worked to that end. However, he was diverted from the work by world events. In any case, education, like civilian science and industrial research, was not the best medium for his genius. Tizard felt happier in military work, because war simplified life. It produced a dominating objective, which justified the ample exercise of authority. It integrated his inner psychological conflicts.

In civilian and educational affairs Tizard's combination of social conventionality with original views on the use and implications of science produced a kind of instability. He was often on edge, and his keen penetration and sharp tongue ruffled people. On the one hand, he believed that the University of Oxford was the most democratic institution in the world; on the other, he had revolutionary ideas on the application of science to strategy.

He had the characteristic upper middle-class belief that there is only a small reservoir of high human ability. Such views as this, and his opinion of Oxford, were not helpful in conceiving policy for the large-scale expansion of scientific and technological education and research.

The brushing away of all social subtleties by Hitler's rise to power in 1933, with the immediate threat to Britain, created the situation in which Tizard could exercise his genius without frustration.

IV

The Second World War

TIZARD had already aimed at securing the participation of science and scientists at the highest levels in government. While not yet succeeding in this, his struggles for the improvement of status had improved the position and conditions of some good scientists, who had consequently been able to make useful progress.

When the rise of the Nazis made the threat of attack evident, a number of good scientists were in the Government administration, even if not in very influential positions. The fact that they were there at all was due in a considerable degree to Tizard.

The existing methods of defence against bombers were based on location of the hostile aircraft by sound-detectors, and by patrols of fighter aircraft. The sound-detectors were quite inadequate against the faster machines, and there were not enough fighters to organize continuous patrols. Consequently, Baldwin was led to make his famous observation that 'the bomber will always get through'.

His attitude was galling to various sections of opinion. One of these was led by Churchill, who was outside the Government, and Lindemann, who believed that it was the political duty of the rulers of the country to adopt a more positive attitude to preparedness. Information on the conditions in Germany suggested that while the Nazi threat was far too serious to be trifled with, the German military position had serious weaknesses which could be exploited. The situation was far from hopeless, and it was essential to explore every possibility for strengthening the British defences, including the development of scientific weapons.

The general public also did not welcome the prospect of the

bombers always getting through. Readers wrote to their newspapers, enquiring whether it might not be possible to invent a death-ray which could be directed onto hostile bombers, and destroy them in the air as they approached.

Government military and scientific officials thought about the problem. As this atmosphere of alertness became more keen, it inspired action. In 1934, A. P. Rowe, the Scientific Assistant to H. E. Wimperis, the Director of Scientific Research at the Air Ministry, studied the files on the subject of scientific methods of defence against air attack. He found them discouraging. The need for new scientific initiative was pressing. Later in the year, Wimperis recommended to the Minister for Air that a new body, a Committee for the Scientific Survey of Air Defence, should be set up, under the chairmanship of Tizard. The other members were to be A. V. Hill and P. M. S. Blackett, together with Wimperis himself, and Rowe as secretary.

It was 'to consider how far recent advances in scientific and technical knowledge can be used to strengthen the present methods of defence against hostile aircraft'. The Air Staff sent officers to represent them, and Tizard promoted frank discussion between the scientists on the one hand, and the fighting officers on the other. He had an outstanding gift for securing the interest of fighting men in the military possibilities of science, and their confidence in scientists.

Before the Committee held its first meeting, Wimperis, apparently on the prompting of Tizard, informally asked Watson Watt whether he believed it might be possible to use radiation as a weapon of defence against air attack. Watson Watt had worked on radio direction-finding in the First World War, and had since become one of the leading authorities on radio transmission. In the course of his researches he had coined the term 'ionosphere', and had latterly carried out extensive investigations on atmospherics. He had shown how their direction and wave-characteristics could be determined visually by the record that they made on a cathode-ray tube.

Watson Watt returned to his laboratory and indicated to one of his assistants the problem to be solved, and asked for the numerical solution. On the basis of the results, Watson Watt found that the radiation to be effective would have to be much more intense than could be produced by any known method. He pointed out, however, that it should be possible to produce radiation strong enough to pick up its echo from a considerable distance. This offered a conceivable method of detecting aircraft by radio.

Watson Watt's remarkable report was submitted to the first meeting of the Tizard Committee, and received strong support. From it sprang the great development of radio location, or radar, which had so important a rôle in the defence of Britain. As chairman of the committee which sponsored radar, Tizard had a unique rôle in encouraging and guiding its development, securing the large funds required for the research and application, and convincing the fighting airmen of its value as a weapon.

Tizard personally persuaded the air chiefs to work out the strategy of air fighting with the aid of radar before radar had actually been completely worked out. He suggested that fighting exercises could be carried out with ordinary radio to simulate radar. This suggestion was adopted, with the consequence that British fighter pilots had learned how to use radar before it had been given to them.

The Luftwaffe was unaware of the changes in air fighting which would be produced by radar, so when it first attacked Britain its losses were enormous, and it was nonplussed. The attacks had to be suspended until the new strategy and tactics had been discovered, and the air crews trained in them.

Tizard's insight into the military use of radar, his success in persuading the fighting men to use it, and his suggestion of how it could be used as a weapon of surprise, were military scientific inspirations of genius, which had great results.

Besides the Committee for the Scientific Survey of Air Defence, of which Tizard was chairman, and which was responsible to the Air Ministry, a sub-committee of the Committee of Imperial Defence was formed on Air Defence Research. It was set up a little later than the Tizard committee, and arose from pressure by Churchill and Lindemann. It was more political in character than his own committee.

Owing to the agitation of Churchill and Lindemann on air defence, Lindemann was invited to become a member of Tizard's committee. He delayed acceptance, because he wanted Tizard's committee to be placed directly under the Air Defence Research Committee, of which Churchill was a member. Lindemann's belief was that the Air Ministry had given Baldwin bad advice on air defence, so research on air defence should not be under the Ministry.

If Tizard's committee had been placed under the Air Defence Research Committee, it would have been more directly open to pressure from Churchill, and hence from Lindemann. Churchill and Lindemann did not succeed in this, so Lindemann accepted membership of the Tizard committee.

Tizard, Hill and Blackett were substantially agreed on what scientific policy should be pursued. Their outlook was that of the ablest professional opinion in the scientific and technical field. Lindemann was in a much more individual position. He had numerous personal scientific proposals and opinions, which were less characteristic of the professional outlook of scientists and technologists. Together with this, he included a much larger political element in arriving at conclusions as to what should be done in air defence.

Tizard and Lindemann, who had long been friends, but had been falling apart, now diverged more and more widely.

From Lindemann's point of view, Tizard had become one of the chief technical pillars of the series of administrations which had dispensed with, or rejected, Churchill, neglected the military safety of the country, and had engaged in appeasement. Lindemann's combination of this attitude with great confidence in the value of his own scientific ideas and opinions, made him an extremely dissident member of Tizard's committee. The former friends became fierce antagonists. The atmosphere grew so bad that Hill and Blackett resigned from the committee. The Air Ministry thereupon dissolved the committee, and reformed it without Lindemann, but again including Blackett and Hill.

The greatest achievement of the Tizard committee was its fostering of radar. Later, it was learned that the idea had been invented in several of the most advanced scientific and industrial countries almost simultaneously. Its development was carried forward far more quickly and effectively in Britain than elsewhere, because it was essential to Britain's defence. For instance, the Germans considered it not so important to them at the beginning of the war because their outlook was offensive, and they believed that it was not essential in the aggressive war they were planning.

The utilization of radar by the Royal Air Force presented a new order of problem in the handling of military equipment.

Hitherto, the instruments used in guiding military action were of a comparatively simple kind, such as telescopes and telephones. The radar apparatus was of a new order of scientific complication and was far more difficult to use. For this, the fighting men needed a deeper kind of technical training. The radar equipment had to be of a robust and convenient design, so that it did not make too great demands on the users. The answers to these questions could be obtained only by sending scientists to study the behaviour of the equipment and its users under fighting conditions.

Further, it was necessary that the scientists should give all their attention to the research, and be free from other duties. They must therefore be on fighting sites, essentially as scientists in a civilian capacity, taking a detached view of the performance of the equipment and its operators.

These studies, beginning with radar, became known as operational research, and spread to the scientific analysis of other aspects of warfare. Thus operational research arose out of, and was fostered by, the activities of the Tizard committee.

The committee stimulated reflection on what the enemy might be doing in similar directions. This led to Tizard suggesting that a scientist, R. V. Jones, should be attached to the intelligence organization, for systematic pursuit of such investigations. Britain appears to have been the first major power to have such a department.

After the discovery of uranium fission, the question of the possibility of atomic bombs arose. Tizard was inclined to believe that it would not be possible. Nevertheless, he attempted to secure a British option on uranium ore in Katanga, and he encouraged investigation of the possibility.

V

The Atomic Bomb

THE development leading to the atomic bomb started from the publication by F. Joliot and his colleagues in Paris, of a letter in *Nature* on April 22nd, 1939, in which they showed that in the fission of a uranium atom more than two neutrons were released. This was concrete evidence for the possibility of a chain reaction in uranium, which might produce an atomic explosion. G. P. Thomson and W. L. Bragg immediately appreciated the implications of these experiments, and concluded that there was probably an even chance that it would be possible to utilize uranium fission as a source of heat and power, and perhaps some chance that it could be utilized as a very powerful explosive. In that case, Britain ought to secure control of uranium, to prevent its being acquired by Germany.

These considerations were brought to the notice of Tizard's Committee on the Scientific Survey of Air Defence. Tizard agreed on the scientific facts, but thought that the chances of their being exploited for military purposes were very much less, perhaps only 1 in 100,000. He nevertheless said that if it were possible, the result would be so important, that even a very small chance should not be ignored. He therefore recommended that Britain should buy or secure the option on uranium.

Consequently, within only four days after the publication of Joliot's letter, the Treasury and the Foreign Office were approached to explore the possibility of action. In a fortnight the president of the Union Minière Company, owning the uranium in the Congo and Belgium, met Tizard in London. But Tizard concluded that the immediate possibilities of exploiting fission had been far too optimistic, and it was not advisable for the Government to spend large sums on purchasing available stocks of uranium. However, experiments were started on a small scale by G. P. Thomson and M. L. E. Oliphant, under Tizard's committee.

When the war started in 1939, the Committee for the Scientific Survey of Air Defence was taken over by Tizard's committee for the Scientific Survey of Air Warfare. Tizard felt that the war situation made the uranium fission possibilities still more remote. Thomson and Oliphant kept their uranium research going through assistants, but themselves went over to other work. Oliphant led the research in which Randall and Boot invented their magnetron, which made accurate radar possible.

This device had more effect on the outcome of the Second World War than any other scientific weapon. The atomic bomb and the large German rockets came into use only after the war had effectively been decided.

By February 1940 Thomson's experiments had still not produced conclusive evidence for the possibility of a chain reaction. About this time, however, O. R. Frisch and R. Peierls, who had not been recruited for war-work because of their alien origin, produced a very cogent short memorandum giving advanced physical reasons why an atomic bomb should be possible. This outstanding paper was referred to Tizard. He sent it to Thomson, who was in charge of uranium work for his committee. The paper stimulated interest; it was decided to set up a sub-committee of the Committee for the Scientific Survey of Air Warfare, to guide further research on the problem. Thomson became chairman, and Chadwick, Oliphant, Cockcroft, Blackett and others were brought into it.

This sub-committee became known as the M.A.U.D., or Maud Committee. Shortly after it was set up, the Committee for the Scientific Survey of Air Warfare was dissolved, as a result of Churchill becoming Prime Minister, with Lindemann as his scientific adviser. But the Maud Committee continued as a committee of the Ministry of Aircraft Production.

Under its guidance a very able research programme was launched. Chadwick, who had independently come to the conclusion that an atomic bomb was probably possible, started making necessary fundamental atomic measurements. The British physicists were greatly strengthened by the arrival of H. Halban and L. Kowarski, Joliot's French colleagues. F. Simon of Oxford came in on the problem of the separation of isotopes of uranium. The Imperial Chemical Industries was brought in to deal with metallurgical problems.

When Tizard went on his mission to the United States in the autumn of 1940, he took Cockcroft with him, to expound the British work on the atomic bomb. They found that the Americans were in the sceptical condition that had obtained in England before the Maud Committee's activities. Their investigations were proceeding on broadly similar lines, but were several months behind.

The British information convinced the Americans of the possibility of the bomb. They were so impressed that they proposed that the project should become Anglo-American. This was not accepted by the British, because they doubted American security precautions, for America was not yet at war, and there was fear that the United States would appropriate the industrial as well as the military fruits, not only of British scientific work, but also of the French and other European scientists who had participated.

After the Japanese attack on Pearl Harbour, when the United States found herself at war, she prosecuted her research and development on the atomic bomb with intense energy, and a unique technological power. She soon left the modest British effort behind, and when the British now suggested a joint Anglo-American project, they were turned down.

The Maud Committee scientists had explored the fundamental problems, outlined the features of atomic bomb production, made estimates of its cost, and reported on their conclusions, within fifteen months.

The Committee made two reports, one on the possibility of using uranium for power, and the other for a bomb. The majority expressed the opinion that the British could make a bomb before the end of 1943. Blackett, in a minority of one, said that he doubted whether so novel and large a project could be carried out in so short a time. The technical problems had not been sufficiently emphasized, nor unforeseen difficulties adequately allowed for. He recommended that the full-scale plant should not be erected in Britain, and that discussions for building it in the United States should be started immediately, with American technologists.

Tizard said that he entirely disagreed with the suggestion that the British could make an atomic bomb before the end of 1943. He compared the situation with the synthesis of ammonia in Germany. The scientific problem was solved in 1909, but the problem of large-scale production was not solved until 1914.

Tizard wrote to Hankey, the chairman of the Scientific Advisory Committee of the War Cabinet, referring to 'the enthusiasm of three well-known Peers' for an immediate British atomic bomb project. Mrs. Gowing suggests that he was referring to Lord Cherwell, and Lords McGowan and Melchett of Imperial Chemical Industries.

In spite of this enthusiasm, it became accepted that Britain had not the resources to build an atomic energy plant during the war. Tizard expressed doubt whether atomic energy would ever be an economic source of power, as an alternative to coal. He doubted whether even a pilot atomic energy plant should be built in Britain during the war, because of the resources which would have to be diverted from making turbo engines for aircraft.

Tizard feared the effects of a British atomic energy project after the war. It might absorb too large a proportion of the scientists required to restore and improve the country's education and industry on which its future depended.

Tizard's severely critical attitude was probably heightened by the complex of interests bearing on atomic energy policy. There were industrialists like McGowan and Melchett, who saw in it one of the prospectively dominating industrial developments of the future. There was Cherwell, who believed that industry should be conducted by private enterprise, or at least by the methods of private enterprise, even if under Government control. There were scientists like Halban, who as a naturalized Frenchman was particularly patriotic. He also believed in private industry and had connections with it. When he came to England he regarded himself as the custodian of the French national interests and patent rights in atomic energy. There were refugee scientists from Nazi Germany, with a full understanding of what Nazi victory would mean, and a desperate desire to make the atomic bomb for the Allies, before the Nazis could make it.

Tizard was the son of a naval officer, and an experimental air pilot officer. He was not at home in this complex of conflicting interests. He looked at the problems of the war in the spirit of an officer called upon to do his duty. He was really the outstanding example of the scientific-officer class. On purely scientific questions of military policy he was unrivalled, but when the political factor in any problem became large, his judgment became less certain.

VI

A Clash of Masterful Spirits

THE appointment of Churchill to the Admiralty after the outbreak of the Second World War complicated Tizard's position. Lindemann accompanied Churchill as his adviser on scientific and economic affairs. He was no longer outside the Government organization. Then, in 1940 he became scientific and economic adviser to the Prime Minister, when Churchill was called to that office.

Lindemann had Tizard's influence curbed, and after this, Tizard considered resignation. But before resigning, he made another major contribution. It had become evident that Britain would have to make extraordinary efforts to secure American support. The British Ambassador in Washington had suggested that there should be an exchange of scientific information and military experience. Tizard suggested that a British scientific attaché should be appointed at Washington, and A. V. Hill was appointed to the post. He found that, in order to influence American official opinion effectively, it was desirable to widen the scope of the scientific information that could be revealed.

It was decided that Tizard should lead a scientific mission to Washington. He was superlatively qualified for the task; it also removed him from the centre of affairs in London, and hence from immediate contact with Lindemann and Churchill. He was permitted to draft his own terms of reference, which were: 'to tell them what they want to know, to give all assistance I can on behalf of the British Government to enable the armed forces of the U.S.A. to reach the highest level of technical efficiency'.

Tizard included in his mission R. H. Fowler, who had been appointed scientific attaché to Ottawa, J. D. Cockcroft, and E. G. Bowen. He insisted on the inclusion of distinguished serving officers. These were Captain Faulkner of the Royal Navy, Colonel F. C. Wallace of the Army, and Group-Captain F. L. Pearce of the Royal Air Force. Wallace had commanded the anti-aircraft guns defending the Dunkirk beaches, and Pearce had joined in the bombing of the *Scharnhorst*.

Among the military scientific secrets which the mission took with them were the 10-centimetre magnetron, which made precise radar possible, and the proximity fuse, which, among many other applications, was to be decisive in the defence against the V1 flying bomb.

Tizard's mission was at first received with caution in the United States, especially by the military. Tizard followed the line that he was there to deliver gifts, not in any way to negotiate. This seemed a very novel point of view. American military scientists were deeply impressed by the magnetron, and were quickly won over. Perhaps the most remarkable impression of all was made on the American military by the sight of such a mission, carrying military scientific information of such profound importance, and containing outstanding serving officers, being led by a civilian whom they regarded as a professor.

It was a deep unspoken lesson on the kind of relations between scientists and fighting men which were now becoming necessary. Tizard's mission is probably the greatest scientific embassy that has yet been made.

After his return to London in the autumn of 1940, Tizard found his scope for direct action in guiding scientific military developments more and more circumscribed. He was appointed to high positions, but these were of an advisory nature, with less power for action.

He became involved in a still more serious dispute with Lindemann on bombing policy. The question turned on several factors. How were the bombing forces to be used? They were necessarily limited. Which targets would be most profitable in contributing to the defeat of the enemy? Should the bomber force be used to break the morale of the German nation? Was this a possible objective? Or should it be used to ensure the survival of Britain by attacking and defeating the U-boats?

This complex question could not be answered without detailed analysis of its various scientific aspects. Nor could it be answered without judgments concerning the political direction of the war. Tizard and most of the scientists who had worked with him were convinced that Lindemann's calculations on the amount of damage that could be done by bombing attacks on the German people in their cities were very seriously wrong. If the bombing force were to be wholly diverted to this object, instead of destroying the U-boats, Britain would lose the war. In fact, just enough of the bomber force was diverted to attacking the U-boats to ensure their defeat.

In this dispute, the balance of the scientific arguments was strongly on Tizard's side. His position in official circles, however, became impossible. His masterful spirit could not be subordinated to that other masterful spirit of Lindemann's. He retired from the centre of affairs, and in 1942 became President of Magdalen College, Oxford. It seemed as if it had become impossible for Tizard and Lindemann to live in the same city.

Tizard tried to represent to himself that he was happy at being President of Magdalen. His military scientific genius was in fact incongruous to the position.

After Churchill was defeated in the General Election of 1945, Lindemann returned to his professorship at Oxford.

It was not long before Tizard resigned the presidency of Magdalen, and came back to London to become the chief adviser on both civilian and military scientific affairs to Attlee's Labour Government. Evidently he felt that his talent was for the formation of science policy, rather than for education.

Tizard's judgment and creative power were at their highest in the use of science for defence. This arose in part from his long preoccupation with the problem of the defence of Britain against air attack. It had nothing to do with lack of ruthlessness; he was quite cold-blooded in considering the possibilities of horrible new weapons, but he was quicker to see the possibilities for defence than offence. When evidence was obtained that the Germans were intending to use radio beams to guide their bombers at night and in bad weather in their raids on Britain, he at first discounted it.

The same orientation predisposed him to doubt the possibility of the successful invasion of Europe in 1944.

His social and political ideas affected his thinking on problems of the offensive. Even at the beginning of 1939, like so many of his colleagues in the Athenaeum, he doubted whether Hitler would launch a major war. His middle-class conventionality inclined him to believe that the head of a state could not be so stupid.

Cherwell's social and political ideas helped him to avoid this kind of misjudgment. He had a better understanding of the psychology of the offensive, even if he made faulty scientific calculations about offensive operations.

Broadly speaking, Tizard was more concerned with saving Britain, Cherwell with smashing the Nazis.

In spite of their bitter contests, they did not become totally and finally estranged. In their last years they met and corresponded occasionally, with a gingerly observation of the ordinary rules of politeness.

VII

Formulator of Science Policy

AFTER the General Election of 1945 and the formation of the Labour Government, the Ministry of Defence, which during the war had been combined with the premiership, was established as a separate ministry. The committee dealing with the scientific aspects of military affairs, of which Cherwell had been chairman, was dissolved. A new committee was set up, to advise the Ministry of Defence on Defence Research Policy.

The new Government also appointed an Advisory Council on Science Policy, to advise on the development of civil science. Tizard was invited to be chairman of both of these committees, resigning his presidency of Magdalen College, and returning to London.

The new plan virtually realized the proposal of Alexander Strange in the 1860's.

The Defence Research Policy Committee was to advise on what lines British defence should be conducted in the new scientific and technological age. It had to take into account the changed position of Britain in the world, with the prospective dissolution of her empire, and comparative decline in economic power. In addition to these factors, there were the internal social changes in the country, accompanied by an alteration in the distribution of the national income, and the resources available for defence expenditure.

Tizard foreshadowed some of the features and concerns of the military science committee in a lecture to the Royal United Service Institution on 'Science and the Services' in 1946. He said that for centuries, from early Chinese and Egyptian times, invention had had a profound influence through the production of new weapons; some of revolutionary significance, such as gunpowder, the change from sail to steam navigation, and the introduction of radio; but the methods of science had been applied to military problems on a comprehensive scale only in the Second World War.

Tizard himself had been told by a famous admiral that he

regarded scientists as mechanics who should do as they were told, but later on the admiral quite changed his view.

During the nineteenth century, the British military service 'like British industry, became lethargic and self-satisfied'. He attributed the first effective break with this attitude to Haldane, through his placing the development of aircraft for military purposes on a scientific basis. This led to the development of military aircraft in the First World War being entrusted to Bertram Hopkinson, with proper status and powers. Tizard believed that Hopkinson was the first to study air tactics by scientific methods.

The position now was that scientists must study the needs as well as supply the wants of the services. They must study the plans for future, as well as the results of past operations. They should help to discover what was most important to do, as well as show how to do it. 'Experience has shown that a nation with toughness, stamina and a will to live and work, can stand far more punishment in the form of bombardment of its cities and homes than most people thought possible before the trial. No one thinks now that it would have been possible to defeat Germany by bombing alone. The actual effort in manpower and resources that was expended in bombing Germany was greater than the value in manpower of the damage caused. . . .'

Consideration of the atomic bomb indicated that 'a future war between highly organized nations may well be a quick fight to the death, and its outcome may depend far more on the state of science, education and industry in the rival countries than on the courage, skill and number of the fighting men.'

He thought it fortunate that the atomic bomb and long-range rockets had been demonstrated before the end of the war, for although they had had little influence on its outcome, 'they opened wide the eyes of the people of the world', who might otherwise have happily gone to sleep again, while these weapons had been developed in secret.

A scientific staff attached to the central Chiefs of Staff organization was required. It should have no executive duties, nor be overburdened with administration, and devote the whole of its time to the study of the influence of ordinary scientific knowledge on military problems.

Tizard welcomed the new committee, which was in fact founded on these lines. In his Haldane Memorial Lecture he called it a 'revolution in organization', impelled by the Second

World War. The new scientific weapons had forced scientists, shortly before it began, to interfere in the tactics of the use of these weapons, and later on, in the strategy. Such ideas had formerly been repugnant to serving officers, but they had become a necessity. War experience had completely changed the serving officers' point of view, and it was they who had pressed for the new committee. The chairman was a scientist, and scientific adviser to the Minister of Defence. He had full access to all relevant information and attended the meetings of the Chiefs of Staff Committee not only when invited, but whenever he judged that his presence would be useful. Consequently, no major recommendation on Defence Policy was made without his knowledge and assistance.

In the earlier stages of the committee, nuclear weapons were excluded from its considerations, owing to the extreme atmosphere of secrecy which surrounded them, until some time after the first Russian nuclear explosions.

Tizard's main achievement with this committee was to consolidate its status as part of the government machinery. As Chairman of the Advisory Committee on Science Policy, which he regarded as a product of Haldane's suggestions of 1924, he aimed at promoting the penetration of science into the general machinery of government.

He considered that the relative ineffectiveness of the earlier committees following on Haldane's suggestions, and of outside bodies of scientists, such as the Royal Society, was due to the separation of scientists and administrators. Members of Parliament were not educated to understand questions with scientific aspects. It was essential, as Sir Edward Bridges had said, that scientific advisers and administrators should work 'cheek by jowl'. Committees consisting entirely of scientists were often ineffective because scientists were inclined to be uncompromising among themselves. Tizard said that this was a cause of the delay in settling a policy of Higher Education in Technology.

The new Advisory Committee on Science Policy included both scientists and administrators, and the chairman was given access to any confidential information necessary for its work.

Tizard held that the most serious difficulty was 'caused by the deplorable intellectual gap that exists between those who have had a scientific education and those who have not'. Nearly all ministers and administrators belonged to the latter class.

Scientists found it bafflingly difficult to explain the scientific aspects of problems to them. One of the ways of reducing this difficulty was to transfer some men from the scientific to the administrative branch of the Civil Service.

Tizard considered that, even if society survived its invention of nuclear weapons, the advances of science and technology would produce serious social dangers. 'The great task of government will be to avoid the social dangers that the changes will involve even in times of peace, without losing the benefits.'

He could not see how this could be done without 'forethought based on real knowledge and understanding', which increasingly involved science in a scientific age. It was for these reasons that he aimed at consolidating the new Advisory Committee on Science Policy, as an essential contribution to social development and safety.

Tizard described in his Messel Lecture the strategy of science as 'the art of so directing the application or advance of science as to make the most rapid progress of society, or of knowledge'.

He regarded research as the tactics of science. He thought that the tactics of British science were very high. They had been successfully continued with good strategy in the Second World War. The problem now was to continue it with a good strategy for industry.

It was difficult to bring British science in adequate combination with industry while British scientists continued, in the phrase of the American civil engineer Professor J. K. Finch, to be so 'high hat'. He agreed with Finch that engineering was still a practical art reinforced by science, but with objectives which were economic and social rather than scientific. It involved industrial and business economics, the planning and direction of labour, and the management of human relations. The study of science alone did not provide an adequate preparation for such work.

From this perspective, there was no point in adding to science, if it could not be utilized in practice. 'It is useless to increase scientific capital if it bears no interest.'

Tizard concluded that 'it is more important now to strengthen our technology than to expand our science; more important to do things than to write about how they might be done. Science is not enough.' In Rutherford's phrase: 'We haven't any money, so we've got to think.'

Tizard said in his Presidential Address to the British Association in 1948 that 'the production of power from uranium cannot bring such economic benefits to this country within twenty years as would the practical application of known methods of economizing coal'. He drew attention to the bearing of features of war science on industrial science. In war, there was rapid solution of practical problems, because 'the incentive to succeed is greater than any profit or ideological incentive in civilian life'. This led to the paradox, that in the desperate desire for victory, more attention was given in war to the study of man in relation to machines, in the design and use of weapons, than is given in civilian peace-time productive industry.

It followed that great increases in industrial production could be expected if there was the incentive for a determined application of science to the whole process, both in its technical and human aspects.

As chairman of the Advisory Committee on Science Policy he had an important part in promoting the expansion of civil scientific research and university science in post-war Britain. The committee was not, however, sufficiently integrated into the government machinery to have the power to do all that was required for adequately incorporating science into the national life.

The position to which Tizard had been appointed was a new office, of higher status within the Civil Service than any previously held by a scientist as such.

Hitherto, during the eighteen years from 1929 until 1947, he had not been a government official, for all his immense work as adviser and chairman of committees. This situation had limited his influence on the execution of policies. It exacerbated a frustration about which he continually complained. But, consciously or unconsciously, he probably preferred this situation, for it absolved him from the ultimate necessity of fitting into the government organization. It left him free, if unpaid, to make criticisms which, while nearly always penetrating, often could not have been borne by official colleagues of comparable status. In his heart, he preferred to be free-speaking rather than prosperous. He had something of the character who would rather lose a friend than suppress a brilliant comment. After he had made such remarks he usually tried to make up for them, but this did not always suffice.

Tizard's work as senior scientist within the government organization was not the most outstanding of his career. His insight into scientific policy exceeded his administrative and political gifts. While seeing what ought to be done, and possessing exceptional powers of personal persuasion for influencing individuals, he was less gifted at creating the administrative and political machinery for carrying it out.

Nevertheless, Tizard did more than any other man to get this first effort at the integration of science and policy working. It was the beginning which could be expanded to the far greater scale which is necessary for the modernization of Britain, and for the salvation of the country.

After the defeat of the Labour Government in 1951, and the return of Cherwell to Whitehall, Tizard soon retired. His health was not good, and he finally left official life in 1952. It was characteristic that he had not secured adequate pension arrangements. He found himself hard up, so he took some directorships in companies with scientific interests.

Tizard was made a Knight Commander of the Bath in 1937 and raised in the order in 1947. The United States awarded him its Medal of Merit in 1947. He received many academic and scientific honours.

He died at his home at Fareham in Hampshire on October 9th, 1959, after a cerebral haemorrhage.

His personal inspiration has been described by Blackett, who has related that 'of all the individuals who have influenced me by their personality, I think Tizard comes next to Rutherford'.

SIR HENRY TIZZARD

Frederick Alexander Lindemann: Lord Cherwell

1886–1957

I

A Scientist in Politics

LINDEMANN was the first scientist to acquire political power in Britain as a scientist. He achieved this by becoming the friend, political collaborator and scientific adviser of Winston Churchill.

Few men have had less immediately obvious qualifications for such an achievement. He had an authoritarian social outlook characteristic of members of the Continental ruling classes, and his surname was regarded by some as German, or German Jewish. He was a tall man with dark hair and pale complexion, who looked very German to ordinary English eyes. He was shy, awkward and rude with strangers; prudish about risky stories, except when he was among people he knew well; a rather extreme vegetarian, virtually a teetotaller, and non-smoker.

It would have seemed impossible for such a man to acquire a unique position in English public life, but under his apparently fatal qualities there were others of a formidable nature. He had a strong, versatile, very quick scientific mind, which enabled him to grasp scientific problems swiftly, and make intelligent comments on them at once. Many good scientists do not have this aptitude, and are able to make useful comments only after solitary meditation.

Lindemann was a strong man physically, though from middle age he looked the reverse of athletic. In his youth he had been a first-class tennis player. He appeared at Wimbledon, and at one time was amateur champion of Sweden. He had the tough mental and physical vitality which helped him to persist in pursuing any aim. His quickness of mind and his energy enabled him to continue a discussion until opponents, whose ideas may have been sounder, were worn down.

Beneath this intellectual equipment and mental energy he had an intense conviction of superiority. He held this in a form common in Continental Europe. In England the social belief in inborn capacity to rule is held as strongly in some circles, but in a less ostentatious way. Lindemann found the nearest English equivalent to his conviction of being born to rule in Churchillian paternalism.

His identification with this set of ideas enabled him to give Churchill great technical help. The two men were remarkably contrasted and complementary personalities. Churchill was gifted in dealing with people. He shared with the majority of mankind a hearty taste for meat, drink and tobacco. He had no head for mathematical calculations, and the quantitative view of phenomena.

Through Churchill, Lindemann could vicariously enjoy the pleasures of life; through Lindemann, Churchill could vicariously engage in mathematical calculations and scientific investigations. They had the attraction of opposites, but based on identity of social and political beliefs.

Lindemann gave some very good and much useful scientific advice to Churchill, but he also gave some that was seriously wrong, and if completely accepted, might have led to the defeat of Britain. On balance, however, as his most important critic, Tizard, contended, he probably did more good than harm. He was an essential part of the Churchillian system. If Churchill was to be the leader, Lindemann had to be accepted. Lindemann could not be removed without removing Churchill.

It was a good thing that a non-scientific leader like Churchill had so gifted a scientist as Lindemann to advise him, even if Lindemann's biggest mistakes were as big as his critics said they were. The alternative to Lindemann was probably not a better but a worse adviser. Here the example of the scientific situation in Germany was instructive.

Nazism had made the position of German Jewish scientists impossible, and nearly all had left the country. Lindemann made a great contribution by providing scope for a number of the most outstanding in England, where they subsequently made a splendid contribution to British science.

But even when the Jewish scientists had left, there were still many able scientists in Germany. Nazism also failed to make proper use of these. The system of scientific and technical development was insufficiently integrated. Many separate scientific and technical laboratories worked under completely independent leaders. In a number of these separate laboratories very good work was done, often better than in the corresponding institutions in England, but the individual products were not sufficiently designed to work together; some were more accurate and better finished than was necessary, and others were not good enough. Hitler's leadership principle prevented the creation of a balanced overall organization of scientific research and development. It was virtually impossible under Hitlerian conditions to develop operational research, which is essential in order to determine the effectiveness of scientific weapons, and the most effective ways of using them; for it was inconceivable that a Hitlerian leader would submit to detached scientific investigation of what he was doing. Hitler was more inclined to listen to magicians and soothsayers than to scientific advisers.

As a civilian scientist, Lindemann appeared a gifted amateur. He either would not or could not settle down to the plodding research along one or more main lines, which marks the professionals, from the greatest to the least.

He started significant developments in several directions by his personal researches, notably on meteors as a source of information on the upper atmosphere, on the kinetics of chemical reactions, and through his invention of an ingenious and much-used type of electrometer. But he was not one of the greatest scientists, because he did not pursue any of the paths he opened, so that he did not himself arrive at any major discovery, or build a great body of new work into a definitive system. He was not a Rutherford or a Maxwell.

His personal contributions to physical science were, however, wider and larger than Tizard's.

His other main scientific achievement was the revival, virtually the creation, of physics at Oxford. He was appointed to the Dr. Lee's Professorship of Experimental Philosophy in 1919. He came to Oxford after considerable scientific achievement, and with a very high reputation for scientific ability. He did not, however, belong educationally or socially to the traditions of the ancient English universities, and soon became very unpopular. He was not prepared to tolerate the degenerate conditions that he found in the teaching of physics, and the provisions for experimental research at Oxford. He started direct assaults on all academic fronts, irrespective of whether they were conducted in keeping with the ancient university traditions. Cambridge men, headed by J. J. Thomson, observed his proceedings from afar without approval.

The noise of disputes at Oxford drowned appreciation of the personal research and stimulation which Lindemann continued to contribute. After a decade of discord, the scientific reputation of Lindemann and Oxford physics declined perhaps further than it should have done. Nevertheless, Lindemann never became universally unpopular.

Then, with the rise of Hitler, a new situation was created in the scientific world. The future of the Jews in Germany was threatened. They included many gifted scientists. Lindemann, whose higher education had been in Germany, resented the persecution of talented scientists with whom he was acquainted, and he understood the reality of the military and political threat of Germany to Britain. He invited Jewish physicists from Germany to Oxford, and created positions for them. In the period of twenty years, these scientists formed the heart of a development of Oxford physics which, by the beginning of the second half of the twentieth century rivalled that of Cambridge physics.

Lindemann was the promoter of this development, which formed a notable achievement in the statesmanship of academic physics.

Lindemann's achievement in rescuing and fostering Jewish scientists reinforced the belief in various quarters that he was of Jewish descent himself. His behaviour strengthened this assumption. He professed an aversion to Jews. This looked like inverted racial prejudice. He was secretive about the details of his origin. He kept these out of standard works of reference. He gave an impression of being Jewish and ashamed of it, and therefore trying to conceal information about himself. Brigadier Lindemann, his elder brother, expressed amazement when he heard of this rumour, and when Lindemann himself was directly asked whether he was of Jewish descent, he categorically denied it.

Lindemann also professed a physical aversion to negroes, and near the end of his life expressed the opinion that the greatest of future dangers was not nuclear energy, but the supersession of the white race.

It seems that much of his personal behaviour which appeared so disagreeable to so many, arose from his social background. He was a son of the cosmopolitan plutocracy, whose ideas were more familiar in Continental Europe than in England.

His father was a financier and engineer. His mother was the daughter of an American engineer of English descent, and the widow of a banker. His parents had an income of £20,000 a year before the First World War, and Lindemann himself, after a life devoted to science and politics, left a fortune of more than £200,000.

His social background, unusual in an Englishman, was of fundamental importance in shaping both his behaviour and his achievement.

II

A Cosmopolitan Youth

LINDEMANN was born at Baden-Baden on April 5th, 1886, whence his mother had gone to have her child. As his father was a naturalized Englishman, Lindemann's nationality was involved in technical complexities. These were such that they caused difficulties in his later obtaining a passport, and in receiving a commission in the First World War. He never forgave his mother for not bothering to ensure that he was born in England. It was one of the causes of a conflict between son and mother which seems to have been an important influence in forming aspects of Lindemann's character.

The tiresome complications about his nationality contributed to Lindemann's secretiveness about his personal life. He became hypersensitive about anything which identified him with Germany. He did not like to refer to his father's familiar name of Adolphus; if others found it funny that Lindemann's father and Hitler had something in common, Lindemann did not.

There was a ludicrous aspect to the facts of Lindemann's situation which made him more sympathetic to those who were well-informed of them, but he could not bring himself to make the facts better known. The majority of people knew only the difficult temper that this excited in Lindemann, not the pathetic facts themselves.

Lindemann's father, Adolphus Frederick, was born in the Palatinate in 1846, and descended from an Alsace-Lorraine family. The head of this family was the Comte de Lindemann, who settled in Paris and married the daughter of Fabre, the shipping magnate.

Lindemann's mother was born in New London, Connecticut, in 1851. She had first married a banker named Davidson, by whom she had three children. With her second husband she had four, three sons and a daughter; Frederick Alexander was the second son. She was a vivacious, beautiful woman, whom her second son seems to have resembled both in features and character.

Adolphus Frederick Lindemann was an engineer with financial and scientific interests. He raised funds in the City of London for building the waterworks, which he owned, at two German cities, Speyer and Pirmasens. He settled in England in the 1860's after which he became naturalized. He was concerned in the construction of the early Atlantic cables.

His wife inherited from her former husband a mansion in Devonshire. Adolphus Frederick set up workshops and laboratories in the grounds, and an astronomical observatory. Enjoying a large income, he was free to pursue his scientific and astronomical interests. His astronomical work became sufficiently well-known for him to have a minor planet, No. 828, named after him. He gave his observatory to Exeter University in 1927, after the death of his wife.

Adolphus Frederick gave the major part of his inheritance to his three sons before he died. Frederick Alexander and his elder brother invested their portions wisely, but the younger brother spent his on the Riviera, where he became a very popular figure in bars and cafés. Frederick Alexander did not approve of his younger brother's way of life, and refused for many years to have any communication with him. He also quarrelled with his sister, after she married a man whom he did not like.

He was compelled to revise his opinion of his younger brother, who carried out notable activities for the Allied Intelligence during the Second World War.

Lindemann's mother exercised her whims in bringing up her children. She insisted on Frederick Alexander being a vegetarian, because she believed it was good for him, though she did not continue one herself. He was given the nickname of 'Peach' in the family.

The Lindemanns engaged tutors for Frederick Alexander from the age of ten, and at thirteen sent him to a school in

Scotland, which prepared boys for entrance to the Army. His father had formed a good opinion of it. Frederick Alexander had difficulties in adjusting his dietary habits, which he found himself now unable to change. He felt ashamed in a kilt, and he was terrified at the thought that the other boys might learn of his nickname. Otherwise, he got along reasonably well. He had a very strong memory and capacity for mental calculations.

His real pleasures were during the holidays in his Devonshire home, and his father's workshops and laboratories. He and his elder brother were able to exercise freely the common boyhood taste for making things and performing experiments.

At the age of sixteen, Lindemann was sent to the Lyceum at Darmstadt, on the recommendation of one of his father's Continental friends. He was well-taught at this excellent school, where he also had the opportunity to play tennis.

From the Lyceum he proceeded, at the age of eighteen, to the Technical High School at Darmstadt. While studying physics there, he was impressed by the need for a glass which was transparent to X-rays. Ordinary glass was opaque. He deduced on theoretical grounds that it should be possible to make such a glass from compounds of elements with very low atomic weight, such as beryllium, boron and lithium. He and his elder brother succeeded in making such a glass in his father's laboratory in Devonshire, and patented the invention. Their father advised them to sell the rights as quickly as possible, as the big industrial companies, with their research laboratories, would find a way round it. They did not do so, and were soon circumvented by the General Electric Company of America.

Through his father's social connections, Lindemann was accepted in the Darmstadt circle of the Grand Duke Ernst Ludwig, a grandson of Queen Victoria and brother-in-law of the Czar. He joined in the Duke's tennis parties, and played with the Kaiser and the Czar.

Lindemann was an outstanding student at the Technical High School. A mutual friend of his father and Nernst recommended him to Nernst for a place in his laboratory at Berlin. Lindemann became one of the foremost of Nernst's pupils, joining in the research into the properties of substances at very low temperatures, which showed striking departures from the classical theory of heat. It had been observed that the specific heat, or heat capacity of diamond at the temperature of liquid hydrogen, decreased to an extraordinarily low figure. This could not be explained in terms of classical theory.

Einstein succeeded in giving a rough explanation in terms of Planck's quantum theory, which had been propounded in 1900, but was not yet widely accepted. Lindemann in his thesis for a doctorate showed that Einstein's explanation was adequate for metals, but not for substances like sulphur.

Lindemann and Nernst then showed in a joint paper that Einstein's explanation in terms of quantum theory could be improved. Shortly afterwards, Debye gave a more complete quantum explanation, which became one of the strongest pieces of evidence in favour of the Quantum Theory, and contributed much to its general acceptance.

Lindemann followed the line of the Nernst school in the experimental and theoretical study of changes of state of substances, in terms of their constitutional properties. In the course of his studies of the theoretical explanation of the properties of solids, he pointed out that the observed strength of solids is much less than would be expected from theory. He suggested that the breaking of crystalline substances was due to the separation of adjacent crystals, and not to the breaking of the crystals themselves.

These conclusions have become of great practical importance, for they suggest that it might be possible to make new materials which are much stronger than the strongest materials yet known.

Lindemann and Tizard met as pupils of Nernst. As Englishmen abroad they became very friendly, but their circumstances were extremely different. Tizard did not find a suitable subject for his abilities and had little money. Lindemann had been educated in Germany; he was at home in the magnificent scientific atmosphere of Nernst, Planck and Einstein. He had done good work in the foundations of quantum physics, and he appeared to have the ability which might enable him at any moment to join this front rank of scientists.

His promise was reflected in his being appointed secretary of the Solvay Conference in 1911. This was attended by twenty-four of the leading physicists of the world, from Planck and Einstein to Marie Curie and Rutherford.

Lindemann's scientific success at Berlin was great, but his social achievement was unique. He and his brother lived as students in the Adlon Hotel, the most famous and fashionable hotel in the capital of Germany. This made a profound impression on his fellow-students, some of whom remembered this more vividly than his scientific activities.

The contrast between Lindemann's and Tizard's situation was piquant. Tizard was deeply impressed by Lindemann, and appears to have suggested, even before the First World War, that Lindemann should be elected to a physics chair at Oxford.

Lindemann affected the manners of the wealthy amateur who did not need to work hard, and could throw off important discoveries through sheer ability. He had the reputation of coming to the laboratory late, while others started at the customary early hour. His tennis-playing impressed his fellow research students almost as much as the Adlon.

Lindemann had a lean athletic figure in his youth. Tizard has said that he and Lindemann used to go to a gymnasium in Berlin to box to keep fit. Tizard was a quicker and more experienced boxer, and apparently scored off Lindemann easily. On one occasion Lindemann completely lost his temper at being outboxed. Tizard thought that perhaps this incident was the beginning of his hostility to him.

When the First World War started, Lindemann was playing in a tennis tournament on the German Baltic coast. He departed only just in time to avoid being interned in Germany.

The outbreak of the war brought him back to England permanently. Thenceforth he lived in the English environment, with a character and habits which had been formed by a cosmopolitan background. His environment and personality were in uneasy interaction for the rest of his life.

III

The First World War

WITHIN a few days of the outbreak of the First World War Lindemann offered himself for military service. The application on his behalf went astray, and he did not begin war work until 1915, when his services as a technical assistant at £3 a week were accepted at the Royal Aircraft Factory, the forerunner of the present Establishment at Farnborough.

His first job was to answer questions on any technical problem which did not come within the scope of existing departments. This brought a wide range of the scientific aspects of flying and air-warfare to his notice.

His best-known work at Farnborough was on aircraft spin. Pilots had already discovered by trial how to recover from spin, but the manoeuvre was little known, and as yet without explanation. Lindemann succeeded in deducing the mechanics of the process by simple general arguments from observations of aircraft which were spinning. He noted that the rate of the spin did not increase as the aircraft went down. The longitudinal axis of the aircraft remained almost vertical, and the rotation was around a vertical axis.

These observations simplified the analysis of the forces acting on the aircraft, and enabled Lindemann to give a correct explanation of the cause of the spin, and how the aircraft should be handled in order to recover from it. He elucidated his reasoning with the assistance of models.

He learned to fly, to test by experiment his theory of how the spin arose, and what manoeuvres should be performed to right the machine. He took up in the machine equipment and an observer to record effects of the spin. As the machine rotated once in every three or four seconds, much strength of mind and courage were required to make reliable observations under such disturbing conditions. From the data so collected, experts on aerodynamics were able to work out Lindemann's approximate theory in detail.

Lindemann made as many as a dozen consecutive spins in his flying experiments; he did this not as a pilot of long experience, but as one who had just learned to fly. This unconcern with death arose from his natural physical courage, and the passionate interest of the scientist who forgets all risks in his effort to prove his theories and discover the truth. His work converted spin from a rather terrifying and obscure event into an understood and manageable danger. It made flying in clouds safer, and provided military aircraft with an additional manoeuvre. W. S. Farren has said that flying in an aircraft with Lindemann at Farnborough made one realize what a great man he was.

Lindemann was on the civilian, not the military staff. He

arrived at the air station every day for his flying lessons in a bowler hat and with an umbrella. The pilots of the Royal Flying Corps were startled at having to teach anyone who wore this garb to fly.

He succeeded in passing the eyesight test for pilots, though his sight was defective. He did this by memorizing the test letters with his good eye; then he guessed successfully what the letters were when they were exposed to his bad eye. He refused ever to wear spectacles. Besides his sight, his body temperature was abnormal, being one degree above the average.

The group of young scientists assembled at Farnborough to assist in the war development of aviation included E. D. Adrian, who was the medical officer, and F. W. Aston, besides G. P. Thomson, G. I. Taylor, B. M. Jones, R. V. Southwell, W. S. Farren and H. Glauert, who were experts on aerodynamics. This superlative company helped Lindemann to overcome some of his awkwardness. They were such that not even he could confidently hold them in contempt.

Aston had just come from Cambridge, where he had been assisting J. J. Thomson in the first successful experiments on the separation of isotopes. This had been achieved by separating the isotopes of neon by electromagnetic deflection in an electrical discharge tube. Some sceptics contended that the particles identified were not isotopes of neon but certain chemical ions of similar mass. Lindemann teased Aston by expounding the case against the reality of the discovery, but presently he joined with Aston in an important paper on the possibility of separating isotopes by various methods. Aston described an unfinished experiment in which he attempted to separate neon isotopes by diffusion through pipe-clay.

Their calculations showed that it was theoretically possible to secure a slight separation by evaporation. Aston's subsequent great work on the separation of isotopes probably owed a good deal to the stimulus of Lindemann on the theoretical side, during their collaboration at Farnborough.

Lindemann's work on this topic made him familiar with a problem which was to be of crucial importance in the development of atomic energy.

In Aston's company Lindemann achieved humour. Aston insisted on taking Lindemann skating against his protests, for he was morbidly sensitive about performing in public anything which he could not do well, or in which he was out of practice. Lindemann staggered onto the ice under Aston's support, but when he reached the centre of the pond, instead of stumbling, he gave an impressive exhibition of figure-skating. In a similar way he concealed his prowess as a pianist and a golfer.

At Farnborough Lindemann showed much scientific versatility. He accomplished important practical research, while promoting several lines of investigation which had significance for the future.

His talented Farnborough colleagues had helped to assimilate him into English life. If they had not got very far, they had at least progressed, which suggested that Lindemann might ultimately become a reasonably comfortable member of English scientific and academic society. After all, he was still only thirty-two.

IV

Oxford

LINDEMANN'S work in Nernst's laboratory in Berlin marked him as a future professor. When the war was over, he had to give serious consideration to his career. Oxford was not the only major prospect; he was sounded for a chair at Chicago. He seems to have been attracted to America because of the social unrest in Europe, which had undermined the kind of aristocratic cosmopolitan society in which he had been brought up.

However, his candidature at Oxford was successful. Among his sponsors were Rayleigh, the Duc de Broglie, Rutherford and Langevin. In the following year, 1920, he was elected a fellow of the Royal Society, at the age of thirty-three.

His chair was associated with Wadham College. One of his first requests was for a bathroom and water closet in his rooms. This was against the Oxford tradition, and led to friction. Lindemann had a horror of undressing in the presence of other people, and was distressed at having to walk to bathroom and lavatories in a dressing-gown through cold, windy passages.

Dr. Lee, after whom Lindemann's chair was named, had been associated with Christ Church, so that college elected him one of its fellows. They did not, however, make him a member of the governing body.

Lindemann lived in Christ Church for the rest of his life. He became established in handsome rooms overlooking Christ Church Meadow, where he steadily adhered to his unusual manner of living. When a scholar of Christ Church was asked whether Lindemann's elevation to the peerage had made any difference to his old life, he pondered for a while and then said: 'In the old days, one read in small letters outside his door, "Professor Lindemann. In." Now one reads in large letters, "LORD CHERWELL. OUT."'

Lindemann retained his interest and participation in Wadham. He bequeathed much of his fortune to this college.

He did not possess the usual Oxford social habits, and did not acquire them easily; when he saw something that was wrong he was directly outspoken. When he was irritated he was often sarcastic, and sometimes brutal. This made enemies.

An incident which was typical of others arose out of a dispute on his place in the order of precedence at dinner at Christ Church. Some held that he should give precedence to younger fellows who were members of the governing body, as he was not. The dispute became so acrimonious that the college sought legal opinion on the point, and were advised that Lindemann must give precedence. Lindemann thereupon consulted Sir John Simon, who gave a contrary opinion. The college gave way and Lindemann got his precedence.

This and other extraordinary disputes involved in Lindemann's eyes not only his own status, but that of science. He was a full professor in a great university. According to German notions, such a person should automatically receive comprehensive privileges.

With his lack of command of the Oxford social idiom, Lindemann was unable to explain to his colleagues in an acceptable manner the glaring faults of Oxford as a school of modern science, which he could see very plainly against his Berlin background. He did not regard with indulgence the backwardness in laboratories and equipment, the small amount of scientific activity compared with that in other studies, and most of all the subordinate status of science.

The obstacles that Lindemann found in his way were bad, and he was right to fight against them, even if he did not command the most appropriate types of English social technique for dealing with them. They diverted his social energy in directions other than operating the university system.

As his academic situation grew more frustrating, his plutocratic and aristocratic connections became comperatively still more important to him. He cultivated industrial magnates, not only to secure money for his laboratory, but because he felt more comfortable with them than with most of his academic colleagues.

In 1920 he was taken to Lord Birkenhead's country house, to join in the tennis parties which were one of its features. He soon became friendly with that statesman, whose qualities appealed to him. Birkenhead also was a man of great ability, who was not in tune with a number of his colleagues.

In the following year Lindemann was introduced to Winston Churchill by the Duke of Westminster. He was overwhelmingly delighted at making his acquaintance. Churchill apparently did not take to him at once. Lindemann tried to please him, and gradually became more intimate.

When Churchill conducted the *British Gazette* during the General Strike of 1926, in which an aggressive attitude to the strikers was adopted, Lindemann was one of his chief assistants. By that time he knew Churchill sufficiently well to make suggestions for submission to the prime minister on how the ending of the strike should be managed. Nothing whatever should be conceded until the strike was over, and then no concession should be made until after an interval which was sufficiently long to demonstrate that it was given only from magnanimity.

Lindemann's personality and habits made him acceptable in fashionable society. He travelled in a Rolls-Royce, with a chauffeur and valet, and he was familiar with society gossip. He became the special authority on science in these particular social circles, and acquired the nickname of 'The Prof.'.

Lindemann helped Churchill in collecting material and notes for articles and books. He became one of his intellectual aides more than ten years before the Second World War.

By 1929, at the end of the first decade of Lindemann's professorship, the scientific promise of 1919 seemed to have declined into squabbling and frustration, relieved by occasional inspiring ideas and papers which started gifted young men on lifetimes of useful work. Lindemann was becoming more absorbed in aristocratic society. He tended to treat his academic duties as necessary

LORD CHERWELL

excursions from this society, rather than the main business of his life. If world affairs had continued without much change, he might have become primarily a unique figure in fashionable society, and more perfunctory as a scientist.

His knowledge of, and liking for aristocratic and plutocratic society widened the gap between his social outlook and that of his scientific colleagues, nearly all of whom were professional and middle-class men. He looked down on their social habits and aims, and they condemned his scientific amateurism.

The rise of National Socialism in Germany changed this situation. As one who was virtually German by education, with cosmopolitan connections, Lindemann understood the danger of the movement to his stratum of society.

Churchill, who by 1929 had a reputation in English politics not unlike that of Lindemann in science, perceived the danger of the violent new German movement to British interests.

Hitler's acquisition of power gave new meaning to the lives both of Lindemann and Churchill. It created a situation in which they could find appropriate scope for their great abilities, without being frustrated by their defects.

V

The Fight for Survival

LINDEMANN had thought of standing for Parliament in the 1920's, but was dissuaded by Birkenhead. After Hitler's seizure of power, he became convinced that he ought to enter Parliament, because of his special knowledge of Germany, and his previous experience of military scientific problems. He tried to secure nomination as one of the Conservative candidates for the University of Oxford in the General Election of 1935.

The Conservatives chose Lord Hugh Cecil, a leading Conservative personality. They were not prepared to accept as their second candidate one who, as the friend of Churchill, was critical of the leadership of the Conservative Party, so they chose a more orthodox man, C. R. M. F. Cruttwell. In the ensuing election, A. P. Herbert stood as an Independent, and J. L. Stocks for Labour.

Lindemann was gratified when Cecil and Herbert were elected, and Cruttwell lost his deposit. Shortly afterwards Lord Hugh Cecil resigned. In the by-election in 1937 for the single vacancy, the Conservatives nominated the professor of medicine and Royal Physician Sir Farquhar Buzzard, and Sir Arthur Salter and Lindemann stood as Independents.

Churchill spoke in Oxford for Lindemann, to the anger of the orthodox Conservatives. The Conservative vote was split, and Salter was elected. Lindemann became still more unpopular in traditional circles.

While Lindemann had been trying, unsuccessfully, to obtain a political footing as a member of the House of Commons, he had continued, with Churchill's support, to fight for a publicly militant defence policy. He wrote to *The Times* in August 1934, asking for new Government action on defence against aircraft. He pointed out that no weapon had yet been invented to which no antidote had been found. He implied that Baldwin's 'the bomber will always get through' contradicted the historical lessons of warfare, and was defeatist.

Lindemann believed that the necessary power for the solution of the decisive problem of air defence could not come from within a single department of state. The magnitude of the political, national and scientific effort required transcended any single office. It could be carried through only by a very high committee, such as that for Imperial Defence. A scientific subcommittee of this committee should therefore be formed for dealing with the air problem.

Lindemann and Churchill pressed for this through their friends among the Conservative ministers. They were then informed that the Air Ministry was setting up its Committee for the Scientific Survey of Air Defence under Tizard, and Lindemann was invited to join it. He did so reluctantly, because the committee was departmental, and did not possess the Cabinet rank which he considered essential. He also probably disliked the idea of sitting under the chairmanship of Tizard.

As already mentioned, the dispute between Tizard and Lindemann became so acrimonious that the committee was dissolved and reformed without Lindemann.

Lindemann had reported what happened in the committee to

Churchill, who then raised the matters in the Air Defence Research Committee of the Committee of Imperial Defence. Lindemann contended that the Tizard Committee had failed to develop many important ideas, such as the detection of aircraft by infra-red radiation. He thought that while the development of radiolocation had been successful, it had been conceived too exclusively as a defensive device, and offensive methods for destroying attacking aircraft, such as his own suggestion of aerial mines, had been neglected.

After Lindemann had been excluded from the committee, he had no avenue of official access. Later on, Lord Swinton was succeeded as Air Minister by Sir Kingsley Wood, who had close relations with Churchill. Kingsley Wood presently invited Lindemann to become a member of the Air Research Defence Sub-Committee of the Committee of Imperial Defence.

Tizard was disturbed by this development. Nevertheless, his influence on the direction of research on air defence continued in full strength until Churchill joined the Government, bringing Lindemann with him as his personal scientific adviser.

The division between Lindemann and Tizard grew irreconcilably wide. Its origins, however, were probably far back in the past. R. V. Jones has said that visible signs of division appeared in 1926, after Tizard failed to secure Lindemann's appointment to membership of the Aeronautical Research Committee.

Brundrett has commented that in their quarrel, Lindemann and Tizard 'behaved like a couple of spoiled children'. The conflict of personalities was the most spectacular aspect of their quarrel. Lindemann rated himself a better scientist than Tizard, and Tizard regarded himself as possessing more scientific judgment.

The most fundamental aspect of the conflict was not a matter of temperament, type of mind, or character; but a clash between the professional middle-class scientist of officer descent on the one side, and the cosmopolitan plutocratic scientist on the other.

For some, Tizard's combination of social conservatism with technological radicalism was upsetting. His officer-like tradition prevented him from looking for, and finding, support in those political directions which were sympathetic to his scientific outlook. Unlike Haldane, whom he admired, he was unskilful at finding his way into the circles which both agreed with his conceptions of scientific development, and could give him effective political support.

Lindemann dealt with his political problem much better. He realized that in order to carry out the kind of scientific policy in which he believed, it was necessary to obtain political power. He therefore set about obtaining that power by identifying himself with Churchill. He succeeded, and used his success to force through at least some of the science policy in which he believed. He was a less good military scientist than Tizard, but had a better understanding of politics and political considerations.

A statesman of science should know how to draw upon political forces to overcome political obstacles.

Tizard and Lindemann were both difficult men. When Tizard was upset he showed signs of nervous excitement, and people felt alarmed, not only for themselves, but for him.

When Lindemann was upset he was preposterous. He made people very angry, which perhaps was a less serious reaction.

VI

The Dark Companion of Sirius

When Lindemann accompanied Churchill to the Admiralty in 1939, he was asked to supply his chief with statistics and quantitative information on a variety of Admiralty concerns, besides science. When Churchill became prime minister in 1940, Lindemann's function was extended to cover many aspects of government.

Churchill has described what Lindemann's help meant to him: '. . . he was my trusted friend and confidant of twenty years. Together we had watched the advance and onset of world disaster. Together we had done our best to sound the alarm. And now we were in it, and I had the power to guide and arm our effort. How could I have the knowledge? Lindemann could decipher the signals of the experts on the far horizons and explain to me in lucid homely terms what the issues were. . . .'

Lindemann's group now became known as the Prime Minister's Statistical Section. It had a staff of about twenty, under

G. D. A. MacDougall, who in 1964, as Sir Donald MacDougall, returned to government service as administrative head of the new Ministry of Economic Affairs. Most of the staff were economists, with one scientist; the majority of the matters dealt with were of an economic or general nature.

Lindemann's own status was raised by his appointment to the peerage in 1941. He took the title of Lord Cherwell, after the small tributary of the Thames in Oxford. In 1942 he was made Paymaster-General, with a seat in the Cabinet.

Cherwell's personal scientific staff was too small. He did not act on Churchill's advice to recruit and organize sufficient technical assistance. While he made use of data collected from other scientific groups, there was too little criticism of his own scientific calculations, before they were submitted to the prime minister. His tendency to deal with all kinds of subjects, and trust to his personal judgment and calculations, led him into some serious mistakes.

His section kept a running quantitative commentary on many aspects of the national effort which were presented daily to Churchill by Cherwell in brief minutes, with graphs and other devices to bring out the point of important information. Broadly speaking, about a third of all the minutes dealt with science, and the rest covered such matters as the armed forces, shipping, food and raw materials, and miscellaneous and post-war problems.

Cherwell helped Churchill to form his decisions on rationing policy. He produced statistics to show that the extra economies produced by very severe rationing were not worth the depression in morale that they caused. The vegetarian was one of the strongest advocates of moderation in rationing.

Cherwell collected information from numerous ministries, abstracted its quantitative significance, and then presented it to the prime minister. Often this was used by the prime minister to draw attention to deficiencies in departmental policy and activities. Departments did not like having their own information used against them. Cherwell's unpopularity began to extend far beyond the frontiers of science.

The tall, dark, saturnine personality with a cold and aloof exterior, German manners, encyclopaedic knowledge, a lightning brain, and a blunt tongue; who made no effort to conceal his belief in his own superiority, and did not observe the normal rules of the administrative system, soon excited fury, which turned in some quarters into fear and hatred.

The irritation caused by his behaviour was to some extent smoothed away by MacDougall's exceptional tact. Cherwell's section was never a department of state; Churchill used it as a kind of private measure for checking whether the official departments were doing their job. The section was so like a department of state in authority, that many regarded it as one, and in addition, one that did not work according to the officially recognized rules.

Cherwell and the section had an early major success in the collection of data on the strength of the Luftwaffe, which revealed that it was not very much larger than the Royal Air Force.

Cherwell exposed the ineffectiveness of the early bombing of Germany by securing an analysis of the flash photographs of the dropping of bombs over a period of months. It revealed that two-thirds of the bombers failed to drop their bombs within five miles of their targets. A shocking waste of human crews and valuable equipment was revealed, and the inaccuracy of aerial navigation made evident. This investigation stimulated the rapid development of radio methods of aircraft navigation.

Cherwell stressed the superiority of German bombs, owing to their higher ratio of explosive charge to weight of shell, and to their content of aluminized explosive. This stimulated the British to the adoption of similar techniques.

Cherwell helped the early development of the proximity fuse, which became one of the most important of the new scientific weapons in the later stages of the war.

The kind of comment in which he excelled is illustrated by his observation from reports of sinkings that submarines were rarely seen before ships were sunk, but if a submarine was seen, the ship had a good chance of escaping. One of the reasons why they were not seen was that the merchant service was supplied with inferior binoculars. Cherwell discovered that the Admiralty had a store of unused high-grade binoculars, and caused some of these to be given to the merchant service.

He was particularly interested in the development of new types of weapons for fighting under conditions different from those envisaged in regular warfare, such as attacks by a few men on tanks and blockhouses.

He encouraged the work of Millis Jefferis, whose department

developed applications of the hollow charge explosive, which produces an extremely penetrating jet that will cut through many feet of steel and concrete. Among the weapons produced were the Bombard, the Sticky Bomb and other anti-tank devices. Cherwell was particularly fond of this department, because it was rather outside the normal government organization, which he disliked.

In the summer of 1940 Cherwell reported to the prime minister that there was evidence that the Germans were preparing to direct bombing by radio beam, so that it could be carried out independently of darkness and fog.

R. V. Jones, a pupil of Cherwell who had started scientific intelligence work at the Air Ministry, on the recommendation of Tizard, and was then twenty-eight years old, was called to a special meeting in the Cabinet room to explain the scientific evidence. On its basis, measures were immediately taken for jamming or deflecting such a beam. When, some three months later, the Germans started to bomb under the direction of radio beams, counter-measures had been sufficiently developed to cause the bombers to stray from their targets and waste a large part of their effort.

Cherwell, like others, saw the necessity for short-wave radar. This made for precision and compactness, for the size of the apparatus is connected with the length of the wave with which it operates. Satisfactory airborne radar required short-wave apparatus. Cherwell had hoped that the research on the invention and development of short-wave oscillators would be centred in his laboratory at Oxford. In fact, it was assigned to Birmingham, with brilliant results. Randall and Boot invented the magnetron.

A simple form of television based on the magnetron was developed by P. I. Dee and A. C. B. Lovell. It was a deadly aid to bombing.

Cherwell had an important part in starting the manufacture of this decisive weapon before it had been perfected. In this way, it was brought into operational use quickly, without loss of time between the completion of the invention in a practical form, and the starting of manufacture.

Cherwell was at his worst on how this new weapon was to be used. He advocated that it should be used for bombing the working-class districts of German cities. He supported his case with erroneous calculations on how much damage could be done, and he used his mistaken figures to argue for the use of the new weapon against the German cities rather than against the U-boats for which it was particularly fitted.

As has been mentioned in the previous chapter, his advice was fortunately not fully taken. Just enough of the new weapons were used to detect the U-boats, and in the space of five months, in 1943, sinkings were reduced from 700,000 to less than 100,000 tons a month, never to recover. This was the most decisive military event for Britain during the later part of the war.

Cherwell succeeded in getting the new equipment used for the bombing attacks on Germany. This led to the Germans capturing portions of it in British aircraft which crashed on the Continent. They were, however, slow in discovering its exact nature, and too late to take effective counter-measures.

Another radar device with which Cherwell had much to do was the use of metal strips for simulating aircraft. When quantities of these, of the correct length, were dropped from high-flying aircraft, they floated slowly to the ground, meanwhile interfering with radar for aircraft detection.

Churchill proposed this device, on the prompting of Cherwell, in 1937. It was developed effectively in 1942, the flying trials being carried out by D. A. Jackson, a distinguished physicist from Cherwell's laboratory at Oxford. Jackson became one of the most expert users of radar weapons in night-fighters; he was twice decorated for his fighting services. In private life he belonged to a wealthy family owning a Sunday newspaper with an enormous circulation. He was a steeplechaser who had ridden in the Grand National. His researches in physics earned him a fellowship of the Royal Society, and a chair at Oxford.

Jackson was a kind of scientist who particularly appealed to Cherwell, and both had the highest regard and understanding for each other.

Cherwell was very successful in his interpretation of evidence for the V1 flying bomb. He made remarkably accurate forecasts, six months before the first flying bomb arrived in England, on its construction and speed. It would have some form of jet propulsion, travel at 400 miles per hour, and carry an explosive charge of less than a ton. He gave a correct estimate of its accuracy, the date when it might be introduced, and the rate at which it could be launched. He thought that it should be practicable to put the launching sites out of operation by bombing.

He was less successful in his forecasts about the rocket-bomb, V2. He doubted the information supplied by intelligence, which had gradually built up a fairly complete account of it. If his views had been accepted, the decision to bomb the V2 plant at Peenemünde and other military action to delay the development and use of V2 might not have been taken. In that case, the perfecting and manufacture of V2 might have been carried to the point where it would have become a decisive weapon.

One reason why he fortunately failed to have his views on this matter accepted, was that the contrary advice was being pressed on Churchill by his own son-in-law, the Parliamentary Secretary to the Minister of Supply, Duncan Sandys.

This mistake, like his other mistakes, arose in part from his confidence in his own individual judgment, and his lack of a team of personal scientific critics. It is astonishing, not that he made serious mistakes, but, acting so much as an individual, he arrived at several important correct conclusions.

A deeper cause of the generally unimpressive performance of the British in the rocket field arose not from personalities, but from the nature of the military contest. Britain was fighting a defensive war in protection of her island. Germany was fighting an aggressive war, to extend her Continental power. Britain's genius was inspired by her needs to invent defensive weapons, Germany's by her offensive needs.

Cherwell's mistake arose in part also from his German scientific background. He was better qualified than most British scientists to appreciate the chemical thermodynamics of such a weapon—had he not been a pupil of Nernst?—and the very formidable scientific and technical problems that had to be solved in making it successful. The invention and construction of V2 involved some of the most difficult of all the technological problems solved in the Second World War.

Cherwell was too sceptical in believing that they could not be solved, at any rate during the current war. But he was correct in his belief, even if for the wrong reasons, that such a rocket would not be important in this war. He rightly held that if it existed, it would not carry an explosive charge of more than one ton, and he refused to believe information that it might carry a charge of ten tons. If it did, the bombardment of London with it might kill more than 100,000 people a month. In the face of this possibility, plans were made for evacuating a million people from London.

The economic side of Cherwell's office dealt with such topics as aircraft production, the rate of growth of supplies of various weapons and equipment, the way in which manpower should be used, the most efficient utilization of machine tools, and particularly the best use of shipping space, such as the transport of motor parts, instead of assembled vehicles.

Cherwell's section showed that disastrous shortages would occur in England unless shipping to the Middle East was heavily cut. He had the strength to get this accepted, even though Montgomery's campaign was in prospect.

Churchill himself gave friendship the first place in his appreciation of Cherwell's qualities. Almost every day Cherwell went to talk with him in the early hours of the morning, after the previous day's work and responsibility. Churchill found understanding and refreshment in Cherwell's mind and company.

Cherwell often had to wait for long hours at night, after his own work was done, in uncomfortable air-raid shelters, and with people with whom he was not at ease, until Churchill was ready for his visit.

Cherwell accompanied Churchill to the Atlantic Conference in August 1941, and to the Quebec Conference in 1943, at which the agreement between Britain, U.S.A. and Canada was made for the development of atomic energy. He was present at the second Quebec Conference in 1944, and proceeded from it to Washington to negotiate the renewal of lease-lend aid. He accompanied Churchill to Potsdam, where he met Stalin.

In the last stages of the war, Cherwell was primarily engaged in post-war considerations of economic policy. His views were similar in some directions to those of Keynes. He was in favour of very close economic cooperation with the United States, and the development of a more closely integrated and flexibly managed international capitalism. He was opposed to the widespread extension of social welfare, and believed that such operations should be limited to 'the prevention of disease and unrest.'

He agreed with Churchill's opposition to all manifestations of socialism, and strove to help him to do everything possible to prevent it from developing, and obtaining power.

VII

Nuclear Politics

CHERWELL at first shared the common scepticism about the possibility of making an atomic bomb. He thought that it would be more dangerous as an instrument of propaganda than as a military weapon. Shortly before the outbreak of the war, Churchill on his advice wrote to the Air Minister, warning him of the danger that Fifth Columnists would spread rumours of a terrifying new weapon, in order to frighten Britain into surrendering to her enemies. It should be understood that though uranium fission was scientifically very interesting, and might ultimately be of great practical importance, it would take several years to make a uranium fission bomb, and such a bomb might not be much more powerful than conventional explosives.

Cherwell did not appreciate the practical possibility of an atomic bomb, until his colleague and friend at Oxford, Professor F. Simon, who was in touch with the Maud Committee, persuaded him in 1940 to listen to an exposition by R. E. Peierls of the theoretical physics involved. He thereafter followed developments closely, and kept Churchill, who in the meantime had become prime minister, fully briefed.

The Maud Committee was replaced by a more formal organization, consisting of a policy and a technical committee. Cherwell or his representative regularly attended the technical committee, which also contained a representative of Imperial Chemical Industries, who were concerned with the problems of manufacture. At Simon's request, Cherwell used his influence with Lord Melchett of I.C.I. to secure a quantity of uranium hexafluoride for research on methods of separation of uranium isotopes.

I.C.I. were very much interested in the prospect of the construction of a plant for making atomic bombs, and Lord McGowan, their chairman, discussed the situation with the chairman of the Scientific Advisory Committee to the War Cabinet. Cherwell was closely in touch with Melchett and

McGowan. These three peers were apparently very much in favour of the plant being immediately built in Britain.

V. Bush and J. B. Conant, the organizers of the American scientific defence effort, suggested on their own initiative that the British and Americans should engage in a joint atomic bomb project. C. G. Darwin, at that time British scientific adviser in the British Embassy at Washington, wrote to London, recommending that a mission should be sent forthwith.

No less than seven months passed before his letter was answered. In the meantime, the Japanese attack on Pearl Harbour had occurred, and the United States had found herself at war. The American situation and attitude were transformed.

The British delay seems to have been due in a large degree to the difficulty of coming to decisions on the post-war implications of the atomic bomb. If the plant were built in America, the United States would be the sole possessor of the bomb, at any rate in the beginning of the post-war world. Britain, after having done so much to start the project, would find herself without atomic weapons, and the United States might become isolationist.

Cherwell advised Churchill that it was essential to go forward with the project for the bomb, for it was becoming scientifically clear that it was feasible. There was an even chance that it could be made, and it would be unforgivable if the Germans were allowed to develop a process by which they could defeat Britain in war, 'or reverse the verdict after they had been defeated'.

He was in favour of making plans for large-scale manufacture, even if it interfered with the turbine manufacture so seriously needed for other armaments. He thought the plant should be in England, or in Canada as a last resort. He believed that if the plant was in England, secrecy would be more secure, and whoever possessed such a plant would have the chance of dictating to the world.

Cherwell's doubts on American security were not without foundation, for Nazi agents had been active in the United States. He felt that it was a mistake to place oneself entirely at the mercy of a neighbour, however trustworthy he might be. He was therefore not in favour of pressing the Americans to build the plant, but going forward with it in Britain; in the meantime just continuing to exchange information with the Americans, without influencing them with regard to construction.

The Scientific Advisory Committee to the War Cabinet

advised against placing the British project with I.C.I., and recommended that it should be conducted by the Department of Scientific and Industrial Research. It was camouflaged under the name of Tube Alloys. The camouflage was subsequently to prove so effective, that Roosevelt's copy of the agreement with Churchill on the future of Anglo-American cooperation on atomic energy became mislaid for years. It was signed after their meeting in Washington in September 1944, and put away in the wrong file. After Roosevelt's death, the Americans had to ask the British for a copy.

Cherwell thought an additional reason for building the plant in Britain, besides the political and military ones, was that the American scientists and technologists had been slow to develop the idea.

He suggested to Churchill that the British atomic energy project should be placed under Sir John Anderson. Churchill sent Cherwell's memorandum on the project to the Chiefs of Staff Committee with his famous minute: 'Although personally I am quite content with the existing explosives, I feel we must not stand in the way of any improvement. . . .'

The Chiefs of Staff were very strongly in favour of the bomb, and that it should be made in England. They said the project should be kept most secret, and the less put down on paper about it the better.

The British project became so secret that it was not discussed by the War Cabinet, and even Attlee, the deputy prime minister, did not know that it was not merely a rather larger kind of conventional bomb until he became prime minister in 1945.

Though the British project was not placed with the I.C.I., an I.C.I. man, W. A. Akers, was placed in charge. The connection of the British project with the I.C.I. was a cause of misunderstanding with the Americans, who suspected that British commercial interests were trying to secure control over the post-war development of atomic energy. The French scientist, H. Halban, who had brought knowledge of the early fundamental research on the release of atomic energy to England, and was a participant in French patents arising out of this work, was also in touch with I.C.I. A complex conflict of British, American and French national, political and commercial interests arose.

As late as June 1942, Cherwell still believed that Britain should start forthwith on the construction of a large-scale atomic plant within the country. He did not agree with the Roosevelt-Churchill understanding in June 1942, that America and Britain should collaborate on a project on equal terms. He was persuaded by Anderson to agree reluctantly that the plant should be built in America.

When the United States began to take the atomic bomb very seriously after she had been attacked, she became extremely possessive in her relation with the British.

Cherwell thought in the spring of 1943 that an intensive effort should still be made on the possibility of building a diffusion plant in Britain for the separation of uranium isotopes. He felt that it was essential that Britain should have her own plant. He told V. Bush, the American organizer of scientific defence, that Britain could not face a future in which she had to rely entirely on the United States for atomic weapons, should Russia or some other power develop them.

The delays in making a decision on an agreement with the Americans for a joint project, in the hope that it would be possible to build an independent plant in Britain immediately, exacerbated Anglo-American relations. The British presently found themselves virtually excluded for a time from the most important scientific development in history, which they had had the chief part in starting.

The situation was clarified by the Quebec Agreement of 1943, signed by Roosevelt and Churchill, governing collaboration between the U.K. and U.S.A. on atomic energy. It contained five clauses. The first three stated that 'this agency' would never be used against each other; that they would not use it against, or communicate information to, third parties, without each other's consent. The fourth said that owing to the heavy burden of production falling on the U.S. 'as the result of a wise division of war effort', it would be left to the President of the U.S. to specify the terms on which advantage was to be taken of post-war developments of an industrial or commercial character, arising from the project. 'The Prime Minister expressly disclaims any interest in these industrial and commercial aspects beyond what may be considered by the President of the United States to be fair and just and in harmony with the economic welfare of the world.'

The fifth clause dealt with the organizational machinery to be set up for the future management of the atomic energy project.

In the end, the main project was American, with some British scientists allowed to take part in it. A subsidiary Anglo-Canadian project was started at Ottawa. British scientists, and French scientists who had left France and joined the Free French movement, participated in the Anglo-Canadian project.

Cherwell was much concerned with the political problems connected with the non-British scientists who participated in the British projects. The most eminent of these was Niels Bohr of Denmark. As the founder of theoretical atomic physics he had a unique position of intellectual authority recognized by all the atomic physicists in the world, from America and Britain to the Soviet Union.

When it became imperative for Bohr to leave Denmark, he fled to Sweden and was brought to London. He learned of the practical progress that had been made towards the release of atomic energy. He visited America, and saw the great atomic laboratories. On his return to London he received through the Soviet Ambassador an invitation to stay in the Soviet Union.

Bohr's intellectual responsiblity as the founder of theoretical atomic physics, his knowledge of the feeling of people on the Continent, his experience of Nazi occupation, his own half-Jewish descent, and his world-wide connections, made him particularly aware of the social and political aspects of atomic energy. At Copenhagen under the Nazi occupation he was scarcely able to think of anything else. He came into the atomic bomb project long after it had been started, and his concern in the making of bombs, unlike the American and British, was not so exclusively military.

He immediately, but tactfully, raised the question of the social and political implications with his British and American hosts. Owing to his connections in America he had acquired information on the atomic project which Churchill thought he ought not to have possessed. When, in addition, Churchill learned that he had received an invitation to stay in the Soviet Union, he was alarmed. He feared that Bohr would transmit atomic information to the Soviet ally, and Cherwell had to persuade him not to take excessive action against him. Churchill went so far as to inform Cherwell that 'It seems to me Bohr ought to be confined or at any rate made to see that he is very near the edge of mortal crimes.'

Cherwell, Anderson and Bush were convinced of Bohr's discretion, and it fell to Cherwell to try to convince Churchill. At last it was arranged that Bohr should meet Churchill, but at the interview nearly all the time was taken up by an irrelevant argument between Cherwell and Churchill, and Bohr said very little.

Bohr continued to give scientific advice to the British and Americans. He returned to Denmark soon after it was liberated.

Anderson, in consultation with Cherwell, wrote a long minute to Churchill in May 1944 on the future control of atomic energy. He suggested that knowledge of the atomic development should be extended to the War Cabinet, Service Ministers and Chiefs of Staff. It was foolish to suppose that the Russians would not make a great atomic effort after the Germans were expelled from their country. He recommended that he and Cherwell should explain the atomic development and its implications to the War Cabinet and the Chiefs of Staff, and that the Foreign Secretary should study its international implications. Churchill sharply disagreed with this proposal.

Cherwell directly urged Churchill to consider the international problem, and told Anderson that he considered plans and preparations for the post-war world would be utterly illusory unless the crucial factor of atomic energy were taken into account. Churchill did not wish to depart from the terms of the Quebec agreement, which he regarded as determining the British attitude towards the future of atomic energy.

According to the published information, it appears that Cherwell fought hard for British interests in atomic energy, as he conceived them, in their relation to American interests. He regarded them as military in the first place, but he was also concerned about their industrial and commercial aspects.

However, he seems to have been prepared to subordinate British entirely to American interests if this was necessary to preserve a monopoly of atomic weapons, for the domination of the rest of the world, and in particular of the Socialist states.

Cherwell, who originally had had doubts on revealing atomic information to the United States for fear that it might reach Nazi agents, was, like Churchill, almost pathologically opposed to the transmission of atomic information to the Soviet Union. The withholding of this information from the ally who was bearing the brunt of the battle had moral and political consequences of an exceedingly serious nature. Cherwell must bear his share of the responsibility for this decision.

VIII

A Luminary of the Lords

After the General Election of 1945 Cherwell returned to Oxford. His new laboratory, opened in 1939, and his scientific staff, had been kept together. Excellent work on very short radio waves had been done, arising out of war research aimed at the development of radar.

In fact, the war had an excellent effect on Oxford physics in several ways. The scientists had remained in the laboratory, while most of the students had left to undertake national service. For the first time, Oxford physicists had been relieved of the excessive college tutoring which had absorbed too much energy, and some very able men had far more opportunity for research than they had enjoyed in the previous ten or twenty years.

The professor's prestige and power increased, so that he was able to give the laboratory still more help in large things; yet he was seldom there, owing to his government duties, so that researches proceeded without disturbance over details.

When Cherwell returned, after being deeply preoccupied in national and world affairs, older and mellower, he was less inclined to disturb the flourishing scientific activity which had grown under the conditions he had created, but had not personally led.

The very short wave radio physics was applied to new fields of research in chemistry and physics with rich results, and the low temperature physics continued in its outstanding development.

Cherwell strengthened the now great Oxford school of physics by helping to secure the conversion of the Wykeham professorship, which had hitherto been for experimental physics, to theoretical physics. While this was an excellent move, Cherwell was not able to develop it without the controversy he so often provoked. He did not provide the proper kind of working collaboration between the theoretical and experimental departments, and this caused friction.

It became evident in the post-war years that the Clarendon

Laboratory had a much stronger position than formerly, in comparison with the Cavendish Laboratory at Cambridge.

Cherwell did not retire from political activities. With the Conservatives in opposition, he spoke in the House of Lords as a member of Churchill's Shadow Cabinet, mainly on scientific and economic affairs.

He asserted in a speech in October 1945, that there was no great scope for the peaceful uses of atomic energy. He passionately hoped and privately worked for American development and control of atomic weapons, which he regarded as the only way of preventing the Soviet Union from acquiring the control of Europe, and the extension of socialism. He publicly supported further trial explosions for the development and perfection of nuclear weapons, and he contended that the dangers of fall-out from nuclear explosions had been greatly exaggerated.

Cherwell presently reversed his early public attitude on the minor importance of the peaceful uses of atomic energy.

He became a consultant on Atomic Energy to the Ministry of Supply in 1946. In his laboratory at Oxford J. L. Tuck began research on the production of controlled thermonuclear reactions, followed a little later by P. C. Thonemann. Tuck subsequently went to the United States to lead a group working on this problem at the Los Alamos Laboratory. Thonemann's research was transferred to Harwell in 1951. From it was developed the well-known Zeta apparatus for producing very high plasma apparatus, as a step towards hydrogen fusion.

As a speaker and lecturer, Cherwell was hard to hear. His normal voice was soft and low; when he raised it to make himself more audible, it became harsh.

Many of his speeches in the House of Lords contained simple expositions of scientific topics for a non-scientific audience; they were expansions of the kind of communications that he supplied to Churchill.

In the notable debate on the extension of scientific research, opened by Lord Samuel in July 1943, Cherwell explained how the solution of the problem of the hydrogenation of coal depended on Nernst's Third Law of Thermodynamics. He referred to the researches of Faraday and Heaviside, which had led to unforeseen discoveries, such as radiolocation, on which the defence of the country had depended. It was essential to promote fundamental scientific research, especially in universities, and extend science teaching in schools. 'I hope that not to have heard of the Law of Conservation of Energy will soon be as shameful as not to have heard of the Norman Conquest.'

He said that scientists, in reacting against their conditions, 'have injured their case by overstating it', but it was 'difficult to overcome in the older foundations the prejudice against science in favour of the "humanities"'. He thought that 'there are probably not more than a few dozen physicists in this country capable of evolving and developing' the various radio devices on which success in this war very largely depended. 'Everyone, I am sure, will agree that it is an anomaly to pay them on lower scales than men of equal educational status who, because they have distinguished themselves in what are usually called humane subjects, are often given war jobs of much higher status and pay than the scientist.'

After the formation of the Labour Government, he became chief opposition speaker in the Lords on scientific and economic affairs. In particular, he opposed the nationalization of steel, and the development of atomic energy by a government department. He argued in detail for private enterprise in steel. 'The majority have not got the aptitude and qualities which enable people to become rich . . . the qualities required may not be very amiable. I do not happen to be particularly attracted to them myself. . . .'

But it was only people like that who could make industry pay, increase exports, and settle the balance-of-payments crisis.

The drift of his arguments for taking the development of atomic energy out of the Civil Service was in the same direction. He aimed at directing it towards private enterprise. In the course of a speech on this topic in 1946 he expressed his position about the place of science in government. 'My view is that the people who run the country should have some knowledge of science, not that scientists should run the country.'

He loaded his speeches with statistics and quantitative information. This increased the difficulty of listening to them. They consisted of almost unrelieved questioning of Government policy on quantitative grounds. He kept querying every figure, drawing attention to possible shortcomings in the data on which the Government was acting.

His style, besides causing impatience, deflected discussion away from his strategic objective, which was to show that the conduct of industry by government was impracticable, and that private enterprise is superior to socialism.

Peers took pleasure in teasing him. At a largely attended luncheon of the Parliamentary and Scientific Committee, the elderly Lord Samuel, boyishly smiling at him, informed the company that he had heard that science was now 'unter den Lindemann'. Cherwell stared coldly towards the ceiling.

When the Conservatives returned to office in 1951, Churchill requested that he should join the Government, and asked Oxford University to release him for a year, which ultimately became two, especially to deal with the scientific side of re-armament, and the organization of the development of atomic energy.

He resumed close collaboration with Churchill, but the situation in peace was not the same as it had been in war. The prime minister's administration was less personal, and individual ministers had more power. Consequently, Cherwell's general influence was less. He concentrated his interest on the organization of atomic energy development.

Soon after the Labour Government was formed, it decided that major development, both for making atomic bombs and atomic power plants, should be undertaken in Britain. A department for the purpose was set up in the Ministry of Supply. Lord Portal was put in charge of production, and Cockcroft of research and development.

The project advanced with extraordinary success. Huge expenditures were involved, and most difficult scientific and technical problems had to be solved. The United States had virtually cut all supplies of atomic information. The British had to re-determine a great deal of information possessed by the Americans, but no longer available from them.

Cherwell was opposed on principle to such a project being carried out by the Civil Service. Atomic energy would ultimately become one of the most important productive activities of the nation. If it remained within the Civil Service, it might become one of the foundations of a future socialist state. Cherwell believed that production was best carried out by private enterprise, and the less the Civil Service had to do with it, the better.

In the general industrial conditions after the war, men in private industry doing work at all comparable in quality and responsibility to that done by the Atomic Energy department of the Ministry of Supply were much better paid, and were less subject to regulation. Some of the men in the Ministry's atomic department became restless, and desired to have salaries and conditions more like those in private industry.

Cherwell sympathized with this attitude. He discussed the idea of a public corporation, which should take over the development of atomic energy from the Civil Service, with Churchill, and believed he had converted him to it.

When Churchill became prime minister again, he assumed that the project would now be carried out by the new Conservative Government. When he brought it forward, he found it strongly opposed by the new Minister of Supply, Duncan Sandys, the son-in-law of the prime minister. The Minister of Supply did not welcome the proposed amputation of one of his most remarkable departments. It became clear that few scientists and other members of the Atomic Energy department wished to leave the Ministry.

A sharp contest then arose in the Cabinet, whether Atomic Energy should remain in the Ministry of Supply, or be conducted by a public corporation, with salaries and conditions more like those of private industry. Churchill decided, after all, that he was in favour of Atomic Energy remaining in the Ministry of Supply.

For the first time in his life Cherwell found himself in disagreement with Churchill on a major question of policy. After painful consideration, he decided that he must appeal to the Cabinet as a whole on what was a question of political principle. Was the Conservative Government's general line of removal of state controls, and placing production more and more under private enterprise, to be carried out also in this new and crucial field?

There was strong doctrinal support for this line, especially from ministers who were beginning to emerge as the Conservative leaders of the new generation.

Cherwell put his project for an Atomic Energy Authority, independent of the Civil Service, to the Cabinet, and carried it against the prime minister and the Minister of Supply.

This was one of Cherwell's most significant actions as a statesman of science. By taking atomic energy out of the Civil Service, he made it more prepared for a future collaboration with, and possible ultimate assimilation by, private industry.

In his last years, Cherwell spoke more and more purely as

himself in the House of Lords. His speeches became surer, more pungent and cogently expressed, and perhaps his last speech on technological education was his best.

One of the last projects in which Cherwell was keenly interested was the foundation of Churchill College, Cambridge. With his German higher education, he was familiar with the excellence of the German technological universities, and the similar institutions in the United States, and other countries. These have the same intellectual and social status as the ancient universities, and have been one of the main causes of the advanced condition of technology in those countries.

Cherwell agitated during his working life for new universities of this type to be founded in Britain, in order to raise the standard, and particularly the extent of the utilization of the most advanced technology in British industry.

He quoted the great technological advances in the Soviet Union, as threatening the future of Britain, which could not be protected without at least keeping up with the best technology elsewhere.

He stimulated Churchill's interest in this question. The references by Churchill and Cherwell in their speeches to Soviet scientific and technological development convinced the majority of the non-socialist world of its reality, though the basic facts about it had been available for nearly twenty years.

No new British technological university was completed in Cherwell's lifetime as a result of his agitation, but Churchill College at Cambridge was created with a bias to science and technology.

Cherwell resigned from the Government in 1953. His health had deteriorated, he wished to return to Oxford, and he could not expect further leave of absence from the University. In 1955 he retired from his chair. In the following year, the Royal Society awarded him its Hughes medal. This was late in the day, and he received the honour coolly.

Cherwell had the detached attitude to the Royal Society which he possessed towards the professional classes as a whole. After serving on its Council in the 1920's he was not elected again. He did not believe that science in Britain should be controlled by the Society. If it were, it would mean that the President would be a member of the Cabinet.

He thought that it was better to have politicians with scientific training, like Anderson and Cripps, rather than have scientists as such, active in politics. He considered the Society was too inbred, and he did not think that its research professors should be eligible to serve on its Council.

He believed, too, that the Society was too small. In addition to the ordinary fellows, there should be 1,500 to 2,000 associate fellows. This would give more scope to younger men for serving on committees, and influencing the course of research.

The human side of Cherwell's character was illustrated by his friend Robert Blake, who referred to 'his personal charm, urbanity and courtesy' at Christ Church. He was very kind, especially to the young and nervous.

His valet and cook were devoted to him. His valet was James Harvey, a retired boxer, who also became his secretary, and was with him for thirty years. Cherwell encouraged him to extend his education, and learn languages, shorthand and typing. Harvey became his amanuensis, and a personal friend. They spent hours together, watching television, including boxing matches, of which Harvey had expert knowledge. Cherwell would not allow Harvey to minister to his wants while a boxing match was on, and would attend to them himself, so that Harvey's view of the fight was not interrupted, and he could report what had happened afterwards. They joined in playful games with a pet cat. Cherwell could not bear to hurt animals, tame or wild.

He was fond of young children, and genuinely entered into their interests. He gave them boxes of chocolates, of which he was himself very fond. His sympathy for young children seems to have been connected with a wistful feeling that in a way he was an unfortunate child that had never grown up, at large in a hostile world.

While he was being savagely rude on the one hand, on the other he was giving unfortunate people secret financial and social help.

His health steadily declined, He died in his rooms in Christ Church on July 3rd, 1957.

Illuminating tributes were paid to Cherwell in the House of Lords after his death. Their most striking feature was their note of affection. Lord Silkin, the Labour peer, described him as 'a great House of Lords man'. He said that he knew that his combination with Churchill was 'the most formidable possible', and had had a great part in winning the war, but he personally remembered him as a debater on a wide range of subjects, and especially on technological education.

The public aspect of his character, as he would have wished to have had it seen, was very well depicted by the then Earl of Home, who described him in a valedictory speech in the House:

'A relentless hunter hurrying along the trail of discovery, there was the same immediate response to a kindred intellect, and the same contempt for a fool. There was a restless impatience with mediocrity and with the generality of mankind who were slow to perceive and accept what to him were the plain highways of progress. There was the same burning patriotism for Oxford and for England, and the same uncompromising hostility to anyone or anything that threatened the welfare of either. . . .' He was 'a character, massive in adversity and undisturbed by calamity, and thus identified himself with the soul of England'.

References

BROUGHAM

1. *The Life and Times of Henry Lord Brougham*, written by himself. 3 vols. London, 1871.
2. *Life of Henry Brougham to 1830*, by Chester W. New. Oxford, 1961.
3. *Henry Brougham*, by Frances Hawes. London, 1957.
4. *Passages of a Working Life*, by Charles Knight. 3 vols. London, 1864–5.
5. *Brougham and his Early Friends*. Edited by R. H. M. B. Atkinson and G. N. Jackson. 3 vols. London, 1908.
6. *An Inquiry into the Colonial Policy of the European Powers*, by Henry Brougham. 2 vols. Edinburgh, 1803.
7. *University College, London, 1826–1926*, by H. Hale Bellot. London, 1929.
8. *George Birkbeck*, by J. G. Godard. London, 1884.
9. *Opinions of Lord Brougham*. London, 1837.
10. *The Works of Lord Brougham*. 11 vols. Edinburgh, 1873.
11. *The Present State of the Law*, by Henry Brougham. London, 1828.
12. *A Letter to Sir Samuel Romilly*, from Henry Brougham upon the *Abuse of Charities*. 6th edition. London, 1818.
13. *Practical Observations upon the Education of the People*, by H. Brougham. London, 1825.
14. *3rd Lecture on the French Revolution*, by William Cobbett. London, 1830.
15. *The Society for the Diffusion of Useful Knowledge*, by Monica C. Grobel. *Thesis* deposited in the Library of University College, London, 1932.
16. *Objects, Advantages and Pleasures of Science*, by Henry Brougham. London, 1827.
17. *Crotchet Castle*, by T. L. Peacock. London, 1831.
18. *The Times*: *1785–1841*. London.
19. *Memoirs of Augustus de Morgan*, by Sophia Elizabeth de Morgan. London, 1882.
20. 'Experiments and Observations on the Inflection, Reflection and Colours of Light', by Henry Brougham. *Phil. Trans. Roy. Soc.*, Vol. 86, pp. 227–77. London, 1796.

21. 'Further Experiments and Observations on the Affection and Properties of Light', by Henry Brougham. *Phil. Trans. Roy. Soc.*, Vol. 87, pp. 352–85. London, 1797.
22. 'General Theorems chiefly Porisms in the Higher Geometry', by Henry Brougham. *Phil. Trans. Roy. Soc.*, Vol. 88, pp. 378–96. London, 1798.
23. *Life of Thomas Young*, by George Peacock. London, 1855.
24. *The Miscellaneous Works of Dr. Thomas Young*. Edited by George Peacock and John Leitch. 3 vols. London, 1855.
25. *Thomas Young*, by Alexander Wood and Frank Oldham. Cambridge, 1954.
26. *Analytical View of Sir Isaac Newton's Principia*, by Henry, Lord Brougham and E. J. Routh. London, 1855.
27. *Tracts*, Mathematical and Physical, by Henry, Lord Brougham. London, 1860.
28. *The Edinburgh Review*, 1802 onwards, especially Nos. I, II, III, V, IX, XXII, LXXXI, LXXXIV, CXLII.
29. *Contributions to the Edinburgh Review*, by Henry, Lord Brougham. 3 vols. London, 1856.
30. *Lives of Men of Letters and Science* who flourished in the time of George III, by Henry, Lord Brougham. 3 vols. London, 1845.
31. *Francis Horner MSS*: Brougham to Horner, Aug. 25, 1796; Sept. 21, 1796; March 27, 1797. London School of Economics.
32. *Papers and Minutes relating to Society for the Diffusion of Useful Knowledge*, 1832–41. Left by H. Ellis and A. Panizzi to the British Museum.
33. *Address of Committee of Society for the Diffusion of Useful Knowledge*, 1832, 43, 46. British Museum.
34. *A Manual for Mechanics' Institutions*, by B. F. Duppa. London, 1839.
35. *The British Almanac and Companion* for the year 1828. London.
36. *Prospectus* for the *Society for the Diffusion of Useful Knowledge*. London, 1825.
37. *Report on Mechanics Institutions*, by Thomas Coates. London, 1841.

GROVE

1. *A Lecture on the Progress of Physical Science*, by W. R. Grove. London, 1842.
2. *The Correlation of Physical Forces*, by W. R. Grove. 6th edition. London, 1874.
3. 'Sir William Robert Grove and the Origins of the Fuel Cell', by R. K. Webb. *Journal of the Royal Institute of Chemistry*, Vol. 85, pp. 291–3, August 1961. London.

4. *Jubilee of the Chemical Society of London: 1891.* London, 1896.
5. Obituaries: *Nature*, August 27, 1896; *Law Journal*, August 8, 1896; *The Times*, August 3, 1896.
6. 'W. R. Grove', *Dictionary of National Biography.*
7. 'William Palmer', *Dictionary of National Biography.*
8. *The Royal Society*, by H. Lyons. Cambridge, 1944.

PLAYFAIR

1. *Memoirs and Correspondence of Lyon Playfair*, by Wemyss Reid. London, 1899.
2. *Subjects of Social Welfare*, by Sir Lyon Playfair. London, 1889.
3. *Memoirs of Sir Robert Peel*, Vol. II. London, 1858.
4. *Jubilee Address to the London Chemical Society*, by Sir Lyon Playfair. London, 1891.
5. *Science in its Relations to Labour*, by Lyon Playfair. Sheffield, 1853.
6. *On the Organization of a Teaching Profession*, by Lyon Playfair. 1877.
7. *On the Effect of Protection on Wages*, by Lyon Playfair. Leeds, 1888.
8. *On the Wages and Hours of Labour*, by Lyon Playfair. Leeds, 1891.
9. 'The Study of Abstract Science essential to the Progress of Industry', by Lyon Playfair. *British Eloquence*, Vol. II. 1855.
10. 'Sir Thomas Wemyss Reid', *Dictionary of National Biography.*
11. 'Lyon Playfair: Reminiscences', by H. E. Roscoe. *Nature*, Vol. LVIII, p. 128, June 9, 1898.
12. *Report on the State of Large Towns in Lancashire.* London, 1845.
13. *Report* of the *British Association.* London, 1845.
14. 'Lyon Playfair's Life', reviewed by H. E. Roscoe. *Nature*, Vol. LXI, p. 121, December 7, 1899.
15. *The Advance of the Fungi*, by E. C. Large. London, 1940.
16. 'Emergence of Potato Blight 1843–46', by P. M. Austin Burke. *Nature*, Vol. 203, pp. 805–8, August 22, 1964.

PRINCE CONSORT

1. *The Prince Consort*, by Theodore Martin. 5 vols. 2nd edition. London, 1875.
2. *The Prince Consort*, by Roger Fulford. London, 1949.
3. *Speeches and Addresses*, by the Prince Consort. London, 1862.
4. *Early Victorian Cambridge*, by D. A. Winstanley. Cambridge, 1940.
5. *The Royal Commission for the Exhibition of 1851*, 1st and 2nd Reports. London, 1852.
6. *The Prince Consort and the Founding of the Imperial College*, by Sir Patrick Linstead, C.B.E., F.R.S. London, 1961.

7. 'The Prince Consort and Science', by J. G. Crowther. *New Scientist*, pp. 689–91, December 14, 1961.
8. *British Scientists of the Nineteenth Century*, by J. G. Crowther, Vol. II. Pelican edition. London, 1941.

THE DUKE OF DEVONSHIRE

1. *The Cavendish Family*, by Francis Bickley. London, 1911.
2. 'First Presidential Address'. *Transactions of the Iron and Steel Institute*, Vol. I, pp. 5–28. London, 1869.
3. 'Presentation to the Institute of a Portrait of His Grace the Duke of Devonshire'. *Journal of the Iron and Steel Institute*, Vol. I, pp. 213–19. London, 1872.
4. Obituaries: *Journal of the Iron and Steel Institute*, Vol. II, 1892; *Proc. Roy. Soc.*, Vol. LI, 1892; *The Times*, December 22, 1891.
5. 'Note on the Duke of Devonshire', *Nature*, Vol. 45, pp. 182–3, 1891.
6. *Life of the Eighth Duke of Devonshire*, by Henry Leach. London, 1904.
7. *Royal Commission on Scientific Instruction and the Advancement of Science*. Reports 1–8, 3 vols. H.M.S.O., London, 1872–5.
8. *Dictionary of National Biography*.

STRANGE

1. *Royal Commission on Scientific Instruction and the Advancement of Science*. 3 vols. H.M.S.O., London, 1872–5.
2. 'On the Necessity for a Permanent Commission on State Scientific Questions', by Lieut.-Col. Alexander Strange, F.R.S. *Journal of the Royal United Service Institution*, Vol. XV, pp. 537–66. London, 1872.
3. 'Science and the State', by R. V. Jones. *The Advancement of Science*. Vol. XX, No. 87, pp. 393–405. London, January 1964.
4. 'The Interaction of Science and Technology', by R. V. Jones. The 1962 Brunel Lecture, *Brunel College of Technology*. London, 1962.
5. 'Obituary of Charles Babbage,' by A. S., *Monthly Notices of the Astronomical Society*, Vol. XXXII, pp. 101–9. London, 1872.
6. 'Report of the Committee on the Provision for Physical Research in the British Isles'. *British Association*, Exeter Meeting, 1869, p. 213. London, 1870.
7. *The Organization of Science in England*, by D. S. L. Cardwell. London, 1957.

8. 'Note on the Duke of Devonshire', *Nature*, Vol. 45, pp. 182–3, 1891.
9. 'Sir Joseph Lockyer', *Dictionary of National Biography*.
10. 'Colonel Alexander Strange', *Dictionary of National Biography*.

HALDANE

1. *Richard Burdon Haldane*: an Autobiography. London, 1929.
2. 'A Scientist in and out of the Civil Service', by Sir Henry Tizard. Haldane Memorial Lecture. *Birkbeck College*, London, 1955.
3. *Education and Empire*, by R. B. Haldane. London, 1902.
4. *The Reign of Relativity*, by Viscount Haldane. London, 1921.
5. *The Life of Richard Burdon Haldane*, by Sir F. Maurice. 2 vols. London, 1937–9.
6. *Essays in Philosophical Criticism*, by R. B. Haldane and A. Seth. London, 1883.
7. *Life of Adam Smith*, by R. B. Haldane. London, 1887.
8. 'Richard Burdon Haldane', by A. Seth Pringle-Pattison. *Proceedings of the British Academy*, Vol. XIV, pp. 405–41. London, 1928.
9. *Science in Public Affairs*, by J. E. Hand, with a preface by R. B. Haldane. London, 1906.
10. 'Viscount Haldane of Cloan, O.M.', by Sir Claud Schuster *et al.* Reprinted from *Public Administration*. London, 1928.

TIZARD

1. *Biographical Memoirs* of Fellows of the Royal Society. Vol. 7, pp. 313–48. 1961.
2. 'Tizard and the Science of War', by P. M. S. Blackett. *Nature*, Vol. 185, pp. 647–53. 1960.
3. *Science and Government*, by C. P. Snow. London, 1961.
4. *Three Steps to Victory*, by Sir Robert Watson Watt. London, 1957.
5. *Britain and Atomic Energy*: *1939–1945*, by Margaret Gowing. London, 1964.
6. 'A Scientist in and out of the Civil Service', by Sir Henry Tizard. Haldane Memorial Lecture. *Birkbeck College*. London, 1955.
7. 'Science and the Services', by Sir Henry Tizard. *Journal of the Royal United Service Institution*, Vol. XCI, pp. 333–46. London, 1946.
8. 'The Strategy of Science', Messel Memorial Lecture by Sir Henry Tizard. *Chemistry and Industry*, pp. 788–92. London, 1952.
9. 'Rutherford Memorial Lecture', by Sir Henry Tizard. *Journal of the Chemical Society*, pp. 980–86. London, 1946.

10. 'Captain Thomas Henry Tizard'. Obituary: *Proc. Roy. Soc.*, A. Vol. CV. 1924.
11. 'Sir William McCormick'. Obituary: *Proc. Roy. Soc.*, A. Vol. XV, p. 130. 1931.
12. 'Nevil Vincent Sidgwick', *Biographical Memoirs* of Fellows of the Royal Society. Vol. 9, p. 237. 1954.
13. *The Rise of the Boffins*, by Ronald W. Clark. London, 1962.
14. Obituary by Sir Frederick Brundrett. *Nature*. Vol. 185, pp. 209–11, 1960.
15. Obituaries: *The Times*, October 10, 12, 13, 15, 19, 1959.
16. *Tizard*, by Ronald W. Clark. London, 1965.

CHERWELL

1. *The Prof in Two Worlds*: The Official Life of Professor F. A. Lindemann, Viscount Cherwell, by the Earl of Birkenhead. London, 1961.
2. *The Prof*, by R. F. Harrod. London, 1959.
3. *Biographical Memoirs* of Fellows of the Royal Society. Vol. 4, pp. 45–71. 1958.
4. *Three Steps to Victory*, by Sir Robert Watson Watt. London, 1957.
5. *The Rise of the Boffins*, by Ronald W. Clark. London, 1962.
6. *Science and Government*, by C. P. Snow. London, 1961.
7. *Parliamentary Debates*, House of Lords, 1943–57.
8. Obituaries: *The Times*, July 4, 5, 8, 1957; *Nature*, Vol. 180, pp. 579–81.
9. *Britain and Atomic Energy*: *1939–1945*, by Margaret Gowing. London, 1964.
10. *The Atom*. Monthly Bulletin of the U.K. Atomic Energy Authority. No. 97, pp. 226–30. November, 1964.

Index